Introduction to Mechanics of Continua

INTRODUCTIONS TO HIGHER MATHEMATICS

A series of brief expository texts designed for use in upper undergraduate courses and in the early years of graduate study.

INTRODUCTION
TO
MECHANICS OF CONTINUA

by William Prager

L. Herbert Ballou University Professor
Brown University

GINN AND COMPANY

Boston New York Chicago Atlanta Dallas Palo Alto Toronto London

161.5
A

Based upon *Einführung in die Kontinuumsmechanik*
by William Prager
and published by arrangement with
Birkhäuser Verlag,
Basel, Switzerland

Library of Congress Catalogue Card Number 61-14659

PRINTED IN THE UNITED STATES OF AMERICA

VNIVERSITATI BRVNENSI

ANNIS VOLVENTIBVS TERTIVM SAECVLVM

Preface

The author teaches at a university that offers an unusually large number of courses in mechanics of continua. The choice of particular courses in this area and the sequence in which they are taken vary widely with the student's major interest. Some repetition in the treatment of the common foundations of mechanics of continua is therefore unavoidable. Though not without didactic value, the repeated discussion of the foundations from the points of view of various special branches is hard to justify at a time when the classical branches of mechanics of continua are growing vigorously and new branches are developing at a remarkable rate. The idea of an introductory course that could serve as the common basis for many special courses in mechanics of continua has long attracted the author. The final decision to write the present book was the outcome of a discussion with Professor P. F. Chenea (Purdue University), which convinced the author that the need for a book of this kind was no less strongly felt at other universities.

The book has a two-fold aim: to provide the foundations for a deeper study of special branches such as hydrodynamics, gasdynamics, elasticity, and plasticity, and to present typical problems and methods of mechanics of continua for the benefit of those who do not plan to specialize in the field. The demands made on the mathematical knowledge of the reader are modest and do not go beyond the usual freshman and sophomore courses on calculus. The necessary concepts and theorems of tensor analysis are developed in Chapter I. The next three chapters are primarily concerned with the general foundations, which can be discussed without assuming a specific constitutive equation. The treatment of the kinematical foundations (Chapter III) differs from the customary one in so far as discussion is restricted to the rate of deformation tensor, the only kinematical tensor needed in the theory of perfect fluids (Chapter V), viscous fluids (Chapter VI), and visco-plastic and perfectly plastic solids (Chapter VII). Chapter VIII introduces the stress rate tensor and discusses the mechanical behavior defined by a homogeneous relation between the components of the stress rate and the rate of deformation. This type of behavior, which was first considered by Jaumann in the first decade of this century, has recently been named "hypoelastic." Restriction to the neighborhood of the homogeneous stress-free state of a hypoelastic solid leads to the classical theory of elasticity. In this way, the introduction of a strain tensor can be postponed until finite strains are to be investigated. Various strain tensors and the associated stress tensors are discussed in Chapter IX without reference to a specific type of mechanical behavior. Chapter X, which is concerned with finite elastic strains, concludes with a discussion of elastic stability.

In working through the book, the reader can check his mastery of the subject on over 160 problems for Chapters I through VIII. Special problems for Chapters IX and X seemed unnecessary, since these chapters make greater demands on the mathematical cooperation of the reader who will have to work out the details of many steps that are only described in general terms.

The author feels indebted to many persons and organisations: to the Corporation of Brown University for sabbatic leave in the academic year 1958–59; to the John Simon Guggenheim Memorial Foundation for a Fellowship, owing to which he could devote the entire year to the writing of the book; to the Council of the Federal Polytechnic Institute in Zürich for his appointment as Visiting Professor, which enabled him to check the suitability of the material while the book was being written; to Professors H. Ziegler (Eidgenössische Technische Hochschule) and E. Sternberg (Brown University) for their critical reading of the entire manuscript and numerous suggestions for improvements; to Professors M. Holt and W. H. Reid (Brown University) for helpful discussions of Chapters V and VI; to Professor R. S. Rivlin (Brown University) for informative remarks on questions of Chapters IX and X; to Professors H. Ziegler (Eidgenössische Technische Hochschule) and E. T. Onat (Brown University) for their invaluable assistance in proof-reading; and to Mrs. Ezoura Fonseca for the careful preparation of the English typescript. (The Swiss edition was typeset from the author's manuscript.)

A special word of thanks is due to the author's wife for her patience in listening to and advising on innumerable passages of both the Swiss and the American edition.

During an earlier stay in Zürich, the author was able to complete the manuscript of a book (*Probleme der Plastizitätstheorie*, Birkhäuser Verlag, Basel) within an unusually short period. When he accepted the invitation of the Council of the Federal Polytechnic Institute and, for the second time, began to write a book during a stay in Zürich, he was by no means certain that the pleasant earlier experience could be repeated. The quiet and hospitable atmosphere of the Hotel Rigihof has again contributed much to the rapid progress of the work.

Last but certainly not least the author would like to thank the publishers, Birkhäuser Verlag (Basel) and Ginn and Company (Boston). Thanks to their splendid cooperation he has the pleasure of seeing well-presented Swiss and American editions of his work appear almost simultaneously.

Providence, R. I. William Prager

Contents

Chapter I · Geometrical Foundations

Chapter II · State of Stress

Chapter III · Instantaneous Motion

Chapter IV · Fundamental Laws

Chapter V · Perfect Fluids

Chapter VI · Viscous Fluids

Chapter VII · Visco-plastic and Perfectly Plastic Materials

Chapter VIII · Hypoelastic Materials; Classical Theory of Elasticity

Chapter IX · Finite Strain

Chapter X · Elastic and Hyperelastic Materials

Introduction to Mechanics of Continua

CHAPTER I

Geometrical Foundations

1. Introduction. Geometrical or physical quantities such as the velocity of a particle are most conveniently specified with reference to an appropriate system of coordinates. At the same time, such a quantity is independent of the coordinate system that may be used in its specification: the specification in *one* coordinate system determines that in any other system. Geometrical or physical quantities may be classified according to the manner in which their specifications change in the transition from one coordinate system to another.

Two of these classes, called *scalars* and *vectors*, are well known from particle mechanics. Mass and kinetic energy belong to the first class, velocity and acceleration to the second. If only very few of these classes need to be considered, the class to which a quantity belongs may be indicated by simple typographical means. For instance, lightface italic type may be used for scalars and boldface roman type for vectors.

The combinations of the various quantities that are found in the applications then suggest the definitions of certain mathematical operations, for which appropriate symbols are introduced. For example, the concept of the resultant $\mathbf{R}$ of two forces $\mathbf{P}_1$ and $\mathbf{P}_2$ that act on the same particle suggests the definition of the *sum* $\mathbf{R} = \mathbf{P}_1 + \mathbf{P}_2$ of two vectors; similarly, the concept of the power L of the force $\mathbf{P}_1$ on the velocity $\mathbf{v}$ of this particle leads to the definition of the *scalar product* $L = \mathbf{P}_1 \cdot \mathbf{v}$. Finally, algebraic rules are established for all meaningful combinations of the newly defined operations. Examples of such rules are the associative law

$$(\mathbf{P}_1 + \mathbf{P}_2) + \mathbf{P}_3 = \mathbf{P}_1 + (\mathbf{P}_2 + \mathbf{P}_3)$$

and the distributive law

$$(\mathbf{P}_1 + \mathbf{P}_2) \cdot \mathbf{v} = \mathbf{P}_1 \cdot \mathbf{v} + \mathbf{P}_2 \cdot \mathbf{v}.$$

In this way one obtains a symbolic algebra that deals directly with the geometrical or physical quantities without reference to a specific coordinate system.

In principle, this *symbolic method* is most attractive, because it yields a natural description of a geometrical or physical situation that avoids all reference to an extraneous coordinate system. For practical reasons, however, the symbolic method is not nearly as useful as this remark would seem to indicate. With each new class of quantities that have to be considered in addition to scalars and vectors, the symbolic method becomes more cumbersome on account of the rapidly increasing numbers of new operations and algebraic rules for their combination. Very soon a point is reached where the complexity of the symbolic method appears to be an excessive price to pay for its conceptual simplicity.

When the symbolic method becomes unmanageable, coordinate methods must be used instead. To avoid having the structure of geometrical or physical formulas reflect special features of the coordinate systems in which they are derived, one may try writing these formulas in such a manner that they are valid in any coordinate system. The fully general execution of this program for rectangular or oblique, rectilinear or curvilinear coordinate systems leads to the general *tensor calculus*. We shall not attempt, however, to develop this calculus in the present book, as the necessity of mastering the new tool would divert the reader's attention from the mechanical content of the mathematical relations. Instead, we shall restrict ourselves to the use of rectangular Cartesian coordinate systems and the discussion of *Cartesian tensors*. In this way, only an indispensable minimum of new mathematical formalism has to be introduced. At the end of this first chapter, the reader should therefore be completely familiar with the new tool and free to concentrate on its use in mechanics of continua.

Where the symbolic method ceases to be useful and the general or the Cartesian tensor calculus becomes preferable, is not sharply defined. In the realm of mechanics, this boundary must doubtless be drawn somewhere in the mechanics of deformable media. The mechanics of particles and rigid bodies can be elegantly treated by the symbolic method. This method also is widely used in the mechanics of ideal fluids, though a larger number of special algebraic rules are needed in this field of application. In the study of Newtonian fluids and Hookean solids the symbolic method is encountered more rarely, and even its most ardent defendants must concede that it is not suited to the treatment of problems involving finite elastic deformations, plastic flow, or non-Newtonian effects. Since this book is concerned with the fundamentals of all these fields of continuum mechanics, the symbolic method and the Cartesian tensor calculus will be developed side by side. Only after the reader has familiarized himself with both can he make a meaningful choice in favor of one or the other when treating a specific problem.

2. Transformation of coordinates. In Figure 1, let O be the origin of the rectangular Cartesian coordinates x, y, z, and P a generic point. The *coordinates* of P may be defined as the projections OX, OY, and OZ of the directed segment OP on the coordinate axes, a projection being considered positive when it has the direction of the corresponding coordinate axis. It follows from this definition that, for instance, the coordinate x depends only on the position of the origin and the positive x-direction but not on the choice of the y- and z-directions, provided only that these are orthogonal to the x-direction.

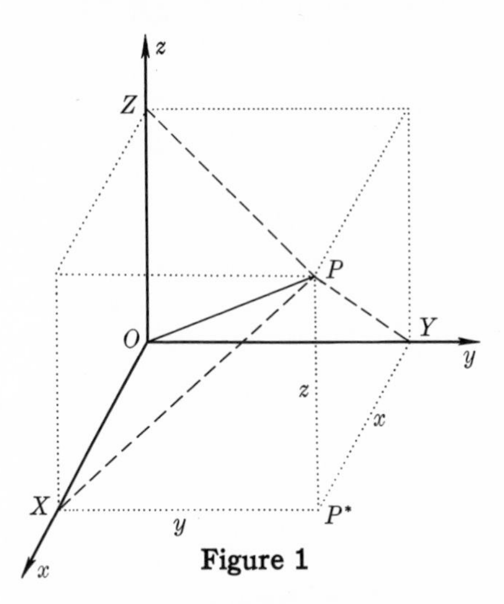

Figure 1

To obtain the coordinate x' in a second coordinate system x', y', z', one must project the directed segment OP on the x'-axis. If P^* (Figure 1) denotes the projection of the point P on the x, y-plane, the projection of OP on the x'-axis may be found by projecting the broken line OXP^*P on this axis. Since the rectilinear segments of this line represent the coordinates x, y, z, one has $x' = x \cos(x', x) + y \cos(x', y) + z \cos(x', z)$, where for instance (x', y) denotes the angle between the axes x' and y. Supplementing this formula by the corresponding ones for y' and z', one obtains the relations

$$\begin{aligned} x' &= x \cos(x', x) + y \cos(x', y) + z \cos(x', z), \\ y' &= x \cos(y', x) + y \cos(y', y) + z \cos(y', z), \\ z' &= x \cos(z', x) + y \cos(z', y) + z \cos(z', z), \end{aligned} \tag{2.1}$$

which represent the transformation from the coordinates x, y, z to the coordinates x', y', z'.

The formulas for the inverse transformation are readily obtained from (2.1) by exchanging primed and unprimed variables and observing that for instance $\cos(x', y) = \cos(y, x')$; thus,

$$\begin{aligned} x &= x' \cos(x', x) + y' \cos(y', x) + z' \cos(z', x), \\ y &= x' \cos(x', y) + y' \cos(y', y) + z' \cos(z', y), \\ z &= x' \cos(x', z) + y' \cos(y', z) + z' \cos(z', z). \end{aligned} \tag{2.2}$$

To derive a formula for the cosine of the angle formed by the directions μ and ν, consider that point P on the ray of the direction μ through the origin, which has unit distance from the origin. The coordinates of this point in the first coordinate system are $x = \cos(\mu, x)$, $y = \cos(\mu, y)$, $z = \cos(\mu, z)$. If the positive x'-direction coincides with the ν direction, the coordinate x' of P equals $\cos(\mu, \nu)$. From the first of the equations (2.1) it follows then that

$$\cos(\mu, \nu) = \cos(\mu, x)\cos(\nu, x) + \cos(\mu, y)\cos(\nu, y) + \cos(\mu, z)\cos(\nu, z). \tag{2.3}$$

It is worth noting that the right-hand side of (2.3) is linear in the direction cosines of each of the two directions.

A more concise manner of writing the transformation formulas (2.1) and (2.2) is achieved as follows. Instead of x, y, z and x', y', z' the notations x_1, x_2, x_3 and x_1', x_2', x_3', respectively, are used for the coordinates. Furthermore, the convention is adopted that lower-case italic subscripts indicate the range 1, 2, 3. This makes it possible to speak of the point with the coordinates x_i or x_j'. Finally, the cosine of the angle between the positive x_i- and x_j'-directions is denoted by c_{ij}. The transformation formulas (2.1) and (2.2) may then be written as follows:

$$x_j' = \sum_{i=1}^{3} c_{ij} x_i, \tag{2.4}$$

$$x_i = \sum_{j=1}^{3} c_{ij} x_j'. \tag{2.5}$$

Each of these relations stands for three equations. To spell out the three equations represented by (2.4), one attributes to the subscript i on the right-hand side successively the values 1, 2, 3, and sums the resulting terms to obtain the relation

$$x_j' = c_{1j}x_1 + c_{2j}x_2 + c_{3j}x_3, \tag{2.6}$$

in which j is the only remaining letter subscript. When this is successively given the values 1, 2, 3, the desired three equations are obtained; except for the different notations for coordinates and direction cosines, they are identical with (2.1).

The summation in (2.4) is extended over the values 1, 2, 3 of the subscript i, which appears twice in the monomial following the summation sign. An analogous remark applies to the subscript j in (2.5). This feature makes it possible to write the transformation formulas still more concisely. Indeed, the summation signs in (2.4) and (2.5) may be omitted if the following convention is adopted: whenever a lower-case italic subscript appears twice in the same monomial, this monomial stands for the sum of the three terms obtained by successively giving to this index the values 1, 2, and 3.

In view of this *summation convention*, (2.4) and (2.5) may be written as follows:

$$x'_j = c_{ij}x_i, \tag{2.7}$$

$$x_i = c_{ij}x'_j. \tag{2.8}$$

As is seen from (2.6), the repeated subscript i in (2.7) disappears after the summation indicated by this subscript has been carried out; this subscript is therefore called a *dummy subscript*. Which lower-case italic letter is used to denote a dummy subscript is immaterial, provided that it differs from the other subscripts in the same monomial. For example, (2.8) might have been written as

$$x_i = c_{ik}x'_k. \tag{2.9}$$

This freedom in the choice of dummy subscripts will often be used in the following. If for instance (2.8) were to be substituted into (2.7), the subscript i would appear four times in the same monomial on the right of the resulting equation and therefore fail to indicate the precise manner in which the double summation is to be carried out. On the other hand, substitution of (2.9) into (2.7) furnishes the relation

$$x'_j = c_{ij}c_{ik}x'_k, \tag{2.10}$$

which clearly indicates the intended double sum. The subscripts in (2.10) obey the following general rule: in a correctly written relation, a lower-case italic subscript may at most appear twice in each monomial; if however such a subscript appears but once in a monomial, it must also appear once in each other monomial, when both sides of the relation are written as sums of monomials.

The relation (2.10) leads to the introduction of an important symbol. Since x'_1, x'_2, x'_3 are independent variables, (2.10) must reduce to the identity $x'_j = x'_j$. The coefficient $c_{ij}c_{ik}$ in (2.10), which depends on the subscripts j and k, therefore equals 1 or 0 according to whether these subscripts have or do not have the same numerical value. The *Kronecker delta* is defined by

$$\delta_{ij} = \begin{cases} 1 & \text{for } i = j, \\ 0 & \text{for } i \neq j; \end{cases} \tag{2.11}$$

with its aid the statement made above may be written as follows:

$$c_{ij}c_{ik} = \delta_{jk}. \tag{2.12}$$

As the roles of the primed and unprimed coordinates may be exchanged, the relation

$$c_{ji}c_{ki} = \delta_{jk} \tag{2.13}$$

holds in addition to (2.12).

To realize the conciseness of the notation introduced above, remark that (2.12) represents six equations. In the notation used at the beginning of this section, these equations are indicated by the relations

$$\cos^2(x', x) + \cos^2(x', y) + \cos^2(x', z) = 1,$$

$$\cos(x', x)\cos(y', x) + \cos(x', y)\cos(y', y) + \cos(x', z)\cos(y', z) = 0,$$

from each of which two further relations may be obtained by cyclic permutation of x', y', z'.

3. Scalar and vector. When suitable units have been chosen, the distance between two points or the kinetic energy of a particle is given by one number, which does not depend on the choice of the coordinate system. Geometrical or physical quantities of this kind are called *scalars*.

The velocity of a particle has already been mentioned in Section 1 as an example of a *vector*. Without reference to a coordinate system, a velocity may be specified by its magnitude, the speed v, and its direction ν. When a scale has been chosen for representing speeds by lengths, a velocity may be represented by a directed line segment. Interpreted as a speed according to the chosen scale, the projection of this line segment on a direction μ will be called the *value* of the velocity for the direction μ and be denoted by $v^{(\mu)}$; it indicates the speed with which the particle progresses in the direction μ. Obviously,

$$v^{(\mu)} = v\cos(\nu, \mu). \tag{3.1}$$

With respect to a rectangular Cartesian coordinate system x_1, x_2, x_3, a velocity is specified by its values for the coordinate axes, which are also called the *components* of the velocity in the considered coordinate system; they are given by

$$v_1 = v\cos(\nu, x_1), \quad v_2 = v\cos(\nu, x_2), \quad v_3 = v\cos(\nu, x_3). \tag{3.2}$$

From (2.3), (3.1), and (3.2), it follows that

$$v^{(\mu)} = v_1\cos(\mu, x_1) + v_2\cos(\mu, x_2) + v_3\cos(\mu, x_3). \tag{3.3}$$

When the considered velocity is specified by its values for the coordinate axes, the relation (3.3) associates a scalar $v^{(\mu)}$ with each direction μ. This remark and the structure of (3.3) suggest the following first definition of the vector concept: *A vector associates a scalar with each direction in space by means of an expression that is linear and homogeneous in the direction cosines.*

This characterization of a vector has the advantage that it uses a single coordinate system (with respect to which the direction cosines are taken). From the point of view of this definition the usual specifications of a vector are obtained as follows: The magnitude of a vector is the maximum of its values for all directions in space; the direction for which this maximum is assumed is the direction of the vector.

A more frequently encountered definition of the vector concept states how the components of a vector change in the transition from one coordinate system to another. If for instance the direction μ in (3.3) is the positive x_1'-direction of a second system of rectangular Cartesian coordinates, this equation furnishes the x_1'-component of the vector as follows:

$$v_1' = v_1 \cos(x_1', x_1) + v_2 \cos(x_1', x_2) + v_3 \cos(x_1', x_3) = c_{i1}v_i. \quad (3.4)$$

The general transformation formula for vector components is obtained by replacing the subscript 1 in the first and last terms of (3.4) by a letter subscript; thus,

$$v_j' = c_{ij}v_i. \quad (3.5)$$

The complete analogy between the tranformation formulas (2.7) and (3.5) is worth noting.

Equation (3.5) suggests the following second definition of the vector concept: *In any rectangular Cartesian coordinate system, a vector is defined by three components that transform according to (3.5) under the coordinate transformation (2.7).*

Equation (3.5) is an abbreviation for the three equations that are obtained from (3.3) by letting the direction μ successively coincide with the positive directions of the primed coordinate axes. It follows that (3.5) and the corresponding second definition of the vector concept do not contain anything that is not implied by (3.3) and the corresponding first definition of the vector concept.

Equation (3.5) is readily solved for the unprimed components by multiplying both sides by c_{kj} and using (2.13); thus,

$$v_k = c_{kj}v_j'. \quad (3.6)$$

Just as it is convenient to speak of the point with the coordinates x_1, x_2, x_3 as the point x_i, so it is convenient to speak of the vector with the components v_1, v_2, v_3 as the vector v_i.

On account of the linearity of the transformation formula (3.5), the sums $u_1 + v_1$, $u_2 + v_2$, $u_3 + v_3$ of corresponding components of two vectors u_i and v_i transform as the components of a vector, which is called the *sum* of the vectors u_i and v_i. In symbolic notation, the sum of the vectors $\mathbf{u}$ and $\mathbf{v}$ is written as $\mathbf{u} + \mathbf{v}$; here the plus sign has a special meaning, which follows from the definition of the sum of two vectors. Strictly speaking, the plus sign in $\mathbf{u} + \mathbf{v}$ should therefore differ from the usual plus sign; for instance a boldface plus sign could be used to indicate vector addition.

On the other hand, the plus sign in the expression $u_i + v_i$ for the typical component of the sum of the vectors u_i and v_i has the conventional algebraic meaning, and the introduction of a special operation symbol is unnecessary. It follows immediately that the commutative and associative laws are valid in vector addition; indeed,

$$u_i + v_i = v_i + u_i, \quad u_i + (v_i + w_i) = (u_i + v_i) + w_i. \tag{3.7}$$

If the symbolic notation is developed without reference to the Cartesian notation, the validity of the corresponding relations

$$\mathbf{u} + \mathbf{v} = \mathbf{v} + \mathbf{u}, \quad \mathbf{u} + (\mathbf{v} + \mathbf{w}) = (\mathbf{u} + \mathbf{v}) + \mathbf{w} \tag{3.8}$$

has to be established by separate proofs.

From the linearity of the transformation formula (3.5) it follows further that the products λv_1, λv_2, λv_3 of the components of a vector v_i with a scalar λ transform as the components of a vector, which is called the *product* of the vector v_i with the scalar λ. In symbolic notation, this product is written as $\lambda\mathbf{v}$. Though no special operation symbol is used the meaning of $\lambda\mathbf{v}$ must be specially explained. On the other hand, no such explanation is needed for the Cartesian notation λv_i. Since

$$\lambda(u_i + v_i) = \lambda u_i + \lambda v_i, \tag{3.9}$$

the distributive law

$$\lambda(\mathbf{u} + \mathbf{v}) = \lambda\mathbf{u} + \lambda\mathbf{v} \tag{3.10}$$

holds for the product of a scalar and a vector.

If the components v_1, v_2, v_3 of a vector are functions of a parameter s, it follows from the linearity of (3.5) that the derivatives of these components with respect to s, that is dv_1/ds, dv_2/ds, dv_3/ds, are the components of a vector. This vector is called the *derivative* of the vector v_i with respect to s and is indicated by dv_i/ds or $d\mathbf{v}/ds$. Similar remarks apply to the higher derivatives of v_1, v_2, v_3 with respect to s.

Next, we consider the sum of the products u_1v_1, u_2v_2, u_3v_3 of corresponding components of two vectors u_i and v_i. From (3.5) and (2.13) it follows that

$$u'_jv'_j = (c_{kj}u_k)(c_{lj}v_l) = c_{kj}c_{lj}u_kv_l = \delta_{kl}u_kv_l. \tag{3.11}$$

According to the definition of the Kronecker delta, we have $\delta_{kl}u_k = u_l$, so that the last term in (3.11) may be written as u_lv_l or u_jv_j, since the name of a dummy subscript is immaterial. Thus,

$$u'_jv'_j = u_jv_j. \tag{3.12}$$

Equation (3.12) shows that the considered sum of products is a scalar; it is called the *scalar product* of the vectors u_i and v_i. In symbolic notation, the scalar product of the vectors $\mathbf{u}$ and $\mathbf{v}$ is written as $\mathbf{u}\cdot\mathbf{v}$.

To discuss the meaning of the scalar product $\mathbf{u}\cdot\mathbf{v}$, we denote the magnitudes of the factors by u and v and their directions by μ and ν, respectively. Using the expressions (3.2) for the components of $\mathbf{v}$ and analogous expressions for those of $\mathbf{u}$ and employing (2.3), one readily verifies that $u_iv_i = u\,v\cos(\mu, \nu)$. The scalar product of two vectors may therefore be obtained by multiplying the magnitude of one of the two vectors by the projection of the other vector on the direction of the first. In this form, the scalar product is usually introduced in mechanics as the power of a force on the velocity of its point of application. When two vectors are orthogonal, their scalar product vanishes. Conversely, when the scalar product of two non-vanishing vectors is zero, the vectors are orthogonal.

From the Cartesian notation $u_i v_i$ there immediately follows the validity of the commutative, distributive, and associative laws, which may be written in symbolic notation as follows:

$$\mathbf{u}\cdot\mathbf{v} = \mathbf{v}\cdot\mathbf{u}, \quad \mathbf{u}\cdot(\mathbf{v}+\mathbf{w}) = \mathbf{u}\cdot\mathbf{v}+\mathbf{u}\cdot\mathbf{w}, \quad \lambda(\mathbf{u}\cdot\mathbf{v}) = (\lambda\mathbf{u})\cdot\mathbf{v} = \mathbf{u}\cdot(\lambda\mathbf{v}). \tag{3.13}$$

The scalar product of a vector v_i with itself,

$$v_i v_i = v_1^2 + v_2^2 + v_3^2, \tag{3.14}$$

is the square of the magnitude v of this vector. Whereas this square is denoted by v^2, it is not advisable to write the left side of (3.14) as v_i^2, because this manner of writing would not clearly indicate that i is a dummy subscript.

A vector of the magnitude 1 is called a *unit vector*. A direction in space is conveniently specified by the unit vector that points in this direction. If μ_i is the unit vector of the direction μ, we have $\mu_i = \cos(\mu, x_i)$ so that (3.3) may be written in the form

$$v^{(\mu)} = v_i \mu_i. \tag{3.15}$$

Whereas the italic indices on the right of (3.15) indicate components that obey the transformation formula (3.5), the Greek superscript on the left does not have this meaning. Indeed, (3.15) shows that $v^{(\mu)}$ is the scalar product of the vectors v_i and μ_i, and as such it is independent of the coordinate system.

4. Tensor. Generalizing the first definition of the vector concept, we stipulate that *a tensor associates a vector with each direction in space by means of an expression that is linear and homogeneous in the direction cosines.* (The term tensor originated in the analysis of the state of stress at a point of a continuum. With each surface element through this point there is associated the vector of the stress that is transmitted across this element. Equilibrium considerations show that the relation between the direction of the normal to the surface element and the stress vector is linear and homogeneous in the direction cosines of the normal. The state of stress at a point of a continuum is therefore specified by a tensor, the *stress tensor* at this point.)

In symbolic notation, tensors will be indicated by block letters. With respect to a rectangular Cartesian coordinate system x_1, x_2, x_3, a tensor T

is specified by the vectors $\mathbf{T}_1$, $\mathbf{T}_2$, $\mathbf{T}_3$ that are associated with the coordinate directions; these vectors will be called the *values* of the tensor T for the coordinate directions. The vector $\mathbf{T}^{(\mu)}$ associated with the direction μ is then given by the formula

$$\mathbf{T}^{(\mu)} = \mathbf{T}_1 \cos(\mu, x_1) + \mathbf{T}_2 \cos(\mu, x_2) + \mathbf{T}_3 \cos(\mu, x_3) = \mathbf{T}_i\mu_i, \quad (4.1)$$

which is analogous to (3.3). With respect to the coordinates x_1, x_2, x_3, the vector $\mathbf{T}_1$ is specified by its components T_{11}, T_{12}, and T_{13} with respect to the coordinate axes. Similarly, the components of the vectors $\mathbf{T}_2$ and $\mathbf{T}_3$ will be denoted by T_{21}, T_{22}, T_{23} and T_{31}, T_{32}, T_{33}, respectively. The nine quantities T_{ij} are called the *components* of the tensor T with respect to the coordinates x_1, x_2, x_3. Just as it is convenient to speak of the vector with the components v_1, v_2, v_3 as the vector v_i, so it is convenient to speak of the tensor with the components T_{11}, T_{12}, $\cdots$, T_{33} as the tensor T_{ij}.

If the direction μ in (4.1) coincides with the positive x_1'-direction of a second system of rectangular Cartesian coordinates x_1', x_2', x_3' and the value of T for this direction is denoted by $\mathbf{T}_1'$, the components μ_i of the unit vector of the direction μ can be identified with the coefficients c_{i1} in the coordinate transformation (2.7). Thus,

$$\mathbf{T}_1' = c_{i1}\mathbf{T}_i. \quad (4.2)$$

The value of the vector $\mathbf{T}_1'$ for the x_l'-direction will be denoted by T_{1l}'. On the other hand, according to (3.5) the value of $\mathbf{T}_i$ for this direction is $c_{jl}T_{ij}$. Equation (4.2) therefore has the Cartesian equivalent

$$T_{1l}' = c_{i1}c_{jl}T_{ij}. \quad (4.3)$$

Similar formulas for the primed components of the vectors $\mathbf{T}_2'$ and $\mathbf{T}_3'$ are obtained by replacing the subscript 1 in (4.3) by 2 or by 3. The general transformation formula for tensor components is accordingly

$$T_{kl}' = c_{ik}c_{jl}T_{ij}. \quad (4.4)$$

This formula is the basis for the following second definition of the tensor concept: *In any rectangular Cartesian coordinate system, a tensor is defined by nine components that transform according to (4.4) under the coordinate transformation (2.7).*

When the nine components of the tensor T are to be displayed, this is usually done in matrix form:

$$\mathsf{T} = \begin{bmatrix} T_{11} & T_{12} & T_{13} \\ T_{21} & T_{22} & T_{23} \\ T_{31} & T_{32} & T_{33} \end{bmatrix}. \quad (4.5)$$

The elements in the first row are the components of the vector $\mathbf{T}_1$, etc. As usual, the first subscript of an element indicates its row and the second its column.

As a first illustration of the transformation formula (4.4), investigate the influence of exchanging the indices k and l in this formula. This exchange yields

$$T'_{lk} = c_{il}c_{jk}T_{ij}. \tag{4.6}$$

As i and j on the right side of (4.6) are dummy subscripts, they may be exchanged without modifying the value of this side. Thus,

$$T'_{lk} = c_{jl}c_{ik}T_{ji} = c_{ik}c_{jl}T_{ji}. \tag{4.7}$$

Comparison of (4.7) and (4.4) furnishes the following result: if the nine values T_{ij} are the components of a tensor $\mathbf{T}$, the values T_{ji} are likewise the components of a tensor. The latter will be called the *transpose* of $\mathbf{T}$ and be denoted by $\mathbf{T}^T$.

As a second illustration of the transformation formula (4.7), consider the tensor $\boldsymbol{\delta}$ that has the components (2.11) in the coordinate system x_1, x_2, x_3. From (4.7), (2.11), and (2.12), it follows that

$$\delta'_{kl} = c_{ik}c_{jl}\delta_{ij} = c_{ik}c_{il} = \delta_{kl}. \tag{4.8}$$

The tensor $\boldsymbol{\delta}$ has therefore the same matrix

$$\boldsymbol{\delta} = \begin{bmatrix} 1 & 0 & 0 \\ 0 & 1 & 0 \\ 0 & 0 & 1 \end{bmatrix} \tag{4.9}$$

in any coordinate system; it is called the *unit tensor*.

A tensor is called *symmetric* if

$$T_{ij} = T_{ji}, \tag{4.10}$$

and *antisymmetric* if

$$T_{ij} = -T_{ji}. \tag{4.11}$$

We leave it to the reader to show by means of the transformation formula (4.4) that these properties are independent of the coordinate system and therefore furnish meaningful concepts.

In the matrix of a tensor, elements in symmetric positions with respect to the main diagonal have the same value if the tensor is symmetric; if it is antisymmetric such elements have the same absolute value but opposite signs, and the elements in the main diagonal are zero. The matrix of a symmetric tensor is therefore specified by six numbers and that of an antisymmetric tensor by three.

In the identity

$$T_{ij} = \tfrac{1}{2}(T_{ij} + T_{ji}) + \tfrac{1}{2}(T_{ij} - T_{ji}), \tag{4.12}$$

the first term of the right side is a symmetric and the second term an antisymmetric tensor. An arbitrary tensor may therefore be written as the sum of a symmetric and an antisymmetric tensor. We leave it to the reader to show that this decomposition is unique.

The two terms of the right side of (4.12) are called the symmetric and the antisymmetric part of the tensor T_{ij}; they are abbreviated by $T_{(ij)}$ and $T_{[ij]}$, respectively. In symbolic notation (4.12) is written as

$$\mathsf{T} = \tfrac{1}{2}(\mathsf{T} + \mathsf{T}^T) + \tfrac{1}{2}(\mathsf{T} - \mathsf{T}^T). \tag{4.13}$$

Strictly speaking, special operation symbols should be used in (4.13) to indicate the sum of two tensors and the multiplication of a tensor by a scalar. Moreover, the distributive and associative laws needed for the verification of (4.13) would have to be established separately, if the symbolic tensor notation were to be developed independently of the Cartesian notation.

Before introducing further operations with tensors, we generalize the tensor concept.

5. Generalization. The first definition of the tensor concept in Section 4 is obtained from the corresponding definition of the vector concept by replacing the words "scalar" and "vector" by the words "vector" and "tensor" respectively. This remark suggests the inductive construction of a hierarchy of quantities. For the purpose of a general definition it is convenient to introduce the alternative terms "tensor of the order zero," "tensor of the order one," and "tensor of the order two" for the scalar, the vector, and the tensor considered above. *A tensor of the order n then associates a tensor of the order n − 1 with each direction in space by means of an expression that is linear and homogeneous in the direction cosines.* Since it is not possible to devise a special typographical characterization for each new order, use of the symbolic notation is restricted to relations involving only the first few orders.

With respect to a coordinate system x_i, a tensor $\mathfrak{T}$ of the third order is specified by three tensors of the second order, namely its *values* for the coordinate directions. If these are denoted by T_1, T_2, T_3, the value of $\mathfrak{T}$ for the direction μ is given by

$$\mathsf{T}^{(\mu)} = \mathsf{T}_1 \cos(\mu, x_1) + \mathsf{T}_2 \cos(\mu, x_2) + \mathsf{T}_3 \cos(\mu, x_3). \tag{5.1}$$

If μ coincides with the x'_1-direction of a second coordinate system, we have again $\mu_i = c_{i1}$ and the value of $\mathfrak{T}$ for the x'_1-direction is

$$\mathsf{T}'_1 = c_{i1}\mathsf{T}_i. \tag{5.2}$$

With respect to the unprimed coordinates, the tensor T_1 is given by its nine components, which will be denoted by T_{1jk}. Similarly, the unprimed components of the tensors T_2 and T_3 will be denoted by T_{2jk} and T_{3jk}, respectively. The twenty-seven quantities T_{ijk} are called the components of $\mathfrak{T}$ in the unprimed coordinate system; the components T'_{ijk} of this tensor in the primed system are defined in an analogous manner.

Consider now those components of the tensor equation (5.2) which correspond to the x'_m- and x'_n-directions. On the left-hand side, we obtain T'_{1mn}, while according to (4.4) the required components of the tensor T_i on the right side have the value $c_{jm}c_{kn}T_{ijk}$. Thus,

$$T'_{1mn} = c_{i1}c_{jm}c_{kn}T_{ijk}. \tag{5.3}$$

Replacing the subscript 1 in (5.3) by l, we obtain the general transformation formula for the components of a tensor of the third order:

$$T'_{lmn} = c_{il}c_{jm}c_{kn}T_{ijk}. \tag{5.4}$$

This transformation formula may be used as the basis of an alternative definition of the concept of a third-order tensor.

The transformation formula for a tensor $\mathfrak{T}$ of the order n can be obtained in a similar manner. The definition given above immediately yields

$$\mathscr{T}_p' = c_{ip}\mathscr{T}_i, \tag{5.5}$$

where the script letters indicate tensors of the order $n - 1$. Specifically, $\mathscr{T}_1'$ is the value of $\mathfrak{T}$ for the direction x'_1, and $\mathscr{T}_i$ the value for the direction x_i. Using the primed components of these tensors and the transformation formula for the components of tensors of the order $n - 1$, one obtains the following transformation formula for the components of tensors of the order n:

$$T'_{pqr\cdots} = c_{ip}c_{jq}c_{kr}\cdots T_{ijk\cdots}; \tag{5.6}$$

here the n subscripts on the left side appear as second subscripts in the n coefficients c on the right side, while the first subscripts of these coefficients are repeated as subscripts of T.

This transformation formula yields the following second definition of the general tensor concept: *In any rectangular Cartesian coordinate system, a tensor of the order n is defined by 3^n components that transform according to (5.6) under the coordinate transformation (2.7).*

To familiarize himself with the transformation formula (5.6), the reader may prove the theorems that form the basis for the following tensor operations.†

(*i*) *Multiplication with a scalar.* Multiplication of all components of a tensor with the same scalar furnishes a second tensor of the same order, which is called the *product* of the first tensor with the scalar. (In symbolic notation, $T_{ij} = \lambda S_{ij}$ is written as $\mathsf{T} = \lambda\mathsf{S}$.)

(*ii*) *Addition.* Addition of corresponding components of two tensors of

† Since the symbolic notation will not be used when tensors of the third or higher orders are involved, examples of this notation are restricted to tensors of the orders zero, one, and two.

the same order furnishes a third tensor of this order, which is called the *sum* of the first two tensors. (In symbolic notation, $T_{ij} = R_{ij} + S_{ij}$ is written as $\mathbf{T} = \mathbf{R} + \mathbf{S}$.)

(*iii*) *Multiplication.* The totality of all products that contain one component each of two tensors constitutes a third tensor, which is called the *product* of the first two tensors. The order of this product is the sum of the orders of the factors. (For example, the product $T_{ijk} = R_{ij}S_k$ of the second-order tensor R_{ij} and the vector S_k is a tensor of the third order. In symbolic notation, $T_{ij} = u_iv_j$ is written as $\mathbf{T} = \mathbf{uv}$. It should be noted that this product of two vectors without a multiplication symbol does not enjoy the commutative property: $\mathbf{vu}$ is the transpose $\mathbf{T}^T$ of the tensor $\mathbf{T} = \mathbf{uv}$.)

(*iv*) *Contraction.* Making two letter subscripts of a tensor of the order n the same, produces a tensor of the order $n - 2$, which is called the *contraction* of the original tensor with respect to these subscripts. (For example, contraction of the second-order tensor T_{ij} furnishes the scalar $T_{ii} = T_{11} + T_{22} + T_{33}$, which is called the *trace* of the tensor T_{ij}. In symbolic notation, the trace of $\mathbf{T}$ is written as $\operatorname{tr} \mathbf{T}$. The scalar product of the vectors a_i and b_j can be regarded as the trace of the tensor $T_{ij} = a_ib_j$. The *powers* of a tensor of the second order furnish further examples of contraction. The square of the tensor T_{ij} is defined as the tensor $T_{ip}T_{pj}$, the cube as $T_{ip}T_{pq}T_{qj}$, the fourth power as $T_{ip}T_{pq}T_{qr}T_{rj}$, etc. In symbolic notation, the powers of the tensor $\mathbf{T}$ are written as $\mathbf{T}^2$, $\mathbf{T}^3$, $\mathbf{T}^4$, etc. Other examples of symbolic notation are $\mathbf{u}\cdot\mathbf{T}$ for the vector u_pT_{pi}, $\mathbf{T}\cdot\mathbf{u}$ for $T_{ip}u_p$, $\mathbf{S}\cdot\mathbf{T}$ for the second-order tensor $S_{ip}T_{pj}$, and $\mathbf{S}:\mathbf{T}$ or $\operatorname{tr}(\mathbf{S}\cdot\mathbf{T})$ for the scalar $S_{pq}T_{qp}$. These examples illustrate the rapid increase in the number of operations that must be considered when tensors of higher orders are involved. The corresponding number of special operation symbols taxes the memory and obstructs the adoption of a uniform notation. For instance, if $\mathbf{S}$ and $\mathbf{T}$ are tensors of the second order, the notation $\mathbf{ST}$ is used by some authors for the second-order tensor $S_{ip}T_{pj}$ and by others for the fourth-order tensor $S_{ij}T_{kl}$.)

(*v*) *Formation of isomers.* Permutation of two subscripts of a tensor furnishes another tensor of the same order, which is called an isomer of the first tensor. (The transpose of a tensor of the second order is the only isomer of this tensor; a tensor T_{ijk} of the third order, however, has the isomers T_{ikj}, T_{jik}, T_{jki}, T_{kij}, T_{kji}.)

A tensor is said to be *symmetric* with respect to two subscripts if it equals the isomer obtained by exchanging these subscripts; if this isomer must be multiplied by -1 to equal the given tensor, the latter is called *antisymmetric.* The reader will easily verify that these definitions include those introduced in Section 4.

In connection with these concepts, the following argument is often used: If $S_{pqij\cdots}$ is symmetric and $T_{pqmn\cdots}$ antisymmetric with respect to the subscripts p and q, then $S_{pqij\cdots}T_{pqmn\cdots} = 0$. Indeed, the sum indicated by the dummy subscripts p and q contains, for instance, the term for $p = 1$, $q = 2$ as well as the term for $p = 2$, $q = 1$. The sum of these two terms vanishes because $S_{12ij\cdots} = S_{21ij\cdots}$ and $T_{12mn\cdots} = -T_{21mn\cdots}$. Using this argument, one readily establishes the following identity for *arbitrary* tensors of the second order:

$$S_{ij}T_{ji} = \{S_{(ij)} + S_{[ij]}\}.\{T_{(ji)} + T_{[ji]}\} = S_{(ij)}T_{(ji)} + S_{[ij]}T_{[ji]}; \quad (5.7)$$

here the notation introduced in Section 4 is used: $S_{(ij)}$ is the symmetric and $S_{[ij]}$ the antisymmetric part of the tensor S_{ij}.

We finally discuss useful criteria for the tensor character of geometrical or physical quantities. With respect to the rectangular Cartesian coordinate systems x_i and x'_i, let such a quantity be determined by the 3^3 numbers A_{ijk} or A'_{ijk} and assume that

$$A'_{pqr}u'_pv'_qw'_r = A_{ijk}u_iv_jw_k \quad (5.8)$$

for any choice of the vectors $\mathbf{u}$, $\mathbf{v}$, and $\mathbf{w}$. It can then be shown that the numbers A_{ijk} and A'_{ijk} are the components of a tensor of the third order with respect to the coordinate systems x_i and x'_i, respectively. To prove this, use (3.6) to express the unprimed vector components in (5.8) by the primed components; thus,

$$(A'_{pqr} - c_{ip}c_{jq}c_{kr}A_{ijk})u'_pv'_qw'_r = 0. \quad (5.9)$$

The left side of this equation is a trilinear form of the components of the vectors $\mathbf{u}$, $\mathbf{v}$, and $\mathbf{w}$, which vanishes identically only when all coefficients vanish, i.e., when the parenthesis in (5.9) vanishes for all values of the subscripts p, q, and r. This condition establishes the fact that A_{ijk} and A'_{ijk} are the components of a third-order tensor with respect to the unprimed and primed coordinate systems.

In a similar manner, it can be shown that A_{ijk} is a tensor of the third order, if it is known that $A_{ijk}B_{ij}$ is a vector for any choice of the second-order tensor B_{ij}.

For the sake of brevity, only a third-order tensor was considered above, but the generalization to tensors of any order is straightforward and can be left to the reader. The general form of this criterion is called the *quotient law* of tensor algebra.

6. The ϵ-tensor. Let u_i, v_j, w_k be the vectors from the origin O to the points U, V, W. The four points O, U, V, W are not supposed to be coplanar and no three of them are supposed to be collinear. In the plane OUV, the directions of the vectors u_i and v_j determine a sense of rotation: the direction of the second vector is obtained from that of the first by a rotation of less than 180° in this sense. This sense of rotation and the direction of the component of w_k that is normal to the plane OUV correspond to the sense of rotation and the direction of progression of either a right-handed or a left-handed screw. The system of the vectors u_i, v_j, w_k is called *right-handed* in the first case, and *left-handed* in the second.

It should be noted that these definitions involve only the directions but not the magnitudes of the three vectors. Applying these definitions to the positive directions of the coordinate axes, one can therefore distinguish between right-handed and left-handed coordinate systems. If thumb, index and middle finger of the right hand are extended to form right angles with each other, they indicate the positive directions of the axes of a right-handed coordinate system.

Consider the parallelepiped specified by the edges OU, OV, and OW. It is known from analytic geometry that the absolute value of the determinant

$$D = \begin{vmatrix} u_1 & v_1 & w_1 \\ u_2 & v_2 & w_2 \\ u_3 & v_3 & w_3 \end{vmatrix} \tag{6.1}$$

represents the volume of this parallelepiped, and that D is positive if and only if the coordinate system and the system of the vectors u_i, v_j, w_k are of the same character, that is, if both are right-handed or both are left-handed.

For fixed vectors u_i, v_j, w_k, the volume of the parallelepiped is independent of the coordinate system, and therefore a scalar. The determinant D, however, changes sign when one passes from a right-handed to a left-handed coordinate system. This kind of quantity is called a *pseudo-scalar*.

Any requirement that a distinction be made between genuine scalars and pseudo-scalars, or generally genuine tensors and pseudo-tensors, would complicate the discussion. To avoid this difficulty, *only right-handed coordinate systems will be considered in the remainder of this book.* Since the determinant D does not change sign in the transition from one right-handed coordinate system to another, this convention lets D appear as a genuine scalar. Quite generally, the restriction to right-handed coordinate systems abolishes the need of distinguishing between genuine tensors and pseudo-tensors.

To write the determinant D in a concise manner, introduce the following quantity:

$$\epsilon_{ijk} = \left\{ \begin{array}{r} 1 \\ -1 \\ 0 \end{array} \right\} \begin{array}{l} \text{according to} \\ \text{whether } i, j, k \end{array} \left\{ \begin{array}{l} \text{form an even} \\ \text{form an odd} \\ \text{do not form a} \end{array} \right\} \begin{array}{l} \text{permutation} \\ \text{of } 1,\ 2,\ 3. \end{array} \tag{6.2}$$

Note that it follows from this definition that

$$\epsilon_{ijk} = \epsilon_{jki} = \epsilon_{kij} = -\epsilon_{jik} = -\epsilon_{ikj} = -\epsilon_{kji}. \tag{6.3}$$

With the use of (6.2), the equation (6.1) may be written as

$$D = \epsilon_{ijk} u_i v_j w_k. \tag{6.4}$$

Indeed, the reader will easily verify that, in view of the definition (6.2) of ϵ_{ijk}, the triple sum indicated by the dummy subscripts i, j, k on the right of (6.4) is the explicit form of the determinant (6.1).

For any choice of the vectors u_i, v_j, w_k in (6.4), the determinant D is a scalar. According to the criterion established at the end of the preceding section, ϵ_{ijk} is therefore a tensor of the third order; it will be called the *ϵ-tensor*. To familiarize himself with this tensor, the reader may prove the following formulas:

$$\left.\begin{aligned} \epsilon_{pqr}\epsilon_{pqr} &= 6, \\ \epsilon_{pqi}\epsilon_{pqj} &= 2\delta_{ij}, \\ \epsilon_{pij}\epsilon_{pkl} &= \delta_{ik}\delta_{jl} - \delta_{il}\delta_{jk}. \end{aligned}\right\} \tag{6.5}$$

The relation

$$t_i = \epsilon_{ijk} T_{jk} \tag{6.6}$$

associates a vector t_i with each second-order tensor T_{jk}. This vector $\mathbf{t}$, which has the components

$$t_1 = T_{23} - T_{32}, \quad t_2 = T_{31} - T_{13}, \quad t_3 = T_{12} - T_{21}, \tag{6.7}$$

is called the *dual vector* of the tensor T. As is seen from (6.7), the dual vector of a tensor of the second order depends only on the antisymmetric part of this tensor. The dual vector of a symmetric tensor vanishes, and conversely, the vanishing of the dual vector shows that the tensor is symmetric.

From (6.6) and the last equation (6.5) it follows that $\epsilon_{ijk} t_i = T_{jk} - T_{kj}$. If the tensor T_{jk} is antisymmetric, the relation (6.6) has therefore the unique inverse

$$T_{jk} = \tfrac{1}{2}\epsilon_{ijk} t_i. \tag{6.8}$$

On the other hand, (6.8) may be considered as the definition of the *dual* (antisymmetric) *tensor* of a given vector.

The product $u_j v_k$ of two vectors u_j and v_k is a tensor; its dual vector

$$w_i = \epsilon_{ijk} u_j v_k \tag{6.9}$$

is called the *vector product* of u_j and v_k. In symbolic notation, (6.9) is written as $\mathbf{w} = \mathbf{u} \times \mathbf{w}$. Scalar multiplication of the vector product with one of its factors, say u_i, furnishes $u_i w_i = \epsilon_{ijk} u_i u_j v_k$. On the right-hand side of this relation, ϵ_{ijk} is antisymmetric with respect to i and j, and $u_i u_j$ is symmetric. The scalar product $u_i w_i$ vanishes therefore, and the same is true for the scalar product $v_i w_i$. In other terms, the vector product $\mathbf{w} = \mathbf{u} \times \mathbf{v}$ is normal to its factors $\mathbf{u}$ and $\mathbf{v}$.

Multiplication of (6.9) with w_i furnishes

$$w_i w_i = \epsilon_{ijk} w_i u_j v_k. \tag{6.10}$$

According to (6.4), the right side of (6.10) represents the algebraic volume of the parallelepiped with the edge vectors w_i, u_j, v_k. Since the left-hand side of (6.10) is a sum of squares and therefore positive, the vectors w_i, u_j and v_k form a right-handed system. Since, moreover, the edge w_i is normal to the base formed by u_j and v_k, the volume of the parallelepiped equals the product of the length w of this edge with the area of the base. On the other hand, (6.10) gives the volume as w^2. It follows that the magnitude w of the vector product $\mathbf{w} = \mathbf{u} \times \mathbf{v}$ represents the area of the parallelogram specified by the factors $\mathbf{u}$ and $\mathbf{v}$. If the magnitudes of these factors are denoted by u and v, and their directions by μ and ν, the magnitude of the vector product is $w = uv \sin(\mu, \nu)$. This magnitude and the facts that $\mathbf{w}$ is normal to $\mathbf{u}$ and $\mathbf{v}$, and that the vectors $\mathbf{w}$, $\mathbf{u}$, $\mathbf{v}$ form a right-handed system, specify the vector product independently of the coordinate system. The vector product of two parallel vectors vanishes, and conversely, when the vector product of two nonvanishing vectors is zero, these vectors are parallel.

To familiarize himself with the vector product, the reader may use the definition (6.9) to establish the following relations:

$$\left.\begin{aligned} \lambda(\mathbf{u} \times \mathbf{v}) &= (\lambda\mathbf{u}) \times \mathbf{v} = \mathbf{u} \times (\lambda\mathbf{v}), \\ \mathbf{r} \times (\mathbf{u} + \mathbf{v}) &= \mathbf{r} \times \mathbf{u} + \mathbf{r} \times \mathbf{v}, \\ \mathbf{u} \times \mathbf{v} &= -\mathbf{v} \times \mathbf{u}; \end{aligned}\right\} \tag{6.11}$$

$$\left.\begin{aligned} \mathbf{t} \times (\mathbf{u} \times \mathbf{v}) &= \mathbf{u}(\mathbf{t}\cdot\mathbf{v}) - \mathbf{v}(\mathbf{t}\cdot\mathbf{u}), \\ (\mathbf{s} \times \mathbf{t})\cdot(\mathbf{u} \times \mathbf{v}) &= (\mathbf{s}\cdot\mathbf{u})(\mathbf{t}\cdot\mathbf{v}) - (\mathbf{s}\cdot\mathbf{v})(\mathbf{t}\cdot\mathbf{u}), \\ (\mathbf{s} \times \mathbf{t}) \times (\mathbf{u} \times \mathbf{v}) &= \mathbf{t}[\mathbf{s}\cdot(\mathbf{u} \times \mathbf{v})] - \mathbf{s}[\mathbf{t}\cdot(\mathbf{u} \times \mathbf{v})]. \end{aligned}\right\} \tag{6.12}$$

In the last of these equations the parentheses on the right-hand side may be omitted, because the multiplications indicated by the dot and cross in, say, $\mathbf{s}\cdot\mathbf{u} \times \mathbf{v}$ can only be combined as $\mathbf{s}\cdot(\mathbf{u} \times \mathbf{v})$.

With the use of the dual tensor of one of its factors (see 6.8), the vector product may be written as follows:

$$\epsilon_{ijk} s_j t_k = s_j \epsilon_{kij} t_k = 2 s_j T_{ij} = s_j (T_{ij} - T_{ji}). \tag{6.13}$$

In (6.13), the antisymmetry of the dual tensor has been used in the transition to the last expression for the vector product.

The following examples for the use of the vector product in mechanics will conclude this section. Let the force $\mathbf{P}$ have the point of application with the radius vector $\mathbf{x}$; the *moment* of this force with respect to the point $\mathbf{x}^{(0)}$ is defined as the vector

$$\mathbf{M} = (\mathbf{x} - \mathbf{x}^{(0)}) \times \mathbf{P}. \tag{6.14}$$

In Cartesian notation, this definition is written as

$$M_i = \epsilon_{ijk}(x_j - x_j^{(0)})P_k. \tag{6.15}$$

The forces $\mathbf{P}^{(\nu)}$ with the points of application $\mathbf{x}^{(\nu)}$ form an equilibrium system, if their sum as well as the sum of their moments with respect to the origin vanishes:

$$\sum_\nu \mathbf{P}^{(\nu)} = 0, \quad \sum_\nu \mathbf{x}^{(\nu)} \times \mathbf{P}^{(\nu)} = 0. \tag{6.16}$$

It follows from (6.16) that the sum of the moments of the forces of an equilibrium system with respect to an arbitrary point vanishes.

Another important application of the vector product is found in kinematics. Consider a rigid body that instantaneously rotates about an axis through the point $\mathbf{x}^{(0)}$. The angular velocity ω, the direction of the axis of rotation, and the sense of rotation can be indicated by a vector $\boldsymbol{\omega}$ of the magnitude ω, which is parallel to the axis of rotation and points in the direction of progress of a right-handed screw that is turning in the same sense as the rigid body. The velocity of the point $\mathbf{x}$ of the rigid body may then be written as

$$\mathbf{v} = \boldsymbol{\omega} \times (\mathbf{x} - \mathbf{x}^{(0)}) \tag{6.17}$$

or

$$v_i = \epsilon_{ijk}\omega_j(x_k - x_k^{(0)}). \tag{6.18}$$

By using the dual tensor

$$\Omega_{jk} = \tfrac{1}{2}\epsilon_{ijk}\omega_i \tag{6.19}$$

of the vector ω_i, one may also write this velocity in the form

$$v_i = 2\Omega_{ki}(x_k - x_k^{(0)}). \tag{6.20}$$

7. Principal axes of a symmetric tensor of the second order. This section will be concerned with the correspondence that a *symmetric* tensor of the second order establishes between vectors and the directions of space.

The direction specified by the unit vector μ_i will be called a *principal direction* of the symmetric tensor T_{ij}, if the associated vector $T_{ij}\mu_i$ is parallel to μ_i, that is, if this vector can be written in the form $T\mu_j$, where T is a scalar. Strictly speaking, the case $T = 0$ should be excluded, since the direction of a vanishing vector is not determined. To avoid this exception, we stipulate that the direction μ_i is also to be considered as principal, if the associated vector $T_{ij}\mu_i$ vanishes. For a principal direction μ_i of a symmetric tensor T_{ij}, we then have the relation $T_{ij}\mu_i - T\mu_j = 0$ or

$$(T_{ij} - T\delta_{ij})\mu_i = 0. \tag{7.1}$$

This relation represents a system of three linear homogeneous equations for the components of the unit vector μ_i. Since the trivial solution $\mu_i = 0$ is not compatible with the condition $\mu_i\mu_i = 1$, the determinant of the coefficients in (7.1) must vanish, if this system is to admit a solution. Indicating this determinant by its typical element, we write this condition in the form

$$|T_{ij} - T\delta_{ij}| = 0. \tag{7.2}$$

Before discussing this condition, we show that it also arises in connection with another problem. To the direction μ_i there corresponds the vector $T_{ij}\mu_i$; its projection on the considered direction is given by $T^{(\mu\mu)} = T_{ij}\mu_i\mu_j$ and will be called the *normal component* of the tensor T_{ij} for the direction μ_i. Considering $T^{(\mu\mu)}$ as a function of the components of μ_i, we propose to determine the latter in such a manner that $T^{(\mu\mu)}$ remains stationary in the transition to neighboring directions. In view of the subsidiary condition $\mu_i\mu_i = 1$, this means that we are looking for the stationary values of

$$(T_{ij} - T\delta_{ij})\mu_i\mu_j, \tag{7.3}$$

where T is a Lagrangian factor. To evaluate the derivative of (7.3) with respect to a component of the vector $\boldsymbol{\mu}$, say with respect to μ_p, we remark that the derivative of μ_i with respect to μ_p is δ_{ip}. Setting the derivative of (7.3) with respect to μ_p equal to zero, we obtain the relation

$$(T_{ij} - T\delta_{ij})(\delta_{ip}\mu_j + \mu_i\delta_{jp}) = (T_{pj} - T\delta_{pj})\mu_j + (T_{ip} - T\delta_{ip})\mu_i = 0,$$

which can be transformed into (7.1) by choosing appropriate dummy subscripts and using the symmetry of the tensors T_{ij} and δ_{ij}.

It is worth noting that the Lagrangian factor T in (7.3) represents the stationary value of the normal component $T^{(\mu\mu)}$. Indeed, multiplication of (7.1) by μ_j shows that

$$T^{(\mu\mu)} = T_{ij}\mu_i\mu_j = T\delta_{ij}\mu_i\mu_j = T, \tag{7.4}$$

as μ_i is a unit vector.

Development of the determinant in (7.2) furnishes a cubic equation for T; this is called the *characteristic equation* of the symmetric tensor T_{ij} and will be written in the form

$$T^3 - \mathcal{T}_{(1)}T^2 - \mathcal{T}_{(2)}T - \mathcal{T}_{(3)} = 0. \tag{7.5}$$

Since the roots of this equation represent the stationary values of the normal component $T^{(\mu\mu)}$, which are independent of the coordinate system, the coefficients $\mathcal{T}_{(1)}$, $\mathcal{T}_{(2)}$, $\mathcal{T}_{(3)}$ must likewise be independent of the coordinate system. These coefficients are therefore scalars; they will be called the *basic invariants* of the symmetric tensor T_{ij}. The first of these invariants

$$\mathcal{T}_{(1)} = T_{ii} \tag{7.6}$$

is the sum of the elements in the main diagonal of the matrix of T_{ij}. The second basic invariant $\mathcal{T}_{(2)}$ is the negative sum of the minors of these elements; † since the minor of the element T_{ij} is

$$t_{ij} = \tfrac{1}{2}\epsilon_{ipq}\epsilon_{jrs}T_{pr}T_{qs}, \tag{7.7}$$

use of the third equation (6.5) furnishes

$$\mathscr{T}_{(2)} = -t_{ii} = \tfrac{1}{2}(T_{ij}T_{ji} - T_{ii}T_{jj}). \tag{7.8}$$

Finally, $\mathscr{T}_{(3)}$ is the determinant of the matrix of T_{ij}; it can be written as

$$\mathscr{T}_{(3)} = \tfrac{1}{6}\epsilon_{ijk}\epsilon_{pqr}T_{ip}T_{jq}T_{kr} \tag{7.9}$$

or

$$\mathscr{T}_{(3)} = \tfrac{1}{6}(2T_{ij}T_{jk}T_{ki} - 3T_{ij}T_{ji}T_{kk} + T_{ii}T_{jj}T_{kk}). \tag{7.10}$$

The fact that the relations (7.6), (7.8), and (7.10) contain only dummy subscripts indicates the scalar character of $\mathscr{T}_{(1)}$, $\mathscr{T}_{(2)}$, and $\mathscr{T}_{(3)}$ independently of the reasons given above.

The roots of the characteristic equation (7.5), which are independent of the coordinate system, are called the *principal values* of the symmetric tensor T_{ij}. At least one of these principal values must be real; it will be denoted by T_{I}.

For $T = T_{\mathrm{I}}$, the linear homogeneous equations (7.1) furnish at least one principal direction μ_i^{I}. If the x_1'-axis of a new coordinate system is given this direction, the associated vector $T_{ij}\mu_i^{\mathrm{I}} = T_{\mathrm{I}}\mu_j^{\mathrm{I}}$ has the primed components $T_{11}' = T_{\mathrm{I}}$, $T_{12}' = T_{13}' = 0$. On account of the symmetry of T_{ij} the characteristic equation of this tensor takes the following form in the primed coordinate system:

$$\begin{vmatrix} T_{\mathrm{I}} - T & 0 & 0 \\ 0 & T_{22}' - T & T_{23}' \\ 0 & T_{23}' & T_{33}' - T \end{vmatrix} = 0$$

or

$$(T_{\mathrm{I}} - T)[T^2 - (T_{22}' + T_{33}')T + T_{22}'T_{33}' - T_{23}'^2] = 0. \tag{7.11}$$

The remaining principal values T_{II} and T_{III} are therefore the roots of the quadratic equation that is obtained by setting the bracket in (7.11) equal to zero. The discriminant

$$(T_{22}' + T_{33}')^2 - 4(T_{22}'T_{33}' - T_{23}'^2) = (T_{22}' - T_{33}')^2 + 4T_{23}'^2 \tag{7.12}$$

of this quadratic equation can be written as the sum of two squares and is therefore non-negative. Accordingly, the roots T_{II} and T_{III} of this quadratic equation are real, and we have the following result: *The principal values of a symmetric tensor are real.*

If the unit vectors μ_i^{II} and μ_i^{III} indicate principal directions corresponding

† In tensor algebra the second invariant is usually defined as the sum of these minors. As in mechanics of continua this sum invariably appears with the minus sign, the definition introduced above is more convenient.

to the principal values T_{II} and T_{III}, respectively, (7.1) furnishes the relations

$$(T_{ij} - T_{\text{II}}\delta_{ij})\mu_i^{\text{II}} = 0, \quad (T_{ij} - T_{\text{III}}\delta_{ij})\mu_i^{\text{III}} = 0. \tag{7.13}$$

Multiplying these equations by μ_j^{III} and μ_j^{II}, respectively, and subtracting, we obtain

$$(T_{\text{II}} - T_{\text{III}})\mu_i^{\text{II}}\mu_i^{\text{III}} = 0. \tag{7.14}$$

For $T_{\text{II}} \neq T_{\text{III}}$, it follows from (7.14) that the principal directions μ_i^{II} and μ_i^{III} are orthogonal: *Principal directions that correspond to distinct principal values are orthogonal.* An important consequence of this result is that the principal directions are uniquely determined when the principal values T_{I}, T_{II}, and T_{III} are distinct. Indeed, if the principal directions were not uniquely determined, each first principal direction would have to be orthogonal to each second and to each third principal direction, and each second principal direction would have to be orthogonal to each third principal direction, in contradiction to the fact that in three-dimensional space not more than three directions can be orthogonal to each other.

The tensor with the distinct principal values T_{I}, T_{II}, T_{III} and the corresponding orthogonal principal directions μ_i^{I}, μ_i^{II}, μ_i^{III} can be written as

$$T_{ij} = T_{\text{I}}\mu_i^{\text{I}}\mu_j^{\text{I}} + T_{\text{II}}\mu_i^{\text{II}}\mu_j^{\text{II}} + T_{\text{III}}\mu_i^{\text{III}}\mu_j^{\text{III}}. \tag{7.15}$$

Indeed, with the direction μ_i^{I} the tensor (7.15) associates the vector $T_{\text{I}}\mu_j^{\text{I}}$, which has this direction, and similar remarks apply to the directions μ_i^{II} and μ_i^{III}. If the coordinate axes are given the principal directions, the matrix of the tensor (7.15) has the diagonal form

$$T = \begin{bmatrix} T_{\text{I}} & 0 & 0 \\ 0 & T_{\text{II}} & 0 \\ 0 & 0 & T_{\text{III}} \end{bmatrix}. \tag{7.16}$$

Conversely, three orthogonal axes are called *principal axes* of a symmetric tensor of the second order, if for these axes the matrix of this tensor assumes the diagonal form. When the principal values are distinct, there exists only a single system of principal axes.

If, on the other hand, $T_{\text{II}} = T_{\text{III}}$, the discriminant (7.12) vanishes, that is, $T'_{22} = T'_{33}$ and $T'_{23} = 0$. The quadratic equation obtained by setting the bracket in (7.11) equal to zero then has the roots $T_{\text{II}} = T_{\text{III}} = T'_{22} = T'_{33}$, and the matrix of the considered tensor has a diagonal form independent of the choice of the x'_2- and x'_3-axes, if the x'_1-axis is given the first principal direction μ_i^{I}.

The preceding discussion shows that *a symmetric tensor of the second order admits at least one system of principal axes.* Let μ_i^{I}, μ_i^{II}, and μ_i^{III} be unit vectors in the principal directions that correspond to the principal values T_{I}, T_{II}, and T_{III}, respectively. It has been shown above that the principal axes are uniquely determined when the principal values are distinct. If two principal values, for instance T_{II} and T_{III}, are equal to each other but distinct from the third principal value (T_{I}), it follows from the linearity of (7.13) that any unit vector obtained by linearly combining μ_i^{II} and μ_i^{III} indicates a principal direction. Since any principal direction corresponding to T_{I} must be orthogonal to all principal directions obtained in this manner, there is only a single principal axis associated with the principal value T_{I}. Accordingly, we have a one-parameter family of systems of principal axes; from one of these all others may be obtained by rotation about the first principal axis. If, finally, all three principal values are equal, any unit vector obtained by linearly combining μ_i^{I}, μ_i^{II}, and μ_i^{III} indicates a principal direction. In other words, any direction of space is a principal direction, and any system of rectangular axes is a system of principal axes.

The reduction of the matrix of a symmetric tensor T_{ij} to diagonal form leads to a simple definition of the powers of such a tensor. In Section 5, the tensor $T_{ip}T_{pj}$ was introduced as the square, the tensor $T_{ip}T_{pq}T_{qj}$ as the cube of T_{ij}, etc. It is readily seen that all these powers are symmetric, if the tensor T_{ij} is symmetric. If (7.16) is the matrix of T with respect to a system of principal axes, the matrix of T^n with respect to the same system of axes is

$$\mathsf{T}^n = \begin{bmatrix} T_{\mathrm{I}}^n & 0 & 0 \\ 0 & T_{\mathrm{II}}^n & 0 \\ 0 & 0 & T_{\mathrm{III}}^n \end{bmatrix}, \tag{7.17}$$

where n is a positive integer. Since the matrix (7.17) has diagonal form, the tensors T and T^n have the same principal axes.

Each of the principal values T_{I}, T_{II}, and T_{III} of the tensor T must fulfill the characteristic equation (7.5). In view of (7.17) these three conditions may be combined to form the following tensor equation

$$\mathsf{T}^3 = \mathscr{T}_{(1)}\mathsf{T}^2 + \mathscr{T}_{(2)}\mathsf{T} + \mathscr{T}_{(3)}\boldsymbol{\delta}, \tag{7.18}$$

which is called the *Hamilton-Cayley equation;* it represents T^3 as a linear combination of the tensors T^2, T, and $\boldsymbol{\delta}$.

Multiplying every term of (7.18) by T in the manner indicated by $\mathsf{T}\cdot$, one obtains

$$\mathsf{T}^4 = \mathscr{T}_{(1)}\mathsf{T}^3 + \mathscr{T}_{(2)}\mathsf{T}^2 + \mathscr{T}_{(3)}\mathsf{T}$$

or, with the use of (7.18),

$$\mathsf{T}^4 = (\mathscr{T}_{(1)}^2 + \mathscr{T}_{(2)})\mathsf{T}^2 + (\mathscr{T}_{(1)}\mathscr{T}_{(2)} + \mathscr{T}_{(3)})\mathsf{T} + \mathscr{T}_{(1)}\mathscr{T}_{(3)}\boldsymbol{\delta}. \tag{7.19}$$

Continuing in this way, one can express all positive integer powers of T as linear combinations of T^2, T, and $\boldsymbol{\delta}$. The coefficients in these linear combinations are polynomials in the basic invariants $\mathscr{T}_{(1)}$, $\mathscr{T}_{(2)}$, and $\mathscr{T}_{(3)}$. According to (7.6), (7.8) and (7.10), these invariants may be expressed in terms of the traces

$$\operatorname{tr} \mathsf{T} = T_{ii}, \quad \operatorname{tr} \mathsf{T}^2 = T_{ij}T_{ji}, \quad \operatorname{tr} \mathsf{T}^3 = T_{ij}T_{jk}T_{ki}. \tag{7.20}$$

The relations between these traces and the basic invariants take particularly simple forms for a *deviator*, that is a second-order tensor with vanishing trace. If the basic invariants of the deviator D are denoted by $\mathscr{D}_{(1)}$, $\mathscr{D}_{(2)}$, and $\mathscr{D}_{(3)}$, we have

$$\mathscr{D}_{(1)} = \operatorname{tr} \mathsf{D} = 0, \quad \mathscr{D}_{(2)} = \tfrac{1}{2} \operatorname{tr} \mathsf{D}^2, \quad \mathscr{D}_{(3)} = \tfrac{1}{3} \operatorname{tr} \mathsf{D}^3. \tag{7.21}$$

8. Tensor fields. With each point P of a finite region R let there be associated a tensor $\mathfrak{T}$ of the order n, the components of which are continuous functions of the position of P. To express this situation concisely, one says that a continuous *tensor field* of the the order n has been defined in R. With respect to the rectangular Cartesian coordinates x_i a continuous tensor field of, say, the order two is specified by nine continuous functions of position $T_{ij}(x_1, x_2, x_3)$. In the following, the letter x will be used to indicate the three arguments x_1, x_2, x_3, and the components of the tensor field $T_{ij}(x_1, x_2, x_3)$ will be written as $T_{ij}(x)$. Unless the contrary is stated explicitly, all derivatives of such functions of position that occur in the investigations are supposed to exist and to be continuous.

The differential operator $\partial \cdots / \partial x_p$ will be abbreviated by ∂_p, the operator $\partial^2 \cdots / (\partial x_p \partial x_q)$ by ∂_{pq}, etc. Unless something else is indicated by parentheses, these operators will act only on the immediately following symbol. (Authors in mechanics of continua, who restrict themselves to the use of rectangular Cartesian coordinates, frequently denote derivatives such as $\partial_p T_{ij}$ and $\partial_{pq} T_{ij}$ by $T_{ij,p}$ and $T_{ij,pq}$, respectively.)

At a generic point $x_i^{(0)}$ of R, we have the Taylor development

$$T_{ijk\cdots}(x) = T_{ijk\cdots}(x^{(0)}) + (x_p - x_p{}^{(0)})\partial_p T_{ijk\cdots}(x^{(0)}) + \cdots, \tag{8.1}$$

where the dots at the end stand for higher-order terms and a remainder term. Each term of this development is a tensor of the order n. Since this statement applies to the last explicitly written term in (8.1) independent of the choice of the vector $x_p - x_p{}^{(0)}$, it follows that $\partial_p T_{ijk\cdots}$ is a tensor of the order $n + 1$. In the transition from one rectangular Cartesian coordinate system to another, the operator ∂_p behaves, therefore, as a vector; the operator $\partial_{pq} = \partial_p \partial_q$ behaves as a tensor of the second order, etc. If, for instance, v_q is a vector field, $\partial_p v_q$ is a tensor field and its trace $\partial_p v_p$ a scalar field. In symbolic notation, the operator ∂_p is represented by the symbolic vector ∇, which is pronounced "del."

A scalar field $\varphi(x)$ is geometrically represented by its *level surfaces* $\varphi =$ constant. To some extent, a vector field $v_k(x)$ is represented by its *field lines*. A field line is an oriented curve; the unit tangent vector at its generic point indicates the direction of the field vector at this point. If a complete geometrical representation of a vector field is desired, the field lines must be supplemented by the level surfaces of the magnitude of the field vector.

The *gradient* of a scalar field $\varphi(x)$ is the vector $\partial_p\varphi$; in symbolic notation, this gradient is written as $\nabla\varphi$ or grad φ. If, from a generic point P of the field, one advances by the infinitesimal distance ds in the direction of the unit vector $\boldsymbol{\mu}$, the scalar φ changes by

$$d\varphi^{(\mu)} = \mu_i\partial_i\varphi\, ds = \boldsymbol{\mu}\cdot\text{grad}\,\varphi\, ds. \tag{8.2}$$

The gradient of φ thus associates with the direction μ the scalar $d\varphi^{(\mu)}/ds$, which is called the *rate of change of* φ *in the direction* μ. The gradient $\nabla\varphi$ therefore points in the direction of the greatest rate of change, and the magnitude of $\nabla\varphi$ represents this greatest rate of change.

If the unit vector $\boldsymbol{\mu}$ is tangential to the level surface of φ through P, the rate of change of φ in the direction of $\boldsymbol{\mu}$ vanishes, that is, the scalar product of $\boldsymbol{\mu}$ and grad φ vanishes. The gradient of φ in P thus is seen to have the direction of the normal of the level surface of φ in P.

Applying the operator ∂_j to a field vector v_k, we obtain the second-order tensor $\partial_j v_k$, which is called the *vector gradient* of the given vector field. If, from a generic point P of the field, we advance by the infinitesimal distance ds in the direction of the unit vector $\boldsymbol{\mu}$, we observe the change

$$dv_k^{(\mu)} = \mu_j\partial_j v_k\, ds. \tag{8.3}$$

In symbolic notation, the right side of (8.3) is written as $(\boldsymbol{\mu}\cdot\nabla)\mathbf{v}\, ds$ or $(\boldsymbol{\mu}\cdot\text{grad})\mathbf{v}\, ds$.

The trace of the vector gradient $\partial_j v_k$ is the scalar $\partial_j v_j$, which is called the *divergence* of the vector field $v_k(x)$; in symbolic notation, this divergence is written as $\nabla\cdot\mathbf{v}$ or div $\mathbf{v}$. Carrying out the summation indicated by the dummy subscript in $\partial_j v_j$, we find

$$\text{div}\,\mathbf{v} = \frac{\partial v_1}{\partial x_1} + \frac{\partial v_2}{\partial x_2} + \frac{\partial v_3}{\partial x_3}. \tag{8.4}$$

The dual vector $\epsilon_{ijk}\partial_j v_k$ of the vector gradient $\partial_j v_k$ is called the *curl* of the vector field $v_k(x)$; in symbolic notation, this curl is written as $\nabla\times\mathbf{v}$ or curl $\mathbf{v}$. The curl has the components

$$(\text{curl}\,\mathbf{v})_1 = \frac{\partial v_3}{\partial x_2} - \frac{\partial v_2}{\partial x_3}, \quad (\text{curl}\,\mathbf{v})_2 = \frac{\partial v_1}{\partial x_3} - \frac{\partial v_3}{\partial x_1}, \quad (\text{curl}\,\mathbf{v})_3 = \frac{\partial v_2}{\partial x_1} - \frac{\partial v_1}{\partial x_2}. \tag{8.5}$$

Contraction of the operator ∂_{ij} furnishes the *Laplace operator*

$$\partial_{ii} = \frac{\partial^2}{\partial x_1^2} + \frac{\partial^2}{\partial x_2^2} + \frac{\partial^2}{\partial x_3^2}. \tag{8.6}$$

In symbolic notation, this operator is written as ∇^2 or Δ.

If the symbolic notation is used, a great number of rules concerning the derivatives of various types of products have to be memorized. Some examples of such rules are:

$$\left.\begin{aligned}\operatorname{div}(\varphi\mathbf{v}) &= \varphi \operatorname{div}\mathbf{v} + \mathbf{v}\cdot\operatorname{grad}\varphi,\\ \operatorname{div}(\mathbf{u}\times\mathbf{v}) &= \mathbf{v}\cdot\operatorname{curl}\mathbf{u} - \mathbf{u}\cdot\operatorname{curl}\mathbf{v},\\ \operatorname{curl}(\mathbf{u}\times\mathbf{v}) &= (\mathbf{v}\cdot\operatorname{grad})\mathbf{u} - (\mathbf{u}\cdot\operatorname{grad})\mathbf{v} + \mathbf{u}\operatorname{div}\mathbf{v} - \mathbf{v}\operatorname{div}\mathbf{u},\\ \operatorname{grad}(\mathbf{u}\cdot\mathbf{v}) &= (\mathbf{u}\cdot\operatorname{grad})\mathbf{v} + (\mathbf{v}\cdot\operatorname{grad}\mathbf{u}) + \mathbf{u}\times\operatorname{curl}\mathbf{v} + \mathbf{v}\times\operatorname{curl}\mathbf{u}.\end{aligned}\right\} \quad (8.7)$$

On the other hand, these rules readily follow from the Cartesian notation for the left-hand sides of (8.7) through application of (6.5) and (6.13). For instance, by means of the last equation (6.5), the i-component of the left side of the third equation (8.7) can be transformed as follows:

$$\begin{aligned}\epsilon_{ijk}\partial_j(\epsilon_{klm}u_lv_m) &= \epsilon_{kij}\epsilon_{klm}(v_m\partial_ju_l + u_l\partial_jv_m)\\ &= (\delta_{il}\delta_{jm} - \delta_{im}\delta_{jl})(v_m\partial_ju_l + u_l\partial_jv_m)\\ &= v_j\partial_ju_i - u_j\partial_jv_i + u_i\partial_jv_j - v_i\partial_ju_j.\end{aligned} \quad (8.8)$$

The last line of (8.8) represents the i-component of the right side of the third equation (8.7). Using (6.13), we readily verify the last equation (8.7) as follows:

$$\begin{aligned}\partial_i(u_jv_j) &= v_j\partial_iu_j + u_j\partial_iv_j\\ &= v_j(\partial_iu_j - \partial_ju_i) + v_j\partial_ju_i + u_j(\partial_iv_j - \partial_jv_i) + u_j\partial_jv_i\\ &= \epsilon_{ijk}v_jR_k + v_j\partial_ju_i + \epsilon_{ijk}u_jS_k + u_j\partial_jv_i;\end{aligned} \quad (8.9)$$

here R_k is the dual vector of ∂_iu_j, that is, the curl of $\mathbf{u}$, and S_k is the dual vector of ∂_iv_j, that is, the curl of $\mathbf{v}$.

We finally mention some combinations of the differential operators introduced above. The curl of the gradient of a scalar field φ is $\epsilon_{ijk}\partial_j(\partial_k\varphi) = \epsilon_{ijk}\partial_{jk}\varphi$. Now, ϵ_{ijk} is antisymmetric and ∂_{jk} is symmetric with respect to the subscripts j and k. Accordingly,

$$\operatorname{curl}\operatorname{grad}\varphi = 0. \quad (8.10)$$

The proof of the relations

$$\operatorname{div}\operatorname{grad}\varphi = \Delta\varphi, \quad (8.11)$$

$$\operatorname{div}\operatorname{curl}\mathbf{v} = 0, \quad (8.12)$$

$$\operatorname{curl}\operatorname{curl}\mathbf{v} = \operatorname{grad}\operatorname{div}\mathbf{v} - \Delta\mathbf{v} \quad (8.13)$$

is left to the reader.

9. Integral theorems. In the region of definition of the tensor field $T_{jkl\cdots}$, consider a convex regular region V, that is, a convex region bounded by a surface S that consists of a finite number of parts with continuously turning tangent plane. The integral of $\partial_1 T_{jkl\cdots}$ extended over V may be evaluated by dividing V into prisms of infinitesimal cross sections by means of two families of planes that are normal to the x_2- and x_3-axes, respectively (Figure 2). The contribution of one of these prisms to the considered integral is

$$(T^{*}_{jkl\cdots} - T^{**}_{jkl}\cdots)\, dx_2\, dx_3, \tag{9.1}$$

where the asterisk and double asterisk refer to the ends of the prism that correspond to greater or smaller x_1-values, respectively. Let $\boldsymbol{\nu}$ be the unit

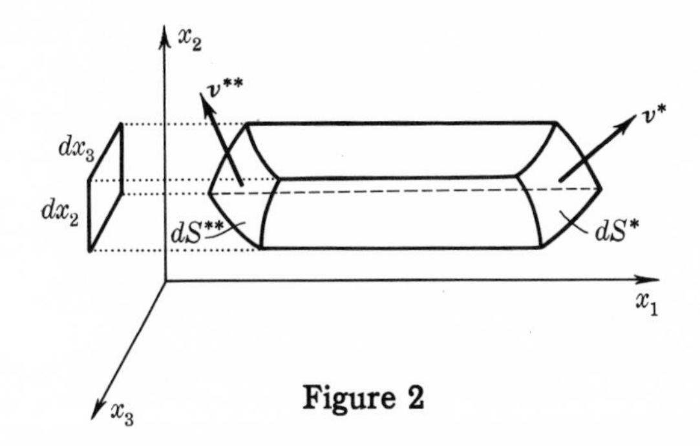

Figure 2

vector along the exterior normal of S. The factor $dx_2\, dx_3$ in (9.1) may then be written in the alternative forms $\nu_1^{*}\, dS^{*}$ or $-\nu_1^{**}\, dS^{**}$, where dS^{*} and dS^{**} are the elements that the prism cuts out of the surface S. The expression (9.1) is therefore equivalent to

$$T^{*}_{jkl\cdots}\, \nu_1^{*}\, dS^{*} + T^{**}_{jkl}\cdots \nu_1^{**}\, dS^{**}. \tag{9.2}$$

Whereas the starred and double-starred terms have opposite signs in (9.1), they have the same sign in (9.2). It is therefore no longer necessary to distinguish the two ends of the prism in this manner. The considered integral may thus be written as

$$\int \partial_1 T_{jkl\cdots}\, dV = \int \nu_1 T_{jkl\cdots}\, dS,$$

where dV and dS denote the elements of V and S, respectively. Replacing the subscript 1 by i, we obtain the *theorem of Gauss:*

$$\int \partial_i T_{jkl\cdots}\, dV = \int \nu_i T_{jkl\cdots}\, dS. \tag{9.3}$$

For the sake of simplicity, the region V was assumed to be convex. If V does not satisfy this condition, but can be decomposed into a finite number of convex regular regions, the validity of the theorem of Gauss is readily established by adding (9.3) written for the component regions. For a more careful discussion of the theorem of Gauss, the reader is referred to Chapter IV of O. D. Kellog's *Foundations of Potential Theory* (J. Springer, Berlin, 1929).

In symbolic notation, important special cases of the theorem of Gauss are written as

$$\left.\begin{aligned}\int \operatorname{grad} \varphi \, dV &= \int \boldsymbol{\nu}\varphi \, dS,\\ \int \operatorname{div} \mathbf{v} \, dV &= \int \boldsymbol{\nu}\cdot\mathbf{v} \, dS,\\ \int \operatorname{curl} \mathbf{v} \, dV &= \int \boldsymbol{\nu}\times\mathbf{v} \, dS.\end{aligned}\right\} \tag{9.4}$$

To obtain a two-dimensional counterpart of the integral theorem (9.3), consider, for instance, a regular domain S of a plane x_3 = constant, that is, a domain bounded by a line L that consists of a finite number of arcs with continuously turning tangent (Figure 3). In a similar manner one finds

$$\int \partial_{\underline{i}} T_{jkl\cdots} \, dS = \int \nu_{\underline{i}} T_{jkl\cdots} \, dL, \tag{9.5}$$

where $\nu_1, \nu_2, 0$ are the components of the unit vector along the exterior

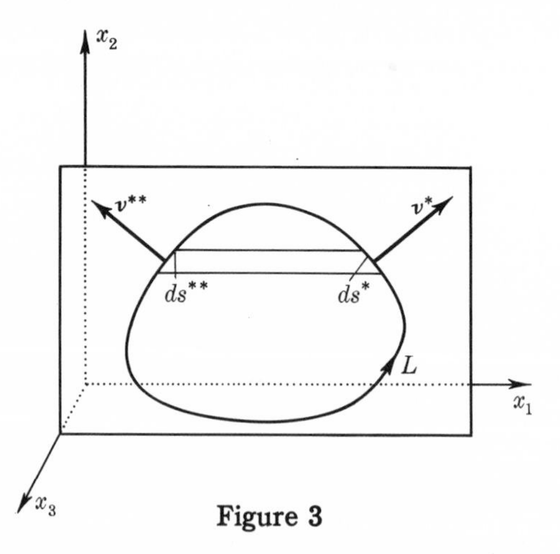

Figure 3

normal of L and underlined subscripts are restricted to the range 1, 2. Because of this restriction, the vector v_i with the components $v_{\underline{i}} = \partial_{\underline{i}}\varphi$, $v_3 = 0$ can only be identified with the gradient of the scalar φ if $\partial_3\varphi = 0$. For a *plane* scalar field of this kind, we have according to (9.5)

$$\int \operatorname{grad} \varphi \, dS = \int \boldsymbol{\nu}\varphi \, dL. \tag{9.6}$$

Similarly, for a *plane* vector field with the components $v_1 = v_1(x_1, x_2)$, $v_2 = v_2(x_1, x_2)$, $v_3 = 0$, we have

$$\left.\begin{aligned} \int \operatorname{div} \mathbf{v}\, dS &= \int \boldsymbol{\nu}\cdot\mathbf{v}\, dL, \\ \int \operatorname{curl} \mathbf{v}\, dS &= \int \boldsymbol{\nu}\times\mathbf{v}\, dL. \end{aligned}\right\} \tag{9.7}$$

Another way of using (9.5) consists in considering a three-dimensional vector field $\mathbf{v}$, but identifying the integrand on the left side of (9.5) with the x_3-component of curl $\mathbf{v}$. In Cartesian notation, one thus obtains the relation

$$\int \epsilon_{3\underline{i}j}\partial_{\underline{i}} v_j\, dS = \int \epsilon_{3\underline{i}j}\nu_{\underline{i}} v_j\, dL. \tag{9.8}$$

The index $\underline{i}$ in (9.8) may be replaced by i, because $\epsilon_{33j} = 0$. The right-hand integrand then contains the factor $\epsilon_{3ij}\nu_i$, which assumes the values $-\nu_2$ and ν_1 for $j = 1$ and $j = 2$, respectively, and vanishes for $j = 3$. This factor therefore represents the j-component of a unit vector, which is tangential to L and is obtained from $\boldsymbol{\nu}$ by means of the same rotation that transforms the positive x_1-direction into the positive x_2-direction. The product of this vector with the infinitesimal length dL represents a directed line element, which will be written as dL_j or $\mathbf{dL}$. The right-hand integrand in (9.8) is then seen to be equivalent to $v_k\, dL_k$ or $\mathbf{v}\cdot\mathbf{dL}$, and (9.8) assumes the form

$$\int (\operatorname{curl} \mathbf{v})_3\, dS = \int \mathbf{v}\cdot\mathbf{dL}. \tag{9.9}$$

The integral of $\mathbf{v}\cdot\mathbf{dL}$ extended over the closed line L is called the *circulation* of the vector $\mathbf{v}$ along L.

The integral theorem (9.9) applies to a closed *plane* line L and the plane domain bounded by it. We now propose to generalize this theorem to an arbitrary closed curve L and a regular surface S bounded by it. We approximate L by an inscribed polygon L^*, and S by an inscribed polyhedral surface S^* that is bounded by L^* (Figure 4). Application of (9.9) to a

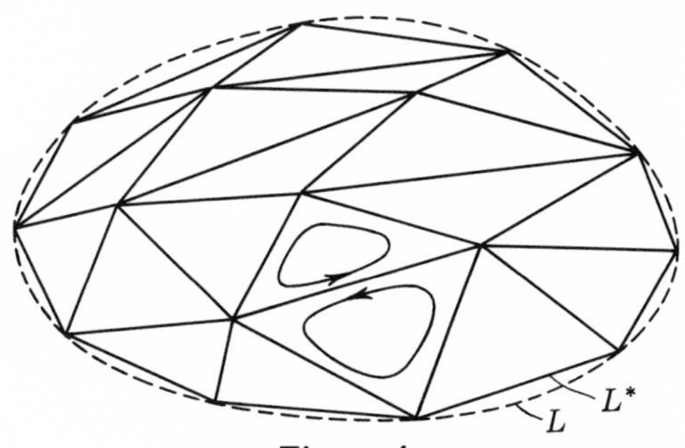

Figure 4

face of S^* shows that the integral of the component of curl $\mathbf{v}$ that is normal to this face equals the circulation of $\mathbf{v}$ along the boundary of the face. Writing this relation for each face and adding, we remark that the contributions of an edge that belongs to the boundaries of two faces cancel each other. Accordingly, the right-hand side of the resulting equation represents the circulation of $\mathbf{v}$ along L^*. As S^* tends towards S, we have therefore

$$\int \boldsymbol{\nu} \cdot \operatorname{curl} \mathbf{v}\, dS = \int \mathbf{v} \cdot \mathbf{dL}, \tag{9.10}$$

where the right-handed screw convention applies to the sense of progression along L and the direction of the unit normal vector $\boldsymbol{\nu}$ of dS. The integral theorem (9.10) is called the *theorem of Stokes*.

We finally give some examples of integral theorems containing higher derivatives. Let φ and ψ be scalar fields. According to the theorem of Gauss (9.3), we have

$$\int \varphi \partial_{ii}\psi\, dV = \int [\partial_i(\varphi \partial_i \psi) - \partial_i \varphi \partial_i \psi]\, dV$$

$$= \int \varphi \nu_i \partial_i \psi\, dS - \int \partial_i \varphi \partial_i \psi\, dV$$

or, in symbolic notation,

$$\int \varphi \Delta \psi\, dV = \int \varphi \frac{\partial \psi}{\partial \nu}\, dS - \int \operatorname{grad} \varphi \cdot \operatorname{grad} \psi\, dV, \tag{9.11}$$

where $\partial\psi/\partial\nu$ is the rate of change of ψ in the direction of the exterior normal $\boldsymbol{\nu}$ of S. The relation (9.11) is called *Green's first identity*. Interchanging φ and ψ in (9.11) and subtracting, we find the relation

$$\int (\varphi \Delta \psi - \psi \Delta \varphi)\, dV = \int \left(\varphi \frac{\partial \psi}{\partial \nu} - \psi \frac{\partial \varphi}{\partial \nu}\right) dS, \tag{9.12}$$

which is called *Green's second identity*.

The following discussion contains typical applications of the integral theorems.

If $\mathbf{v} = \operatorname{grad} \varphi$, the curl of $\mathbf{v}$ vanishes according to (8.10). We propose to show that, conversely, a vector field that is defined in a simply connected region R and has identically vanishing curl in R is the gradient field of a scalar field φ. To this end, we join the generic point P of R to a fixed point O of R by means of two arcs L_1 and L_2, which are contained in R and directed from O towards P. The arc L_1 and the reversed arc L_2 form a closed line. Since R is simply connected, this line can be considered as the boundary of a surface S that is contained in R. Applying the theorem of

Stokes, we obtain, in readily understandable notation,

$$\int_O^P \mathbf{v}\cdot d\mathbf{L}_1 - \int_O^P \mathbf{v}\cdot d\mathbf{L}_2 = 0, \tag{9.13}$$

because the curl of $\mathbf{v}$ is supposed to vanish. This relation shows that the integral

$$\varphi = \int_O^P \mathbf{v}\cdot d\mathbf{L} \tag{9.14}$$

along a path leading from the fixed point O to the point P depends only on the position of P but not on the choice of the path in the region of definition of the vector field $\mathbf{v}$. Accordingly, this integral is a scalar function of position $\varphi(P)$. To prove that the gradient of φ is the vector $\mathbf{v}$, we consider a neighboring point P' of P. Let ds be the infinitesimal distance PP' and $\boldsymbol{\mu}$ the unit vector with the direction from P towards P'. Evaluating $\varphi(P')$ by means of the path OPP', we obtain the increment

$$d\varphi^{(\mu)} = \varphi(P') - \varphi(P) = \boldsymbol{\mu}\cdot\mathbf{v}\, ds. \tag{9.15}$$

Combining (9.15) with (8.2), we find

$$\boldsymbol{\mu}\cdot(\mathbf{v} - \operatorname{grad}\varphi) = 0. \tag{9.16}$$

Since the unit vector $\boldsymbol{\mu}$ can be chosen arbitrarily, the parenthesis in (9.16) must vanish. This establishes the fact that *a vector field with vanishing curl is a gradient field.*

As an application of Green's first identity, we prove that *a vector field* $\mathbf{v}$ *is uniquely determined in a regular region* R, *if its divergence and curl are given throughout* V *and its normal component is given on the bounding surface* S *of* V. Assume that there exist two distinct vector fields $\mathbf{v}^{(1)}$ and $\mathbf{v}^{(2)}$ that fulfill these conditions, and denote the difference $\mathbf{v}^{(1)} - \mathbf{v}^{(2)}$ by $\mathbf{w}$, and the unit vector along the exterior normal of S by $\boldsymbol{\nu}$. It follows from the conditions for $\mathbf{v}^{(1)}$ and $\mathbf{v}^{(2)}$ that

$$\operatorname{div}\mathbf{w} = 0, \quad \operatorname{curl}\mathbf{w} = 0 \text{ in } V \tag{9.17}$$

and

$$\boldsymbol{\nu}\cdot\mathbf{w} = 0 \text{ on } S. \tag{9.18}$$

Since according to the second equation (9.17) the field $\mathbf{w}$ has vanishing curl, $\mathbf{w}$ must be the gradient of a scalar field which will be denoted by φ:

$$\mathbf{w} = \operatorname{grad}\phi. \tag{9.19}$$

According to (8.11) and the first equation (9.17) we have

$$\Delta\varphi = 0 \text{ in } V, \tag{9.20}$$

and (9.18) furnishes

$$\boldsymbol{\nu}\cdot\operatorname{grad}\varphi = \frac{\partial\varphi}{\partial\nu} = 0 \text{ on } S. \tag{9.21}$$

Setting $\varphi = \psi$ in Green's first identity and taking account of (9.20) and (9.21), we obtain

$$\int (\text{grad } \varphi)^2 \, dV = 0. \tag{9.22}$$

Since the integrand in (9.22) is non-negative the integral can only vanish if the integrand vanishes identically. From grad $\varphi = 0$ follows $\mathbf{w} = 0$, that is $\mathbf{v}^{(1)} = \mathbf{v}^{(2)}$. Therefore the assumption that there exist two distinct vector fields which satisfy the conditions of the problem leads to a contradiction.

10. Curvilinear coordinates. For the discussion of the principles of mechanics of continua and for the derivation of the general equations, rectangular Cartesian coordinates are adequate. In the treatment of a special problem, however, it is often desirable to use orthogonal curvilinear coordinates which are more suited to the problem. A method must therefore be developed by which equations in this kind of coordinate system can be derived from the equations in a rectangular Cartesian coordinate system. The general tensor calculus furnishes, of course, equations that are valid in any coordinate system. Since this calculus is not to be treated in this book, a special method suitable for orthogonal curvilinear coordinates will be discussed.

To avoid any conflict with the summation convention, which refers to lower case italic subscripts, we denote the orthogonal curvilinear coordinates by Greek letters; α, β, γ will be used in the general discussion, ρ, θ, ζ for cylindrical coordinates, and ρ, θ, φ for spherical coordinates. Thus, $T_{\rho\rho}$ represents, say, the radial stress, and not the first basic invariant of the stress tensor.

In general, the distance ds_α between the points with the orthogonal curvilinear coordinates α, β, γ and $\alpha + d\alpha$, β, γ is not given by $d\alpha$ but by $ds_\alpha = h_\alpha d\alpha$, where h_α is a function of the coordinates α, β, γ; the functions h_β and h_γ are defined in a similar manner.

With each point we associate a system of orthogonal unit vectors $\mathbf{e}^{(\alpha)}$, $\mathbf{e}^{(\beta)}$, $\mathbf{e}^{(\gamma)}$, which will be called the *basis vectors* at this point; the vector $\mathbf{e}^{(\alpha)}$ points in the direction of the maximum rate of change of α, and similar statements hold for $\mathbf{e}^{(\beta)}$ and $\mathbf{e}^{(\gamma)}$. We suppose that the coordinates are labelled α, β, γ in such a sequence that the basis vectors $\mathbf{e}^{(\alpha)}$, $\mathbf{e}^{(\beta)}$, $\mathbf{e}^{(\gamma)}$ form a right-handed system. Their components with respect to the rectangular Cartesian coordinates x_i will be denoted by $e_i^{(\alpha)}$, $e_i^{(\beta)}$, $e_i^{(\gamma)}$; they are functions of the coordinates α, β, γ of the considered point.

The components v_α, v_β, v_γ of a vector v_j in the system α, β, γ are defined by

$$v_j = e_j^{(\alpha)} v_\alpha + e_j^{(\beta)} v_\beta + e_j^{(\gamma)} v_\gamma, \tag{10.1}$$

the components $T_{\alpha\alpha}$, $T_{\beta\beta}$, $\cdots$, $T_{\gamma\gamma}$ of a second-order tensor T_{ij} by

$$T_{ij} = e_i^{(\alpha)} e_j^{(\alpha)} T_{\alpha\alpha} + e_i^{(\alpha)} e_j^{(\beta)} T_{\alpha\beta} + \cdots + e_i^{(\gamma)} e_j^{(\gamma)} T_{\gamma\gamma}, \tag{10.2}$$

etc. If we are only concerned with quantities that are defined at one and the same point, the orthogonal curvilinear components can therefore be identified with the rectangular Cartesian components in a system x_i, the positive coordinate directions of which are indicated by the basis vectors. For example, $T_{\alpha\alpha} = T_{11}$, $T_{\alpha\beta} = T_{12}$, $\cdots$. On the other hand, all differential operators require the comparison of quantities that are defined at neighboring points. In carrying out this comparison, one must keep in mind that the transition to a neighboring point involves not only a change of the curvilinear components but also a change of the basis vectors.

To illustrate this, we derive some important expressions in cylindrical coordinates ρ, θ, ζ. From $ds_\rho = d\rho$, $ds_\theta = \rho\, d\theta$, $ds_\zeta = d\zeta$, it follows that $h_\rho = h_\zeta = 1$, $h_\theta = \rho$. If one advances from a generic point in the radial direction towards a neighboring point, the basis vectors $\mathbf{e}^{(\rho)}$, $\mathbf{e}^{(\theta)}$, $\mathbf{e}^{(\zeta)}$ remain constant. On the other hand, Figure 5 shows that

$$\frac{\partial \mathbf{e}^{(\rho)}}{\partial \theta} = \mathbf{e}^{(\theta)}, \quad \frac{\partial \mathbf{e}^{(\theta)}}{\partial \theta} = -\mathbf{e}^{(\rho)}, \quad \frac{\partial \mathbf{e}^{(\zeta)}}{\partial \theta} = 0. \tag{10.3}$$

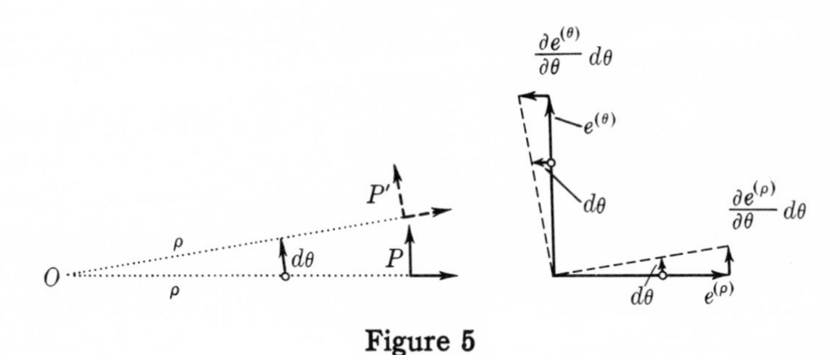

Figure 5

We start with the gradient of a scalar φ. Its component in an arbitrary direction gives the rate of change of φ in this direction. We therefore have the relation

$$\operatorname{grad} \varphi = \left(\mathbf{e}^{(\rho)} \frac{\partial}{\partial \rho} + \mathbf{e}^{(\theta)} \frac{1}{\rho} \frac{\partial}{\partial \theta} + \mathbf{e}^{(\zeta)} \frac{\partial}{\partial \zeta} \right) \varphi, \tag{10.4}$$

where the parenthesis is the equivalent of the del operator in cylindrical coordinates. In Cartesian notation, (10.4) takes the form

$$\partial_i \varphi = \left(e_i^{(\rho)} \frac{\partial}{\partial \rho} + e_i^{(\theta)} \frac{1}{\rho} \frac{\partial}{\partial \theta} + e_i^{(\zeta)} \frac{\partial}{\partial \zeta} \right) \varphi. \tag{10.5}$$

Applying the operator ∂_i, which is given by the parenthesis in (10.5), to the vector

$$v_j = e_j^{(\rho)} v_\rho + e_j^{(\theta)} v_\theta + e_j^{(\zeta)} v_\zeta, \tag{10.6}$$

and taking account of (10.3), we obtain the vector gradient

$$
\begin{aligned}
\partial_i v_j = \;& e_i^{(\rho)} p_j^{(\rho)} \frac{\partial v_\rho}{\partial \rho} + e_i^{(\rho)} e_j^{(\theta)} \frac{\partial v_\theta}{\partial \rho} + e_i^{(\rho)} e_j^{(\zeta)} \frac{\partial v_\zeta}{\partial \rho} \\
&+ e_i^{(\theta)} e_j^{(\rho)} \frac{1}{\rho}\left(\frac{\partial v_\rho}{\partial \theta} - v_\theta\right) + e_i^{(\theta)} e_j^{(\theta)} \frac{1}{\rho}\left(\frac{\partial v_\theta}{\partial \theta} + v_\rho\right) + e_i^{(\theta)} e_j^{(\zeta)} \frac{1}{\rho}\frac{\partial v_\zeta}{\partial \theta} \\
&+ e_i^{(\zeta)} e_j^{(\rho)} \frac{\partial v_\rho}{\partial \zeta} + e_i^{(\zeta)} e_j^{(\theta)} \frac{\partial v_\theta}{\partial \zeta} + e_i^{(\zeta)} e_j^{(\zeta)} \frac{\partial v_\zeta}{\partial \zeta}.
\end{aligned}
\tag{10.7}
$$

By reason of the orthogonality of the basis vectors, (10.7) immediately furnishes

$$
\begin{aligned}
\operatorname{div} \mathbf{v} = \partial_i v_i &= \frac{\partial v_\rho}{\partial \rho} + \frac{1}{\rho}\left(\frac{\partial v_\theta}{\partial \theta} + v_\rho\right) + \frac{\partial v_\zeta}{\partial \zeta} \\
&= \frac{1}{\rho}\frac{\partial}{\partial \rho}(\rho v_\rho) + \frac{1}{\rho}\frac{\partial v_\theta}{\partial \theta} + \frac{\partial v_\zeta}{\partial \zeta}.
\end{aligned}
\tag{10.8}
$$

Replacement of the vector v_i in (10.8) by the gradient (10.5) yields the following expression for the Laplace operator in cylindrical coordinates:

$$
\Delta \varphi = \left[\frac{1}{\rho}\frac{\partial}{\partial \rho}\left(\rho \frac{\partial}{\partial \rho}\right) + \frac{1}{\rho^2}\frac{\partial^2}{\partial \theta^2} + \frac{\partial^2}{\partial \zeta^2}\right] \varphi. \tag{10.9}
$$

To obtain the components of curl $\mathbf{v}$, we multiply (10.7) by ϵ_{pij} and replace the vector products of the basis vectors in the resulting equation by their values; thus

$$
\begin{aligned}
\epsilon_{pij} \partial_i v_j = e_p^{(\rho)} \left(\frac{1}{\rho}\frac{\partial v_\zeta}{\partial \theta} - \frac{\partial v_\theta}{\partial \zeta}\right) + e_p^{(\theta)} \left(\frac{\partial v_\rho}{\partial \zeta} - \frac{\partial v_\zeta}{\partial \rho}\right) \\
+ e_p^{(\zeta)} \left[\frac{\partial v_\theta}{\partial \rho} - \frac{1}{\rho}\left(\frac{\partial v_\rho}{\partial \theta} - v_\theta\right)\right].
\end{aligned}
\tag{10.10}
$$

The ζ-component of curl $\mathbf{v}$ can also be written in the form

$$
(\operatorname{curl} \mathbf{v})_\zeta = \frac{1}{\rho}\left[\frac{\partial}{\partial \rho}(\rho v_\theta) - \frac{\partial v_\rho}{\partial \theta}\right]. \tag{10.11}
$$

In view of its importance in stress analysis, we finally establish the expression for $\partial_i T_{ij}$ in cylindrical coordinates, where

$$
\begin{aligned}
T_{ij} = \;& e_i^{(\rho)} e_j^{(\rho)} T_{\rho\rho} + e_i^{(\rho)} e_j^{(\theta)} T_{\rho\theta} + e_i^{(\rho)} e_j^{(\zeta)} T_{\rho\zeta} \\
&+ e_i^{(\theta)} e_j^{(\rho)} T_{\theta\rho} + e_i^{(\theta)} e_j^{(\theta)} T_{\theta\theta} + e_i^{(\theta)} e_j^{(\zeta)} T_{\theta\zeta} \\
&+ e_i^{(\zeta)} e_j^{(\rho)} T_{\zeta\rho} + e_i^{(\zeta)} e_j^{(\theta)} T_{\zeta\theta} + e_i^{(\zeta)} e_j^{(\zeta)} T_{\zeta\zeta}
\end{aligned}
\tag{10.12}
$$

is a tensor of the second order. Applying the operator ∂_i as given by (10.5) to the tensor (10.12) and using the orthogonality of the basis vectors, we obtain

$$\begin{aligned}\partial_i T_{ij} = \quad & e_j^{(\rho)}\left[\frac{\partial T_{\rho\rho}}{\partial\rho} + \frac{1}{\rho}\left(\frac{\partial T_{\theta\rho}}{\partial\theta} + T_{\rho\rho} - T_{\theta\theta}\right) + \frac{\partial T_{\zeta\rho}}{\partial\zeta}\right] \\ & + e_j^{(\theta)}\left[\frac{\partial T_{\rho\theta}}{\partial\rho} + \frac{1}{\rho}\left(\frac{\partial T_{\theta\theta}}{\partial\theta} + T_{\rho\theta} + T_{\theta\rho}\right) + \frac{\partial T_{\zeta\theta}}{\partial\zeta}\right] \\ & + e_j^{(\zeta)}\left[\frac{\partial T_{\rho\zeta}}{\partial\rho} + \frac{1}{\rho}\left(\frac{\partial T_{\theta\zeta}}{\partial\theta} + T_{\rho\zeta}\right) + \frac{\partial T_{\zeta\zeta}}{\partial\zeta}\right].\end{aligned} \tag{10.13}$$

The symmetrical stress field $T_{ij} = T_{ji}$ in a continuum that is in equilibrium in the absence of body forces satisfies the equilibrium condition $\partial_i T_{ij} = 0$. According to (10.13) this equilibrium condition is equivalent to the following equations:

$$\left.\begin{aligned}\frac{\partial T_{\rho\rho}}{\partial\rho} + \frac{1}{\rho}\frac{\partial T_{\rho\theta}}{\partial\theta} + \frac{\partial T_{\zeta\rho}}{\partial\zeta} + \frac{1}{\rho}(T_{\rho\rho} - T_{\theta\theta}) &= 0, \\ \frac{\partial T_{\rho\theta}}{\partial\rho} + \frac{1}{\rho}\frac{\partial T_{\theta\theta}}{\partial\theta} + \frac{\partial T_{\theta\zeta}}{\partial\zeta} + \frac{2}{\rho}T_{\rho\theta} &= 0, \\ \frac{\partial T_{\zeta\rho}}{\partial\rho} + \frac{1}{\rho}\frac{\partial T_{\theta\zeta}}{\partial\theta} + \frac{\partial T_{\zeta\zeta}}{\partial\zeta} + \frac{1}{\rho}T_{\zeta\rho} &= 0.\end{aligned}\right\} \tag{10.14}$$

For cylindrical coordinates, the expressions (10.3) for the derivatives of the basis vectors with respect to the coordinates were readily obtained from Figure 5. The corresponding expressions for arbitrary orthogonal curvilinear coordinates can be derived as follows. In terms of the orthogonal curvilinear coordinates α, β, γ of a point, its rectangular Cartesian coordinates may be given by the three functions $x_i = x_i(\alpha, \beta, \gamma)$, so that

$$\frac{\partial x_i}{\partial\alpha}\frac{\partial x_i}{\partial\alpha} = h_\alpha^2, \tag{10.15}$$

and

$$\frac{\partial x_i}{\partial\alpha} = h_\alpha e_i^{(\alpha)}. \tag{10.16}$$

Differentiation of (10.16) with respect to β yields

$$\frac{\partial x_i}{\partial\alpha\partial\beta} = h_\alpha\frac{\partial e_i^{(\alpha)}}{\partial\beta} + \frac{\partial h_\alpha}{\partial\beta}e_i^{(\alpha)}. \tag{10.17}$$

Since the basis vectors are orthogonal, multiplication of (10.17) by $e_i^{(\beta)}$ or

$e_i^{(\gamma)}$ furnishes

$$\frac{1}{h_\alpha}\frac{\partial^2 x_i}{\partial\alpha\partial\beta}e_i^{(\beta)} = \frac{\partial e_i^{(\alpha)}}{\partial\beta}e_i^{(\beta)}, \tag{10.18}$$

$$\frac{1}{h_\alpha}\frac{\partial^2 x_i}{\partial\alpha\partial\beta}e_i^{(\gamma)} = \frac{\partial e_i^{(\alpha)}}{\partial\beta}e_i^{(\gamma)}. \tag{10.19}$$

It follows from these equations that the left-hand sides represent the β- and γ-components of the derivative $\partial\mathbf{e}^{(\alpha)}/\partial\beta$. On the other hand, the derivative of the unit vector $\mathbf{e}^{(\alpha)}$ is orthogonal to this vector, so that the α-component of $\partial\mathbf{e}^{(\alpha)}/\partial\beta$ is zero. Accordingly,

$$\frac{\partial e_j^{(\alpha)}}{\partial\beta} = \frac{1}{h_\alpha}\frac{\partial^2 x_i}{\partial\alpha\partial\beta}(e_i^{(\beta)}e_j^{(\beta)} + e_i^{(\gamma)}e_j^{(\gamma)}). \tag{10.20}$$

Similar formulas can be written for the other derivatives of the basis vectors with respect to the coordinates.

PROBLEMS

2.1.† Let the primed coordinate system be obtained from the unprimed one by a small rotation about the x_3-axis. Denoting the angle of rotation by $d\theta$, and letting the sense of rotation correspond to that of the rotation by a right angle that transforms the positive x_1-direction into the positive x_2-direction, show that the coefficients in (2.7) have the values

$$c_{11} = c_{22} = c_{33} = 1, \quad c_{12} = -c_{21} = -d\theta,$$

$$c_{13} = c_{23} = c_{31} = c_{32} = 0.$$

2.2. Prove that

$$\delta_{ij}\delta_{ij} = 3.$$

2.3. Show that the expression

$$A = \delta_{ip}\delta_{jq} - \delta_{iq}\delta_{jp}$$

assumes the following values:

$$A = \begin{cases} 1, & \text{if } i = p \text{ and } j = q, \text{ but } i \neq j, \\ -1, & \text{if } i = q \text{ and } j = p, \text{ but } i \neq j, \\ 0, & \text{if } i = j \text{ or } p = q. \end{cases}$$

3.1. How do the components of a vector transform under the infinitesimal rotation in Problem 2.1?

† The number 2.1 indicates that this is the first problem concerning the material in Section 2.

3.2 The components of the vectors **u** and **v** are continuously differentiable functions of a scalar parameter s. Prove that

$$\frac{d}{ds}(\mathbf{u}\cdot\mathbf{v}) = \frac{d\mathbf{u}}{ds}\cdot\mathbf{v} + \mathbf{u}\cdot\frac{d\mathbf{v}}{ds}.$$

3.3. The components of a unit vector **u** are continuously differentiable functions of a parameter s. Show that $d\mathbf{u}/ds$ is perpendicular to **u**.

4.1. Investigate the influence of the coordinate transformation $x_1' = -x_1$, $x_2' = x_2$, $x_3' = x_3$ on the components of a tensor T.

4.2. How do the components of a tensor T transform under the infinitesimal rotation in Problem 2.1?

4.3. A tensor is called *isotropic* if it has the same components with respect to any rectangular Cartesian coordinate system. Using the transformations in Problems 4.1 and 4.2, prove that an isotropic tensor has the form $\lambda\boldsymbol{\delta}$, where λ is a scalar and $\boldsymbol{\delta}$ the unit tensor.

4.4. Prove that the decomposition of a tensor into a symmetric and an antisymmetric part is unique.

5.1. Show that the contracted product $S_{ij}T_{ij}$ of a tensor T_{ij} with a symmetric tensor S_{ij} is independent of the antisymmetric part of T_{ij}.

5.2. Consider a physical quantity that is specified by nine numbers A_{ij} in a given rectangular Cartesian coordinate system. Let it be known that, in the transition to another coordinate system of this kind, $A_{ij}v_iv_j$ transforms as a scalar for any choice of the vector v_i. Prove that the quantities $A_{ij} + A_{ji}$ are the components of a tensor of the second order.

5.3. Consider a physical quantity that is specified by twenty-seven numbers A_{ijk} in a given rectangular Cartesian coordinate system. In the transition to another coordinate system of this kind, let $A_{ijk}B_{jk}$ transform as a vector for any choice of the *antisymmetric* tensor B_{jk}. Prove that the quantities $A_{ijk} - A_{ikj}$ are the components of a tensor of the third order.

6.1. Prove the formulas (6.5) and (6.12).

6.2. Let t_{ij} be the minor of the element T_{ij} in the determinant of the second-order tensor T. Establish the relation

$$t_{ij} = \tfrac{1}{2}\epsilon_{ipq}\epsilon_{jrs}T_{pr}T_{qs},$$

which shows that the minors t_{ij} are the components of a tensor of the second order.

6.3. Show that the determinant D of the second-order tensor T can be written in the form

$$D = \tfrac{1}{6}\epsilon_{ijk}\epsilon_{pqr}T_{ip}T_{jq}T_{kr}.$$

6.4. The determinant in Problem 6.3 can also be written as

$$D = \epsilon_{ijk}T_{i1}T_{j2}T_{k3} = \epsilon_{ijk}T_{1i}T_{2j}T_{3k},$$

and we have

$$\epsilon_{pqr}D = \epsilon_{ijk}T_{ip}T_{jq}T_{kr} = \epsilon_{ijk}T_{pi}T_{qj}T_{rk}.$$

Use these formulas to prove that the product of the determinants of the tensors S_{ij} and T_{ij} is the determinant of the tensor $S_{il}T_{lj}$.

6.5. Let **t**, **n**, and **b**, represent the unit vectors along the tangent, normal, and binormal of a curve in space. If these vectors are considered as functions of the arc length s of this curve, their derivatives with respect to s are given by Frenet's formulas

$$d\mathbf{t}/ds = \kappa\mathbf{n},$$

$$d\mathbf{n}/ds = -\kappa\mathbf{t} + \tau\mathbf{b},$$

$$d\mathbf{b}/ds = -\tau\mathbf{n},$$

in which κ and τ denote the *curvature* and *torsion* of the curve. Let the vertex of the trihedron formed by **t**, **n**, and **b**, move with unit velocity along the curve in the direction of increasing values of s. The corresponding motion of the trihedron can be obtained by superimposing a rotation about the vertex on the translation given by the motion of the vertex. Determine the vector of the angular velocity of this rotation (Darboux' vector).

6.6. At the typical point P of a curve in space consider unit forces that have the positive directions of the tangent, normal and binormal of this curve in P. Denote the moments of these forces with respect to the coordinate origin by **T**, **N**, and **B**, respectively. Considering these moment vectors as functions of the arc length s of the curve, show that $d\mathbf{T}/ds = \kappa\mathbf{N}$, and establish the corresponding formulas for $d\mathbf{N}/ds$ and $d\mathbf{B}/ds$.

7.1. Considering a finite number of particles, show that their moment of inertia with respect to an axis that passes through the origin and has the direction μ is the normal component of a symmetric tensor of the second order for this direction and that in the matrix of this *inertia tensor* the elements of the principal diagonal are the moments of inertia with respect to the coordinate axes while the other elements represent the negative products of inertia.

7.2. Let the system of particles considered in Problem 7.1 perform a rigid-body rotation about the origin. Denoting the vector of the instantaneous angular velocity of this rotation by ω_i, show that the moment of momentum of the system with respect to the origin is given by the relation $W_j = T_{ij}\omega_i$, in which T_{ij} denotes the inertia tensor introduced in Problem 7.1. Determine the kinetic energy of the system.

7.3. Let S_{ij} be a symmetric tensor of the second order with the nonvanishing principal values S_{I}, S_{II}, and S_{III}. The *reciprocal tensor* S^*_{ij} is defined as the symmetric tensor of the second order that has the same principal axes and the principal values S_{I}^{-1}, S_{II}^{-1}, and S_{III}^{-1}. Prove the relation

$$S_{ip}S^*_{pj} = S^*_{ip}S_{pj} = \delta_{ij},$$

which justifies the use of the word "reciprocal."

7.4. Let T_{ij} be a second tensor of the kind considered in Problem 7.3 and denote its reciprocal tensor by T^*_{ij}. Prove that the tensors $U_{ij} = S_{ip}T_{pj}$ and $U^*_{ij} = T^*_{iq}S^*_{qj}$, which, as a rule, are not symmetric, are reciprocal in the sense that

$$U_{ir}U^*_{rj} = U^*_{ir}U_{rj} = \delta_{ij}.$$

7.5. Let $\mathbf{S}$ be a tensor of the kind considered in Problem 7.3. Represent $\mathbf{S}^2$ as a linear combination of $\mathbf{S}$, $\boldsymbol{\delta}$, and $\mathbf{S}^*$, where $\boldsymbol{\delta}$ is the unit tensor and the tensor $\mathbf{S}^*$ is the reciprocal of $\mathbf{S}$. Give the corresponding representation of the tensor $\mathbf{Q}^*$ that is reciprocal to $\mathbf{Q} = \mathbf{S}^2$.

8.1. The instantaneous velocity field $v_i(x)$ of a rigid body can be written as

$$v_i = a_i + \epsilon_{ijk}b_jx_k,$$

where the vectors a_i and b_j do not depend on the position of the considered particle. Show that the curl of this velocity field is $2b_i$ while the divergence vanishes.

8.2. Let $\mathbf{r}$ be the radius vector of the typical point in a field and r the magnitude of $\mathbf{r}$. Show that the relations

$$\text{div}\,(r^n\mathbf{r}) = (n+3)r^n, \quad \text{curl}\,(r^n\mathbf{r}) = 0$$

are valid everywhere for $n \geq 0$ and everywhere except at the origin for $n < 0$.

8.3. In the vector field $\mathbf{v}(x)$, let there exist a surface on which $\mathbf{v} = 0$. Show that, at an arbitrary point of this surface, curl $\mathbf{v}$ is tangential to the surface or vanishes, while div $\mathbf{v}$ is given by the rate of change of the normal component of $\mathbf{v}$ in the direction of the normal of the surface.

8.4. Let the field lines of the vector field $\mathbf{v}(x)$ coincide with those of the gradient field $\mathbf{u} = \text{grad}\,\varphi$ of the scalar field $\varphi(x)$. Prove that curl $\mathbf{v}$ at the typical point of the field is perpendicular to the field vector $\mathbf{v}$ at this point.

8.5. Prove the formulas (8.7), (8.11), (8.12), (8.13).

9.1. Let V be the volume of a simply connected regular region of space, dS the typical element of its surface, $\boldsymbol{\nu}$ the unit vector along the exterior normal of dS, and $\mathbf{x}$ the radius vector of dS. Prove that $\int x_i\nu_j\,dS = V\delta_{ij}$.

9.2. Show that the centroid of the region considered in Problem 9.1 has the radius vector $X_i = (2V)^{-1}\int x_jx_j\nu_i\,dS$.

9.3. Let the typical surface element dS of the region considered in Problem 9.1 be subjected to the force $\boldsymbol{\nu}\,dS$. Show that these surface forces form an equilibrium system, i.e., that the integrals $\int \boldsymbol{\nu}\,dS$ and $\int \mathbf{x} \times \boldsymbol{\nu}\,dS$ vanish.

9.4. Prove the following generalization of Green's first identity, in which φ, ψ, and χ are continuously differentiable scalar fields:

$$\int \varphi \operatorname{div}(\chi \operatorname{grad} \psi)\, dV = \int \chi\varphi \frac{\partial \psi}{\partial n}\, dS - \int \chi \operatorname{grad} \varphi \cdot \operatorname{grad} \psi\, dV.$$

9.5. Let the scalar field χ be defined in the simply connected regular region V of space, and assume that χ is positive throughout this region. Furthermore, assume that the scalar field ψ satisfies the differential equation $\operatorname{div}(\chi \operatorname{grad} \psi) = 0$ in V, while the normal derivative $\partial\psi/\partial n$ vanishes on the surface S of V. Using the theorem in Problem 9.4 show that $\psi =$ constant throughout V.

9.6. Let the vector field $\mathbf{v}(x)$ be defined in the simply connected regular region V, and assume that div $\mathbf{v}$ and curl $\mathbf{v}$ vanish throughout this region. Show that this vector field is the gradient field of a scalar field φ that satisfies the differential equation $\Delta\varphi = 0$.

10.1. Establish the expressions for grad φ, div $\mathbf{v}$, curl $\mathbf{v}$, and $\Delta\varphi$, in spherical coordinates ρ, θ, ψ.

10.2. *In the neighborhood* of a plane arc c without points of inflection, let the plane curvilinear coordinates α and β of a typical point P be defined as follows. On c choose an origin O and a positive sense of progression. Denote by P^* the point on c that has the least normal distance from P, and choose the direction from P^* to the corresponding center of curvature of c as the negative direction of the normal P^*P. The algebraic distance P^*P then is to be used as the coordinate α of P, and the angle that the current normal P^*P forms with the fixed normal at O as the coordinate β. To specify the shape of the arc c, its radius of curvature ρ is to be given as a function of β. Prove that for a plane scalar field $\varphi(\alpha, \beta)$ one has

$$\Delta\varphi = \frac{\partial^2\varphi}{\partial\alpha^2} + \frac{1}{\rho + \alpha}\frac{\partial}{\partial\beta}\left(\frac{1}{\rho + \alpha}\frac{\partial\varphi}{\partial\beta}\right) + \frac{1}{\rho + \alpha}\frac{\partial\varphi}{\partial\alpha}.$$

CHAPTER II

State of Stress

1. Stress tensor. Particle mechanics is concerned with systems of discrete particles. Mechanics of continua, on the other hand, deals with the equilibrium or motion of gases, liquids, or solids, which are conceived as having continuously distributed mass. The *density* ρ at a point P in a continuum is defined by a limit process, which may be summed up by the following statement: A volume element dV that encloses the point P contains the mass $\rho\, dV$. The density may also be characterized as the specific mass or, in a convenient but less precise manner, as the mass per unit volume.

As the mass of a continuum is continuously distributed, so any force stemming from the mass, for instance gravity, is also continuously distributed. When referred to the unit of mass, this type of force is called *specific body force*. For example, the specific body force corresponding to gravity is a downward vertical vector that has the acceleration of free fall as intensity.

In stress analysis, forces that are distributed over surfaces drawn in the continuum are considered in addition to the body forces, which are distributed over the volume. To explain the basic assumptions regarding these surface forces, consider a regular region V of the continuum. Let P be a point of the surface S of V and dS an element of S that contains the point P, and let the orientation of dS be given by the unit vector $\boldsymbol{\nu}$ along the exterior normal of S in P. That side of dS towards which the vector $\boldsymbol{\nu}$ is directed will be called the positive side, and the other the negative side of dS.

We assume that in the surface element dS the continuum outside V transmits a force $\mathbf{T}^{(\nu)}\, dS$ but no couple onto the continuum in V. The force $\mathbf{T}^{(\nu)}\, dS$ will be called the surface force and the vector $\mathbf{T}^{(\nu)}$ the *surface traction* transmitted from the positive onto the negative side of dS, and it will be assumed that the surface traction depends only on the position of the point P and the direction of the normal vector $\boldsymbol{\nu}$ but not on the shape of either the surface element dS or the surface S. At the considered point P, we therefore have an association of the vectors $\mathbf{T}^{(\nu)}$ of the surface traction with the directions $\boldsymbol{\nu}$ of space.

To show that this association is governed by a law that is linear and homogeneous in the direction cosines, we use the following *equilibrium principle* of stress analysis. In a continuum that may be at rest or in motion, consider a finite region V with the surface S; the surface forces transmitted onto the continuum inside V then are at each instant in equilibrium with the body forces acting on this part of the continuum, provided that for the moving continuum the inertia forces are included in the body forces.

Apply this principle to the infinitesimal tetrahedron $PQ_1Q_2Q_3$, the edges PQ_1, PQ_2, and PQ_3 of which have the positive coordinate directions (Figure 6). Let dS be the area of the face $Q_1Q_2Q_3$, and $\boldsymbol{\nu}$ its exterior unit normal. The faces PQ_2Q_3, PQ_3Q_1, and PQ_1Q_2 have the areas $dS_1 = dS \cos(\nu, x_1)$, $dS_2 = dS \cos(\nu, x_2)$, and $dS_3 = dS \cos(\nu, x_3)$, respectively, while their

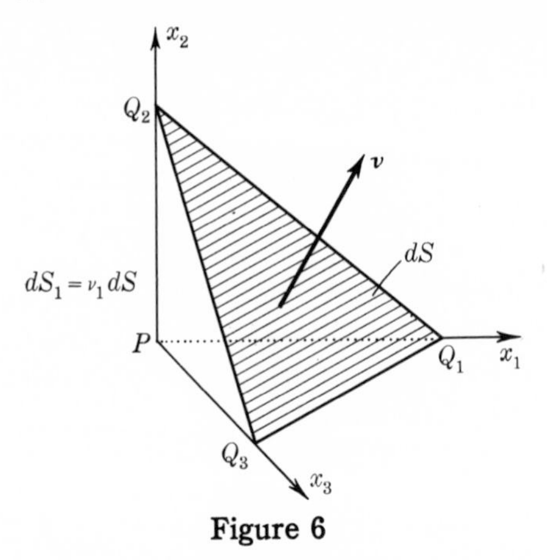

Figure 6

exterior normals have the negative coordinate directions. The surface traction transmitted onto the tetrahedron in the face dS will be denoted by $\mathbf{T}^{(\nu)}$; it is the vector associated with the direction ν. The vectors associated with the positive coordinate directions will be denoted by $\mathbf{T}_1$, $\mathbf{T}_2$, and $\mathbf{T}_3$. The surface forces acting on the tetrahedron then have the resultant

$$\mathbf{T}^{(\nu)}\,dS - \mathbf{T}_1\,dS_1 - \mathbf{T}_2\,dS_2 - \mathbf{T}_3\,dS_3$$
$$= [\mathbf{T}^{(\nu)} - \mathbf{T}_1 \cos(\nu, x_1) - \mathbf{T}_2 \cos(\nu, x_2) - \mathbf{T}_3 \cos(\nu, x_3)]\,dS. \quad (1.1)$$

The resultant of the body forces acting on the tetrahedron is proportioned to its volume dV. If we let all linear dimensions of the tetrahedron decrease in the same ratio, the resultant of the body forces tends more rapidly to zero than that of the surface forces. In the limit, the equilibrium of the tetrahedron requires that

$$\mathbf{T}^{(\nu)} = \mathbf{T}_1 \cos(\nu, x_1) + \mathbf{T}_2 \cos(\nu, x_2) + \mathbf{T}_3 \cos(\nu, x_3) = \mathbf{T}_i\nu_i. \quad (1.2)$$

As is seen from this relation, the *state of stress* at the point P is specified by the stress tensor T, which associates with an arbitrary direction ν the surface traction $\mathbf{T}^{(\nu)}$ transmitted at P from the positive onto the negative side of a surface element that is normal to ν.

Let T_{11}, T_{12}, T_{13} be the components of the vector $\mathbf{T}_1$; similarly, denote the components of the vectors $\mathbf{T}_2$ and $\mathbf{T}_3$ by T_{21}, T_{22}, T_{23} and T_{31}, T_{32}, T_{33}, respectively. The mechanical significance of these nine *stress components* is found as follows. The vector $\mathbf{T}_1$ with the components T_{11}, T_{12}, T_{13} is the surface traction across a surface element that is normal to the x-axis. Accordingly, T_{11} is that component of this surface traction which is normal to the considered surface element; T_{11} is therefore called the *normal stress* for this surface element. The components T_{12} and T_{23} of the surface traction $\mathbf{T}_1$ are tangential to the considered surface element and are called *shearing stresses*. Similarly, T_{22} and T_{33} are the normal stresses for surface elements that are normal to the x_2- and x_3-axes, respectively, and T_{21}, T_{23} and T_{31}, T_{32} are the corresponding shearing stresses (Figure 7).

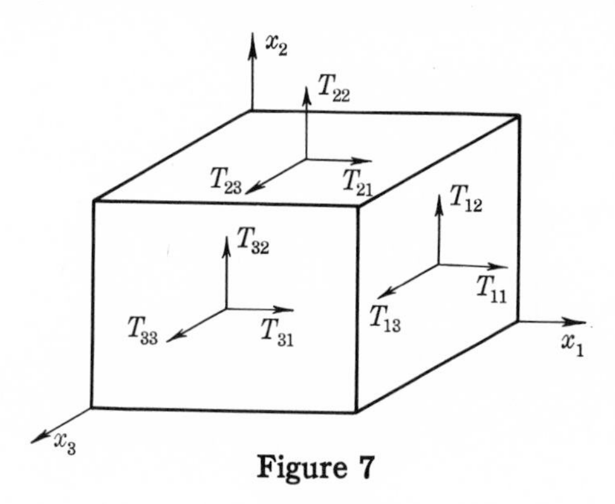

Figure 7

In engineering literature, the coordinates are usually denoted by x, y, z. The normal stress for a surface element that is normal to the x-axis is then denoted by σ_x, and the shearing stresses for this element by τ_{xy} and τ_{xz}. Similarly, the notations σ_y and σ_z are used for the normal stresses acting on surface elements normal to the x_2- and x_3-axes, and the notations τ_{yx}, τ_{yz} and τ_{zx}, τ_{zy} for the corresponding shearing stress.

The normal stress on a surface element with the unit normal vector ν is given by

$$T^{(\nu\nu)} = \mathbf{T}^{(\nu)} \cdot \boldsymbol{\nu} = T_{ij}\nu_i\nu_j \tag{1.3}$$

and is, therefore, the normal component (see Chapter I, Section 7) of the stress tensor T for the direction $\boldsymbol{\nu}$.

2. Conditions of equilibrium. Let us apply the equilibrium principle of stress analysis to a finite volume V of the continuum that is bounded by a surface S with piecewise continuously turning tangent plane.

Let the specific body force in the continuum be specified by the vector field $F_i(x)$ and the stresses by the tensor field $T_{ij}(x)$. The body force $\rho F_k\, dV$ acting on the typical element of volume with the radius vector x_j has the moment $\epsilon_{ijk}x_j\rho F_k\, dV$ with respect to the coordinate origin. Denote the typical element of the surface S of V by dS, and the unit vector along its exterior normal by ν_l. The surface force $T_{lk}\nu_l\, dS$ that is transmitted across dS on the continuum in V has the moment $\epsilon_{ijk}x_jT_{lk}\nu_l\, dS$ with respect to the origin. According to the equilibrium principle we therefore have the equations

$$\int T_{lk}\nu_l\, dS + \int \rho F_k\, dV = 0, \tag{2.1}$$

$$\int \epsilon_{ijk}x_jT_{lk}\nu_l\, dS + \int \epsilon_{ijk}x_j\rho F_k\, dV = 0, \tag{2.2}$$

in which the volume integrals are to be extended over V and the surface integrals over S.

With the aid of Gauss' theorem the surface integrals can be transformed as follows:

$$\int T_{lk}\nu_l\, dS = \int \partial_l T_{lk}\, dV, \tag{2.3}$$

$$\begin{aligned} \int \epsilon_{ijk}x_jT_{lk}\nu_l\, dS &= \int \partial_l(\epsilon_{ijk}x_jT_{lk})\, dV \\ &= \int \epsilon_{ijk}T_{jk}\, dV + \int \epsilon_{ijk}x_j\partial_l T_{lk}\, dV. \end{aligned} \tag{2.4}$$

In the transition to the last line of (2.4) the following facts were used: the components of the ϵ-tensor are independent of the coordinates, and $\partial_l x_j = \delta_{lj}$. Substitution of (2.3) and (2.4) into (2.1) and (2.2), respectively, yields the relations

$$\int (\partial_l T_{lk} + \rho F_k)\, dV = 0, \tag{2.5}$$

$$\int \epsilon_{ijk}[T_{jk} + x_j(\partial_l T_{lk} + \rho F_k)]\, dV = 0. \tag{2.6}$$

These volume integrals with continuous integrands must vanish for any volume V, i.e., their integrands must vanish identically. The relations (2.5) and (2.6) thus furnish the equilibrium conditions

$$\partial_l T_{lk} + \rho F_k = 0, \tag{2.7}$$

$$\epsilon_{ijk}T_{jk} = 0, \tag{2.8}$$

since the parenthesis in the integrand of (2.6) vanishes according to (2.7).

The left side of (2.8) is the dual vector of the stress tensor; its vanishing establishes the symmetry of the stress tensor (see I, 6.7):

$$T_{ij} = T_{ji}. \tag{2.9}$$

On account of this symmetry, the stress field is specified by six rather than nine functions of position.

After the symmetry of the stress field has been recognized once and for all, the three equations indicated by (2.7) are the only conditions of equilibrium imposed on the stress field. Of course, these three equations do not suffice for the determination of the six functions of position that specify the stress field. This situation may be expressed by the statement that the stress field of a continuum is *statically indeterminate.* To determine the stress field, we must obviously supplement the equation of equilibrium (2.7) by some other relation that cannot be derived from statical considerations. The first example of such a relation will be given in Section 6 of this chapter. In Section 3 some consequences of the symmetry of the stress tensor will be discussed, and Sections 4 and 5 will be concerned with geometrical representations of the stress tensor.

3. Principal stresses and principal shearing stresses. Section 7 of Chapter I was concerned with symmetric tensors of the second order. The results obtained there apply in particular to the symmetric stress tensor

At an arbitrary point P of a continuum, we therefore have at least one system of principal axes: across surface elements that are normal to these orthogonal axes only normal stresses but no shearing stresses are transmitted. The corresponding normal stresses T_{I}, T_{II}, T_{III} are called *principal stresses.* If they are distinct, no other system of principal axes exists at P. If, on the other hand, we have, say, $T_{\mathrm{I}} \neq T_{\mathrm{II}} = T_{\mathrm{III}}$, an arbitrary rotation of the considered system about the principal axis corresponding to T_{I} furnishes another system of principal axes. If, finally, $T_{\mathrm{I}} = T_{\mathrm{II}} = T_{\mathrm{III}}$, any set of three orthogonal axes through P can be regarded as a system of principal axes at the point P.

Let $T_{\mathrm{I}} > T_{\mathrm{II}} > T_{\mathrm{III}}$ be the principal stresses, assumed to be distinct, and let $\mu_i^{(\mathrm{I})}$, $\mu_i^{(\mathrm{II})}$, and $\mu_i^{(\mathrm{III})}$ be the unit vectors along the corresponding principal directions. Considered as a function of the direction ν, the normal stress $T^{(\nu\nu)}$ is stationary in the neighborhood of a principal direction. Thus, T_{I} is the maximum and T_{III} the minimum normal stress, whereas T_{II} represents a saddle value; it is the minimum normal stress for all directions in the plane determined by $\mu_i^{(\mathrm{I})}$ and $\mu_i^{(\mathrm{II})}$ and the maximum normal stress in the plane determined by $\mu_i^{(\mathrm{II})}$ and $\mu_i^{(\mathrm{III})}$.

The following decomposition of the stress tensor is often useful. Since the trace of a tensor is independent of the coordinate system, the arithmetic mean of the principal stresses has the value

$$\mathscr{T} = \tfrac{1}{3}T_{kk}, \tag{3.1}$$

which is called the *mean normal stress*. Subtracting the product of the unit tensor $\boldsymbol{\delta}$ by the mean normal stress from the stress tensor, we obtain the *stress deviator*

$$T'_{ij} = T_{ij} - \mathscr{T}\delta_{ij}. \tag{3.2}$$

As is readily seen, $T'_{ii} = 0$. According to the definition given at the end of Chapter I, Section 7, the expression (3.2) represents a deviator.

If the unit vector μ_i is directed along a principal axis of the stress tensor, we have as in (I, 7.1)

$$(T_{ij} - T\delta_{ij})\mu_i = 0, \tag{3.3}$$

where T is the principal stress associated with the principal direction μ_i. Solving (3.2) with respect to T_{ij} and substituting the result into (3.3), we obtain

$$[T'_{ij} - (T - \mathscr{T})\delta_{ij}]\mu_i = 0. \tag{3.4}$$

This relation shows that the vector μ_i also indicates a principal direction of the stress deviator, and that the corresponding principal value of the stress deviator is

$$T' = T - \mathscr{T}. \tag{3.5}$$

The discussion of the state of stress at a point P of a continuum can often be simplified by giving to the coordinate axes x_1, x_2, x_3 the principal directions that are associated with the principal stresses T_{I}, T_{II}, T_{III}, respectively. The traction $\mathbf{T}^{(\nu)}$ transmitted across a surface element dS with the unit normal vector $\boldsymbol{\nu}$ then has the components $T_{\text{I}}\nu_1$, $T_{\text{II}}\nu_2$, $T_{\text{III}}\nu_3$. Since the normal stress $T^{(\nu\nu)}$ appears frequently in the following formulas, it will be abbreviated by T_N. According to (1.3), we have

$$T_N = T_{\text{I}}\nu_1^2 + T_{\text{II}}\nu_2^2 + T_{\text{III}}\nu_3^2. \tag{3.6}$$

The surface traction $\mathbf{T}^{(\nu)}$ can be considered as the resultant of the *normal traction* $T_N\,\boldsymbol{\nu}$, which is normal to dS, and a *tangential traction* that is parallel to dS. Since these tractions are perpendicular to each other, the intensity T_S of the tangential traction follows from

$$\begin{aligned} T_S^2 &= \mathbf{T}^{(\nu)}\cdot\mathbf{T}^{(\nu)} - T_N^2 \\ &= T_{\text{I}}^2\nu_1^2 + T_{\text{II}}^2\nu_2^2 + T_{\text{III}}^2\nu_3^2 - (T_{\text{I}}\nu_1 + T_{\text{II}}\nu_2 + T_{\text{III}}\nu_3)^2. \end{aligned} \tag{3.7}$$

Note that (3.6) and (3.7) contain only the squares of the direction cosines; T_N and T_S therefore do not change when the direction ν is reflected on one of the coordinate planes. Accordingly, the following discussion can be restricted to directions in the first octant, for which ν_1, ν_2, ν_3 are non-negative.

In (3.7), replace ν_3^2 by $1 - \nu_1^2 - \nu_2^2$, treating ν_1 and ν_2 as the independent variables. Thus,

$$\begin{aligned} T_S^2 = \nu_1^2(T_{\text{I}}^2 - T_{\text{III}}^2) + \nu_2^2(T_{\text{II}}^2 - T_{\text{III}}^2) + T_{\text{III}}^2 \\ - [\nu_1^2(T_{\text{I}} - T_{\text{III}}) + \nu_2^2(T_{\text{II}} - T_{\text{III}}) + T_{\text{III}}]^2. \end{aligned} \tag{3.8}$$

To determine stationary values of T_S^2, we set the derivatives of the right side of (3.8) with respect to ν_1 and ν_2 equal to zero:

$$\begin{aligned} \nu_1(T_{\mathrm{I}} - T_{\mathrm{III}})\{T_{\mathrm{I}} - T_{\mathrm{III}} - 2[\nu_1^2(T_{\mathrm{I}} - T_{\mathrm{III}}) + \nu_2^2(T_{\mathrm{II}} - T_{\mathrm{III}})]\} &= 0, \\ \nu_2(T_{\mathrm{II}} - T_{\mathrm{III}})\{T_{\mathrm{II}} - T_{\mathrm{III}} - 2[\nu_1^2(T_{\mathrm{I}} - T_{\mathrm{III}}) + \nu_2^2(T_{\mathrm{II}} - T_{\mathrm{III}})]\} &= 0. \end{aligned} \tag{3.9}$$

These equations are obviously fulfilled if $\nu_1 = \nu_2 = 0$ and hence $\nu_3 = 1$. As is seen from (3.8), the non-negative quantity T_S^2 has the value zero for this principal direction, which therefore furnishes a minimum of T_S^2. A similar remark applies to the other principal directions.

A second possibility of satisfying the equations (3.9) consists in setting $\nu_1 = 0$ to satisfy the first equation and then solving the second with respect to ν_2. In this manner, one obtains the directions specified by

$$\nu_1 = 0, \quad \nu_2^2 = \nu_3^2 = \tfrac{1}{2}. \tag{3.10}$$

According to (3.8), the corresponding stationary value of the intensity of the tangential traction equals

$$T_S = \tfrac{1}{2}|T_{\mathrm{II}} - T_{\mathrm{III}}|. \tag{3.11}$$

As the labeling of the principal axes is arbitrary, the directions given by

$$\nu_1^2 = \nu_2^2 = \tfrac{1}{2}, \quad \nu_3 = 0 \tag{3.12}$$

furnish the stationary value

$$T_S = \tfrac{1}{2}|T_{\mathrm{I}} - T_{\mathrm{II}}|, \tag{3.13}$$

and the directions

$$\nu_1^2 = \tfrac{1}{2}, \quad \nu_2 = 0, \quad \nu_3^2 = \tfrac{1}{2} \tag{3.14}$$

the stationary value

$$T_S = \tfrac{1}{2}|T_{\mathrm{I}} - T_{\mathrm{III}}|. \tag{3.15}$$

We leave it to the reader to prove that for distinct principal stresses there exist no further ways of satisfying the equations (3.9). If the distinct principal stresses are labeled so that $T_{\mathrm{I}} > T_{\mathrm{II}} > T_{\mathrm{III}}$, then (3.15) represents the maximum intensity of the tangential traction. According to (3.14) the corresponding surface elements contain the second principal axis and the bisectors of the angles formed by the first and third principal axes.

The values of T_S given by (3.11), (3.13), and (3.15) are called the *principal shearing stresses.* The discussion of the cases of two or three equal principal stresses will be left to the reader as an exercise.

We finally determine the intensity of the tangential traction on surface elements that have the same orientation with respect to the principal axes as the faces of an octahedron have with respect to its axes. For the face in the first octant, we have $\nu_1 = \nu_2 = \nu_3 = 1/\sqrt{3}$ and hence, by (3.7),

$$T_S^2 = \tfrac{1}{3}[T_{\mathrm{I}}^2 + T_{\mathrm{II}}^2 + T_{\mathrm{III}}^2 - \tfrac{1}{3}(T_{\mathrm{I}} + T_{\mathrm{II}} + T_{\mathrm{III}})^2]. \tag{3.16}$$

This expression for the square of the *octahedral shearing stress* can be simplified as follows. According to (3.2), the stress tensor differs from the stress deviator by the isotropic tensor $\mathcal{T}\delta_{ij}$. For a generic surface element with the unit normal vector $\boldsymbol{\nu}$, this isotropic tensor furnishes the surface traction $\mathcal{T}\boldsymbol{\nu}$, which is normal to the surface element, so that the stress tensor and the stress deviator yield the same tangential traction for this element. The principal stresses in (3.16) can therefore be replaced by the principal values T'_{I}, T'_{II}, T'_{III} of the stress deviator. Since their sum is zero, (3.16) reduces to

$$T_S^2 = \tfrac{1}{3}[T_{\mathrm{I}}'^2 + T_{\mathrm{II}}'^2 + T_{\mathrm{III}}'^2] = \tfrac{2}{3}\mathcal{T}'_{(2)}, \tag{3.17}$$

where $\mathcal{T}'_{(2)}$ is the second basic invariant of the stress deviator.

4. Mohr's representation of states of stress. Plane state of stress. Let the principal stresses be distinct and so labelled that $T_{\mathrm{I}} > T_{\mathrm{II}} > T_{\mathrm{III}}$. Replacing the parenthesis in (3.7) by T_N, and supplementing the resulting relation by (3.6) and the equation $\nu_i\nu_i = 1$, we obtain a system of linear equations for the squares of the direction cosines; its solution is

$$\left.\begin{aligned} \nu_1^2 &= \frac{(T_{\mathrm{II}} - T_N)(T_{\mathrm{III}} - T_N) + T_S^2}{(T_{\mathrm{II}} - T_{\mathrm{I}})(T_{\mathrm{III}} - T_{\mathrm{I}})}, \\ \nu_2^2 &= \frac{(T_{\mathrm{III}} - T_N)(T_{\mathrm{I}} - T_N) + T_S^2}{(T_{\mathrm{III}} - T_{\mathrm{II}})(T_{\mathrm{I}} - T_{\mathrm{II}})}, \\ \nu_3^2 &= \frac{(T_{\mathrm{I}} - T_N)(T_{\mathrm{II}} - T_N) + T_S^2}{(T_{\mathrm{I}} - T_{\mathrm{III}})(T_{\mathrm{II}} - T_{\mathrm{III}})}, \end{aligned}\right\} \tag{4.1}$$

Following O. Mohr,† we associate with the generic direction ν a stress point with the abscissa T_N and the ordinate T_S. Since T_S is by definition non-negative, all stress points lie in the upper half-plane.

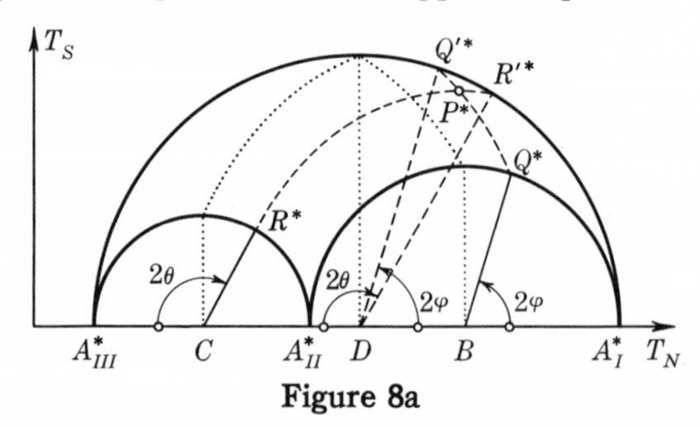

Figure 8a

In Figure 8a, the stress points A_{I}^*, A_{II}^*, A_{III}^* with the coordinates $(T_{\mathrm{I}}, 0)$, $(T_{\mathrm{II}}, 0)$, $(T_{\mathrm{III}}, 0)$ correspond to the principal directions; they will be called

† O. Mohr, Zivilingenieur *28* (1882) 113.

the *principal points* of the Mohr diagram. The centers of the segments $A_{\mathrm{I}}^*A_{\mathrm{II}}^*$, $A_{\mathrm{II}}^*A_{\mathrm{III}}^*$, and $A_{\mathrm{III}}^*A_{\mathrm{I}}^*$, will be denoted by B, C, and D, respectively.

Considering a fixed value of ν_3, we investigate surface elements that envelop a straight circular cone, the axis of which coincides with the third principal axis. As follows from the third equation (4.1), the values of T_N and T_S for these surface elements satisfy the equation

$$T_S^2 + [T_N - \tfrac{1}{2}(T_{\mathrm{I}} + T_{\mathrm{II}})]^2 = \tfrac{1}{4}(T_{\mathrm{I}} - T_{\mathrm{II}})^2 + \nu_3^2(T_{\mathrm{I}} - T_{\mathrm{III}})(T_{\mathrm{II}} - T_{\mathrm{III}}), \tag{4.2}$$

which shows that the stress points corresponding to a fixed value of ν_3 form a circular arc with the center B. The radius of this arc is given by the square root of the right-hand side of (4.2); as ν_3 varies between 0 and 1, this radius varies between $\frac{1}{2}(T_{\mathrm{I}} - T_{\mathrm{II}})$ and $\frac{1}{2}(T_{\mathrm{I}} + T_{\mathrm{II}}) - T_{\mathrm{III}}$. In Figure 8a, these bounds are represented by the segments $BA_{\mathrm{I}}^* = BA_{\mathrm{II}}^*$ and BA_{III}^*; in particular, the upper semicircle with the diameter $A_{\mathrm{I}}^*A_{\mathrm{II}}^*$ corresponds to the value $\nu_3 = 0$.

Similarly, the stress points corresponding to fixed values of ν_1 or ν_2 form circular arcs with the centers C or D, respectively. The radius of the first kind of arc varies between $CA_{\mathrm{II}}^* = CA_{\mathrm{III}}^*$ and CA_{I}^*, and that of the second kind between $DA_{\mathrm{I}}^* = DA_{\mathrm{III}}^*$ and DA_{II}^*. In particular, the upper semicircles with the diameters $A_{\mathrm{II}}^*A_{\mathrm{III}}^*$ and $A_{\mathrm{I}}^*A_{\mathrm{III}}^*$ correspond to the values $\nu_1 = 0$ and $\nu_2 = 0$, respectively.

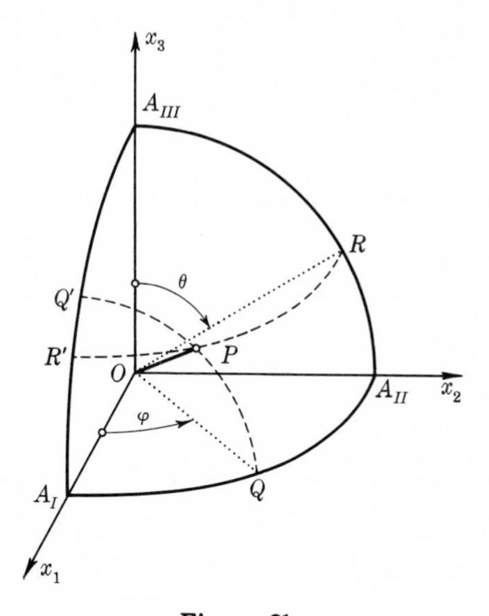

Figure 8b

In the first quadrant of the x_1, x_2-plane, consider the direction OQ that forms the angle φ with the x_1-axis (Figure 8b). With $\nu_1 = \cos\varphi$, $\nu_2 = \sin\varphi$,

$\nu_3 = 0$, (3.6) and (3.7) furnish

$$T_N = T_{\mathrm{I}} \cos^2 \varphi + T_{\mathrm{II}} \sin^2 \varphi$$

$$= \tfrac{1}{2}(T_{\mathrm{I}} + T_{\mathrm{II}}) + \tfrac{1}{2}(T_{\mathrm{I}} - T_{\mathrm{II}}) \cos 2\varphi, \tag{4.3}$$

$$T_S^2 = T_{\mathrm{I}}^2 \cos^2 \varphi + T_{\mathrm{II}}^2 \sin^2 \varphi - (T_{\mathrm{I}} \cos^2 \varphi + T_{\mathrm{II}} \sin^2 \varphi)^2$$

$$= [\tfrac{1}{2}(T_{\mathrm{I}} - T_{\mathrm{II}}) \sin 2\varphi]^2. \tag{4.4}$$

Let Q^* be the stress point for the direction OQ. Since $\nu_3 = 0$, this stress point lies on the upper semicircle with the diameter $A_{\mathrm{I}}^* A_{\mathrm{II}}^*$, and according to (4.3) and (4.4) the angle $A_{\mathrm{I}}^* BQ^*$ equals 2φ (Figure 8a). Consider now all directions that form the angle φ with the x_1-axis. Since ν_1 has the fixed value $\cos \varphi$ for these directions, the corresponding stress points form a circular arc with the center C, and since OQ is one of these directions, this circular arc passes through Q^*. In particular, the intersection Q'^* of this circular arc with the upper semicircle of the diameter $A_{\mathrm{I}}^* A_{\mathrm{III}}^*$ corresponds to the direction OQ' in the first quadrant of the x_1, x_3-plane that forms the angle φ with the positive x_1-axis. The angle $A_{\mathrm{I}}^* DQ'^*$ equals 2φ, as does the angle $A_{\mathrm{I}}^* BQ^*$.

In the first quadrant of the x_2, x_3-plane, let the direction OR form the angle θ with the x_3-axis. It can then be shown that the stress point R^* for this direction lies on the upper semicircle with the diameter $A_{\mathrm{II}}^* A_{\mathrm{III}}^*$ and that the angle $A_{\mathrm{III}}^* CR^*$ equals 2θ (Figure 8a). The stress points for all directions that form the angle θ with the x_3-axis therefore lie on a circular arc of center B that passes through R^*. The intersection R'^* of this arc with the upper semicircle of the diameter $A_{\mathrm{I}}^* A_{\mathrm{III}}^*$ corresponds to the direction OR' in the first quadrant of the x_1, x_3-plane that forms the angle θ with the x_3-axis. The angle $A_{\mathrm{III}}^* CR'^*$ equals 2θ.

Consider now the direction OP in the first octant, that forms the angles φ and θ with the x_1- and x_3-axes, respectively. The corresponding stress point P^* is the intersection of the circular arcs $Q^*Q'^*$ and $R^*R'^*$. In this way, the normal stress T_N and the shearing stress T_S for an arbitrary direction can be determined by means of graphical representation of the state of stress, which requires the knowledge of the principal axes and values of the stress tensor. As is shown by the dotted lines in Figure 8a, the maximum of T_S is assumed for $\varphi = \theta = 45°$, i.e., for the bisector of the angle formed by the positive x_1- and x_3-axes; this maximum has the value $\tfrac{1}{2}(T_{\mathrm{I}} - T_{\mathrm{III}})$ and the associated value of T_N is $\tfrac{1}{2}(T_{\mathrm{I}} + T_{\mathrm{III}})$.

A state of stress is called *plane* if one and only one principal stress vanishes. The principal axes that correspond to the two other principal stresses specify the *plane* of the considered state of stress.

A state of stress with two and only two vanishing principal stresses is called *uniaxial*. The principal axis that corresponds to the third principal stress is called the *axis* of the considered state of stress.

As Mohr has shown, the graphical representation given above can be usefully modified for plane states of stress, provided that the discussion is restricted to directions in the plane of stress. To describe this modification, we assume that $T_{\mathrm{I}} > T_{\mathrm{II}}$ but no longer insist that $T_{\mathrm{III}} = 0$ must be smaller than T_{I} and T_{II}. We also drop the assumption that the x_1- and x_2-axes, which are to lie in the plane of stress, coincide with the principal axes in this plane.

Since all directions that are to be considered lie in the plane of stress, $\theta = 90°$, and the stress points lie on the circle with the diameter $A_{\mathrm{I}}^* A_{\mathrm{II}}^*$. Mohr's graphical representation of general states of stress furnishes only the intensity T_S of the tangential traction but not its direction. In the present case, however, the tangential traction acts along the trace of the considered surface element in the plane of stress. The direction of the tangential traction can therefore be specified by treating the intensity T_S of this traction as an algebraic quantity. The usual sign convention is shown in Figure 9. The considered surface element is indicated by its trace

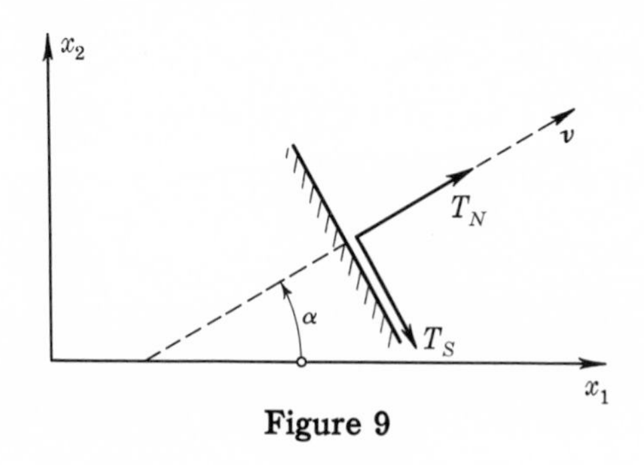

Figure 9

in the x_1, x_2-plane. The angle between the normal vector $\boldsymbol{\nu}$ and the positive x_1-axis will be denoted by α. The vectors T_N and T_S in the figure are the normal and tangential tractions transmitted onto the shaded negative side of the surface element. As usual, the intensity T_N of the normal traction is considered positive if this traction has the direction of $\boldsymbol{\nu}$. The intensity T_S of the tangential traction will be regarded as positive, if the direction of this traction and that of $\boldsymbol{\nu}$ have the same relation to each other as the positive x_1- and x_2-directions, respectively. It should be noted that, according to this sign convention, $T_S = T_{12}$ for $\alpha = 90°$ but $T_S = -T_{12}$ for $\alpha = 0°$.

Since T_S can now assume negative values, the graphical representation is no longer restricted to the upper T_N, T_S-plane. We therefore use the full circle of the diameter $A_{\mathrm{I}}^* A_{\mathrm{II}}^*$ instead of its upper half. Figure 10a shows several directions in the x_1, x_2-plane, and Figure 10b the corresponding points of this *stress circle*. Whereas all considered surface elements pass through the origin, the normal and tangential tractions transmitted in these elements are shown as acting at some distance from the origin in the interest of clarity. The negative sides of the surface elements are again indicated by shading. The angle α introduced in connection with Figure 9 is formed by the positive x_1-axis and the normal vector $\boldsymbol{\nu}$; alternatively, α can be defined as the angle formed by the negative x_2-axis and the positive T_S-direction on the trace of the surface element. This second definition of the angle α is used in Figures 10a and 10b.

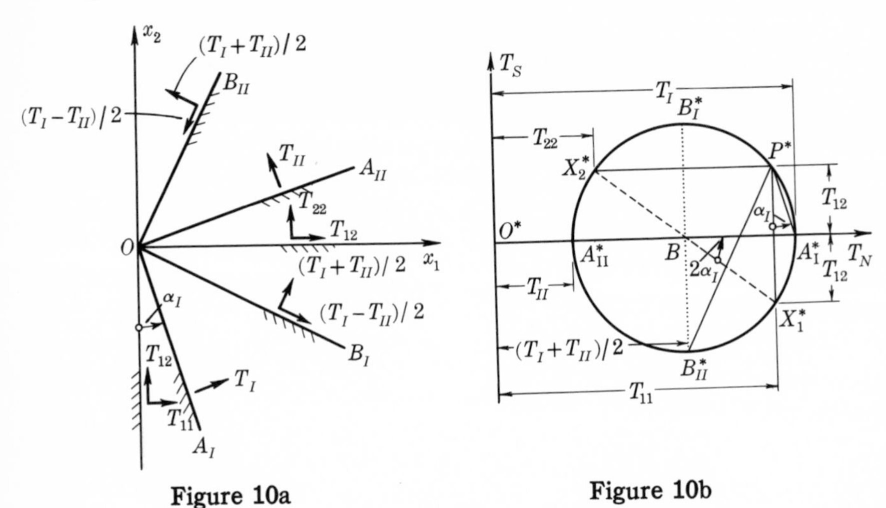

Figure 10a Figure 10b

Let the value $\alpha = \alpha_{\mathrm{I}}$ specify the orientation of the surface element in which the greatest principal stress T_{I} is transmitted (Figure 10a); the corresponding stress point is A_{I}^* (Figure 10b). To the value $\alpha = 0$, on the other hand, corresponds the stress point X_1^* with the coordinates $T_N = T_{11}$, $T_S = -T_{12}$, and the central angle $X_1^*BA_{\mathrm{I}}^*$ equals $2\alpha_{\mathrm{I}}$.

Through X_1^* and A_{I}^*, draw lines parallel to the traces of the corresponding surface elements. The intersection P^* of these lines lies on the stress circle, because the angle $X_1^*P^*A_{\mathrm{I}}^*$ equals the peripheral angle over the arc $X_1^*A_{\mathrm{I}}^*$. The point P^* is called the *pole* of the stress circle; its coordinates are T_{11}, T_{12} (Figure 10b).

If the stress circle and its pole are given, the stress point for an arbitrary surface element that is normal to the stress plane is found by drawing, through the pole, the parallel to the trace of the surface element; the second intersection of this parallel with the stress circle is the desired stress point.

Leaving the detailed study of Figures 10a and 10b to the reader, we restrict ourselves to the following remarks. To the surface elements with the traces OA_{I} and OA_{II} in Figure 10a correspond the principal stresses, and to the surface elements with the traces OB_{I} and OB_{II}, the principal shearing stresses. A plane state of stress is specified by the stress components T_{11}, T_{22}, and T_{12}, which determine the diameter $X_1^*X_2^*$ of the stress circle.

The principal directions and stresses of a plane state of stress can therefore be graphically determined by compass and straightedge. The corresponding problem of determining the principal axes and stresses of a general triaxial state of stress from the stress components cannot be solved in this manner. Indeed, the characteristic equation (I, 7.5) is cubic and, in general, does not admit a graphical solution by compass and straightedge.

5. Cauchy's stress quadrics. Cauchy † has developed another geometrical representation of general states of stress. Though less valuable than Mohr's from the quantitative point of view, it helps one visualize the directions of the tractions transmitted across various surface elements.

To discuss the state of stress T_{ij} at a point P of the continuum, let the origin of the coordinates x_i coincide with P and consider the scalar field

$$\varphi = T_{ij}x_ix_j. \tag{5.1}$$

Its level surfaces are geometrically similar quadrics of the common center P, which are called *Cauchy's stress quadrics.*

Choosing suitable units of length and stress, let Φ_1 and Φ_{-1} be the stress quadrics with the equation $\varphi = 1$ and $\varphi = -1$, respectively. The ray from P that has the direction of the unit vector $\boldsymbol{\nu}$ intersects Φ_1 or Φ_{-1} according to whether the normal stress

$$T_N = T_{ij}\nu_i\nu_j \tag{5.2}$$

for the direction ν is positive (tensile) or negative (compressive).

Let PQ be a ray of the first kind, and denote its intersection with Φ_1 by Q. If the unit vector along PQ is denoted by ν_i and the distance PQ by r, the coordinates of Q are $x_i = r\nu_i$. The gradient of the scalar field φ at Q is therefore given by

$$\partial_j\varphi = 2T_{ij}x_i = 2rT_{ij}\nu_i = 2rT_j^{(\nu)}, \tag{5.3}$$

where $T_j^{(\nu)}$ is the surface traction associated with the direction ν. According to (5.3), this traction has the direction of grad φ at Q; it is therefore perpendicular to the tangent plane of the level surface Φ_1 at Q, and it points from Q into that half-space bounded by this tangent plane which does not contain P. It follows immediately that the axes of the stress quadrics coincide with the principal axes of the stress tensor.

The magnitude $T^{(\nu)}$ of the surface traction $T_j^{(\nu)}$ can be determined as follows. Since the coordinates of Q are $x_i = r\nu_i$, the equation $\varphi = 1$ of the stress quadric Φ_1 together with (5.1) and (5.2) show that the normal component T_N of the surface traction is inversely proportional to the square of the distance PQ. It then follows from the similarity of the triangles PQR and PAB in Figure 11, that $T^{(\nu)}$ is inversely proportional to the product hr,

† A. L. Cauchy, *Exercises de Mathématiques*, Vol. 2, Paris, 1827, p. 42.

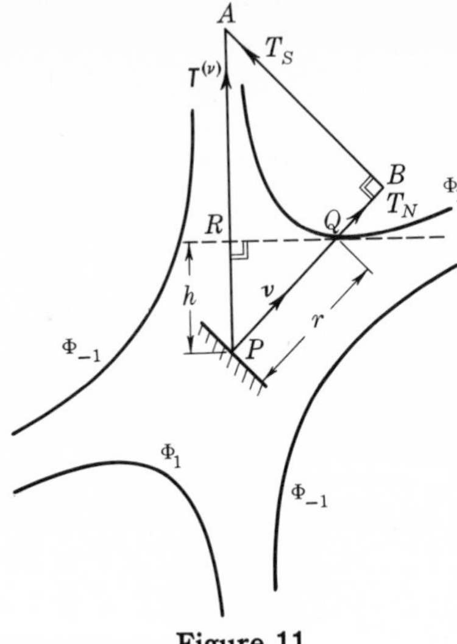

Figure 11

where h is the distance of P from the tangent plane of Φ_1 at Q and r is the distance PQ.

A similar discussion applies if the considered ray encounters the quadric Φ_{-1}, except that in this case the surface traction $\mathbf{T}^{(\nu)}$ points into that half-space bounded by the tangent plane which contains P.

When all principal stresses are positive, Φ_1 is an ellipsoid and Φ_{-1} is imaginary; for negative principal stresses, Φ_1 is imaginary and Φ_{-1} is an ellipsoid. When the principal stresses are different from zero and do not all have the same sign, Φ_1 and Φ_{-1} are hyperboloids. The generators of the common asymptotic cone of these hyperboloids indicate the directions ν for which the normal stress (5.2) vanishes; only shearing stresses are transmitted across the corresponding surface elements.

The stress quadrics for a plane state of stress are elliptic or hyperbolic cylinders according to whether the nonvanishing principal stresses have the same or opposite signs. In the first case, one of the quadrics Φ_1 and Φ_{-1} is imaginary. For a uniaxial state of stress one of these quadrics degenerates into a pair of planes while the other is imaginary.

6. Hydrostatics. As has already been remarked, the equation of equilibrium (2.7) does not suffice for the determination of the stress field but must be supplemented by some other relation, which cannot be derived from statical considerations. In hydrostatics, such a relation follows from the assumption that shearing stresses cannot be transmitted in a fluid at rest. According to (3.11), (3.13), and (3.15), distinct principal stresses always involve shearing stresses. At a typical point of a fluid that is at rest, the three principal stresses must therefore be equal to each other; their common value is denoted by $-p$, and p is called the *hydrostatic pressure* at the considered point. It follows that the stress field in a fluid at rest is of the form

$$T_{ij} = -p\delta_{ij}, \tag{6.1}$$

where p is a scalar field. According to (2.7), this pressure field must satisfy the equation of equilibrium

$$\partial_k p = \rho F_k \quad \text{or} \quad \text{grad}\, p = \rho \mathbf{F}, \tag{6.2}$$

where ρ denotes the density and $\mathbf{F}$ the specific body force.

The pressure p, the density ρ, and the absolute temperature Θ satisfy the *equation of state* of the fluid:

$$f(p, \rho, \Theta) = 0. \tag{6.3}$$

For an ideal gas, for instance, we have

$$\frac{p}{\rho} = R\Theta, \tag{6.4}$$

where R is the gas constant.

On account of (I, 8.10), the equation of equilibrium (6.2) shows that

$$\text{curl}\,(\rho \mathbf{F}) = 0 \tag{6.5}$$

is a necessary condition for the existence of a pressure field that satisfies (6.5). On the other hand, it has been shown in Chapter I, Section 9 that a vector field with identically vanishing curl is a gradient field. Thus, (6.5) is not only a necessary but also a sufficient condition. We leave it to the reader to prove that this condition may be written in the form

$$\mathbf{F} \times \text{grad}\, \rho - \rho\, \text{curl}\, \mathbf{F} = 0. \tag{6.6}$$

The specific body force $\mathbf{F}$ can frequently be derived from a *potential* U according to $\mathbf{F} = -\text{grad}\, U$. Since the curl of a gradient vanishes identically, (6.6) then shows that the force $\mathbf{F}$ is parallel to grad ρ, i.e., that the level surfaces of the density coincide with those of the potential. This can also be shown as follows. If the specific body force admits a potential U, the equation of equilibrium (6.2) takes the form

$$\text{grad}\, p = -\rho\, \text{grad}\, U, \tag{6.7}$$

which shows that the level surfaces of p coincide with those of U. The pressure p therefore is a function $p(U)$ of the potential, and we have

$$\text{grad}\, p = \frac{dp}{dU}\, \text{grad}\, U. \tag{6.8}$$

Substitution of this relation into (6.7) yields

$$\rho = -\frac{dp}{dU}, \tag{6.9}$$

i.e., the density is also a function of the potential. The equation of state (6.3) shows, finally, that the absolute temperature Θ is a function of the potential.

To illustrate these relations, consider the equilibrium of the atmosphere under the assumption that air can be treated as an ideal gas. If x_3 denotes the elevation above sea level, the potential of the force of gravity is

$$U = gx_3, \tag{6.10}$$

where g is the acceleration of free fall. Thus, pressure, density, and temperature depend only on the elevation x_3.

Assume in particular that the temperature decreases linearly with the elevation according to

$$\Theta = \Theta_0(1 - x_3/h), \tag{6.11}$$

where Θ_0 is the absolute temperature at sea level and h denotes the elevation at which the absolute temperature zero would be reached if the formula (6.11) had unrestricted validity.

With the use of (6.11), the equation of state (6.4) yields

$$\rho = \frac{p}{R\Theta_0(1 - x_3/h)}, \tag{6.12}$$

and substitution of this expression for the density into the equation of equilibrium (6.2) furnishes the differential equation

$$\frac{dp}{dx_3} = -\frac{gp}{R\Theta_0(1 - x_3/h)}. \tag{6.13}$$

Integrating this equation, we find

$$p = p_0(1 - x_3/h)^{gh/(R\Theta_0)}, \tag{6.14}$$

where p_0 denotes the pressure at sea level.

The term *isothermal equilibrium* implies that the temperature field is supposed to be uniform. The equation of state (6.3) then furnishes the density as a function $\rho(p)$ of the pressure. Choosing a reference pressure p_0, we introduce the quantity

$$P(p) = \int_{p_0}^{p} \frac{dp}{\rho(p)}. \tag{6.15}$$

Since

$$\text{grad } P = \frac{dP}{dp} \text{ grad } p = \frac{1}{\rho(p)} \text{ grad } p, \tag{6.16}$$

the equation of equilibrium (6.7) shows that

$$P + U = \text{constant}. \tag{6.17}$$

In particular, in an incompressible fluid with the constant density ρ,

$$p + \rho U = \text{constant.} \tag{6.18}$$

The relation (6.18) contains Pascal's principle. In an incompressible fluid at rest, let the pressure at one point be raised by a certain amount; according to Pascal's principle, the pressure then rises by this amount throughout the fluid.

PROBLEMS

1.1. Let the vectors $\mathbf{T}_1$, $\mathbf{T}_2$, $\mathbf{T}_3$ be the surface tractions transmitted across surface elements that are normal to the coordinate axes. Show that the sum of the squares of the magnitudes of these vectors is independent of the orientation of the coordinate axes.

1.2. If μ_i is a unit vector and S a positive scalar, the stress tensor $T_{ij} = S\mu_i\mu_j$ represents the "uniaxial" state of stress whose intensity and direction of axis are respectively given by S and μ_i. Let the surface traction transmitted across the surface element with the unit normal ν_i be decomposed into two components, one of which is parallel and the other perpendicular to $\boldsymbol{\nu}$. Considering the values of these components as functions of the direction ν, show that they have the maxima S and $S/2$, respectively.

2.1. Using spherical coordinates, establish the equivalent of the condition of equilibrium (2.7).

2.2. Consider a uniaxial stress field with variable intensity but constant direction of axis (see Problem 1.2). Show that, in the absence of body forces, the gradient of the intensity must be perpendicular to the axis.

2.3. The spheres about the origin O with the radii $a > 0$ and $b > a$ bound a region V in which a stress field is defined as follows. The state of stress at the typical point P is uniaxial (see Problem 1.2); its intensity is independent of the position of P, and its axis has the direction of the radius vector OP. Determine the body and surface tractions that must act in the region V and at its surface to make this an equilibrium field of stress.

2.4. Prove that, in the absence of body forces, an equilibrium field of stress T_{ij} can be derived from a symmetric tensor field Φ_{rs} by means of $T_{ij} = \epsilon_{ipr}\epsilon_{jqs}\partial_{pq}\Phi_{rs}$. Discuss the special cases in which the matrix of the tensor Φ_{rs} has one of the forms

$$\text{(a)} \quad \begin{bmatrix} \varphi & 0 & 0 \\ 0 & \psi & 0 \\ 0 & 0 & \chi \end{bmatrix}, \qquad \text{(b)} \quad \begin{bmatrix} 0 & \chi & \psi \\ \chi & 0 & \varphi \\ \psi & \varphi & 0 \end{bmatrix}$$

in the considered coordinate system, φ, ψ, and χ being twice continuously differentiable functions of position.

2.5. With reference to Problem 2.4,a, discuss the special case in which $\varphi = \psi = 0$ and $\chi = \chi(x_1, x_2)$. Show that, at the typical point P, the surface traction transmitted across a surface element that is parallel to the x_2, x_3-plane is normal to the x_3-axis and tangential to the level surface of the function $f = \partial_2 \chi$ through P.

2.6. Let $\boldsymbol{\nu}$ and $\boldsymbol{\nu}'$ be unit vectors and $\mathbf{T}^{(\nu)}$ and $\mathbf{T}^{(\nu')}$ the surface tractions transmitted at the typical point P in surface elements that are normal to these vectors. Prove that $\boldsymbol{\nu} \cdot \mathbf{T}^{(\nu')} = \boldsymbol{\nu}' \cdot \mathbf{T}^{(\nu)}$.

3.1. Determine the principal stresses and axes of the state of stress given by the stress tensor $T_{ij} = \alpha(\lambda_i \lambda_j' + \lambda_j \lambda_i')$, where α is a scalar and $\boldsymbol{\lambda}$ and $\boldsymbol{\lambda}'$ are unit vectors. (Hint: To simplify the computation, choose the x_1-axis parallel to $\boldsymbol{\lambda}$ and the x_3-axis normal to $\boldsymbol{\lambda}$ and $\boldsymbol{\lambda}'$.)

3.2. Prove that the decomposition of the stress tensor into a deviatoric and an isotropic part (i.e., a part with vanishing trace and a part that is proportional to the unit tensor) is unique.

3.3. Show that the second basic invariant $\mathscr{T}_{(2)}'$ of the stress deviator equals 1.5 times the sum of the squares of the principal shearing stresses.

3.4. Let $T_{\mathrm{I}} > T_{\mathrm{II}} > T_{\mathrm{III}}$ be the principal stresses at the point P. Determine the vector of the tangential traction for the surface element through P the normal of which has the direction cosines ν_1, ν_2, ν_3 with respect to the principal directions μ_{I}, μ_{II}, μ_{III}.

3.5. Let $T_{\mathrm{I}} > T_{\mathrm{II}} > T_{\mathrm{III}}$ be the principal stresses at the point P, and g the straight line through P that has the direction cosines

$$(T_{\mathrm{I}} - T_{\mathrm{II}})^{1/2}/(T_{\mathrm{I}} - T_{\mathrm{III}})^{1/2},\ 0,\ (T_{\mathrm{II}} - T_{\mathrm{III}})^{1/2}/(T_{\mathrm{I}} - T_{\mathrm{III}})^{1/2}$$

with respect to the principal directions μ_{I}, μ_{II}, μ_{III}. Show that the vector of the tangential traction for any surface element at P that passes through g has the direction of g.

4.1. Let the principal stresses at the point P satisfy the relation $T_{\mathrm{II}} = \frac{1}{2}(T_{\mathrm{I}} + T_{\mathrm{III}}) > 0$. Determine the orientation of the surface element for which normal and tangential tractions have the values $T_N = T_{\mathrm{II}}$, $T_S = (T_{\mathrm{I}} - T_{\mathrm{III}})/4$.

4.2. Let the state of stress at the point P be plane, and denote by T_N', T_N'', and T_N''' the normal tractions on surface elements through P that are normal to the plane of stress and form angles of 120° with each other. Determine the principal stresses.

5.1. On the typical ray through the coordinate origin O, determine the point P whose distance from O is inversely proportional to the magnitude of the surface traction transmitted at O across the surface element that is normal to OP. Assuming the principal stresses to be different from zero, show that the locus of the points P is an ellipsoid, the axes of which coincide with the principal axes of stress.

5.2. If Cauchy's stress quadrics are hyperboloids, the construction indicated in Figure 11 fails for the directions given by the generators of the asymptotic cone. Show how this difficulty may be overcome by the use of the stress ellipsoid in Problem 5.1.

6.1. A fluid that is subject to gravity rotates with the constant angular velocity ω about an axis that forms the angle α with the vertical. Determine the level surfaces of the pressure.

6.2. Consider a fluid with the equation of state $\rho = a + bp$, in which a and b are constants. Assuming that gravity is the only body force acting on this fluid, determine the dependence of the pressure p on the depth d below the surface of the fluid, which is exposed to the pressure p_0.

CHAPTER III

Instantaneous Motion

1. Rate of rotation and rate of deformation. In the discussion of the instantaneous motion of a continuum, use of the term "point" could easily cause misunderstanding, since it might refer either to a fixed point of space or to a point of the moving continuum. In the interest of clarity, the term "point" will be exclusively used for fixed points of space, and the term "particle" for points of the continuum. In describing geometrical configurations such as line or surface elements, the adjectives "spatial" or "material" will be used to indicate that these configurations are formed by points or particles, respectively.

The instantaneous motion of a continuum is described by its *velocity field* $v_k(x)$, which specifies the velocity components v_k of a typical particle P as functions of the instantaneous position x_1, x_2, x_3 of this particle. The field lines of the velocity field are called *stream lines.* Since the stream lines are determined by the instantaneous velocity field, they do not, as a rule, coincide with the trajectories of the particles.

Consider neighboring particles P and P' with the instantaneous coordinates x_k and $x_k + dx_k$, respectively. According to (I, 8.3), the relative velocity of P' with respect to P is given by

$$dv_k = dx_j \, \partial_j v_k, \tag{1.1}$$

where the vector gradient $\partial_j v_k$ is to be taken at the particle P.

It will be convenient to regard this vector gradient as the sum of its antisymmetric and symmetric parts:

$$\partial_j v_k = \partial_{[j} v_{k]} + \partial_{(j} v_{k)}. \tag{1.2}$$

In (1.2) the parenthesis and brackets at the subscript level are to be interpreted as in Chapter I, Section 4, although here they enclose subscripts of distinct symbols. In analogy to this decomposition of the vector gradient of the velocity field, we decompose the relative velocity (1.1) as follows:

$$dv_k = dv_k^* + dv_k^{**}, \tag{1.3}$$

where

$$dv_k^* = dx_j \, \partial_{[j} v_{k]}, \quad dv_k^{**} = dx_j \, \partial_{(j} v_{k)}. \tag{1.4}$$

To study the relative velocity dv_k^*, which corresponds to the antisymmetric tensor $\partial_{[j} v_{k]}$, we denote the dual vector of this tensor by $2w_i$. We therefore have

$$w_i = \tfrac{1}{2}\epsilon_{ijk}\partial_{[j}v_{k]} = \tfrac{1}{2}\epsilon_{ijk}\partial_j v_k = \tfrac{1}{2}\,(\text{curl }\mathbf{v})_i \tag{1.5}$$

or

$$w_1 = \tfrac{1}{2}(\partial_2 v_3 - \partial_3 v_2), \quad w_2 = \tfrac{1}{2}(\partial_3 v_1 - \partial_1 v_3), \quad w_3 = \tfrac{1}{2}(\partial_1 v_2 - \partial_2 v_1). \tag{1.6}$$

According to (I, 6.8), the inverse of (1.5) is

$$\partial_{[j}v_{k]} = \epsilon_{ijk}w_i. \tag{1.7}$$

The contribution of the antisymmetric part of the vector gradient $\partial_j v_k$ to the relative velocity (1.3) is therefore given by

$$dv_k^* = \epsilon_{kij}w_i\,dx_j. \tag{1.8}$$

Comparison of the right-hand sides of (1.8) and (I, 6.18) shows that the relative velocities dv_k^* in the neighborhood of the particle P correspond to a rigid-body rotation of this neighborhood about an axis through P. The vector (1.5) indicates the angular velocity, the direction of the axis and the sense of the rotation in the manner that has been discussed in Section 6 of Chapter I. The vector (1.5) is called the *vorticity* of the velocity field. The field lines of the vorticity field are called *vortex lines*.

If the vector gradient $\partial_j v_k$ at the particle P is antisymmetric, the symmetric part is zero, and the neighborhood of P instantaneously moves as a rigid body. Conversely, it can be shown that the symmetric part of the vector gradient $\partial_j v_k$ at P vanishes, if the neighborhood of P instantaneously moves as a rigid body. To this end, consider, in addition to P, the neighboring particles P' and P'', and denote the coordinates of the three particles by x_j, $x_j + dx_j$, and $x_j + \delta x_j$, respectively. In analogy to (1.1), the expression

$$\delta v_k = \delta x_j\,\partial_j v_k \tag{1.9}$$

represents the relative velocity of P'' with respect to P, that is, the instantaneous rate of change of the coordinate difference δx_k. The scalar product $dx_k\,\delta x_k$ therefore changes at the rate

$$\begin{aligned}(dx_k\,\delta x_k)^{\cdot} &= dv_k\,\delta x_k + dx_k\,\delta v_k = \partial_j v_k\,dx_j\,\delta x_k + \partial_j v_k\,dx_k\,\delta x_j \\ &= (\partial_j v_k + \partial_k v_j)\,dx_j\,\delta x_k = 2\partial_{(j}v_{k)}\,dx_j\,\delta x_k,\end{aligned} \tag{1.10}$$

where the dot superscript indicates the *material rate of change*, i.e., the rate of change of a quantity that is defined with reference to specific particles of the moving continuum.

If the neighborhood of P instantaneously performs a rigid-body motion, the material triangle $PP'P''$ instantaneously retains its shape. The material rate of change (1.10) then vanishes for any choice of the particles P' and P'' in the neighborhood of P, that is, for any choice of the infinitesimal vectors dx_k and δx_k. It follows from the last term of (1.10) that the tensor

$$V_{jk} = \partial_{(j}v_{k)} \tag{1.11}$$

must vanish, if the neighborhood of P instantaneously moves as a rigid body. In view of the remark at the beginning of the preceding paragraph, the vanishing of the tensor (1.11) is thus a necessary and sufficient condition for the instantaneous rigidity of the considered neighborhood. The symmetric tensor V_{jk} will be called the *rate of deformation* at the particle P.

To discuss the mechanical significance of the components of the rate of deformation, denote the instantaneous lengths of the material line elements PP' and PP'' by ds and δs, respectively, and their angle by θ, so that

$$\begin{aligned}(dx_k\,\delta x_k)^{\cdot} &= (ds\,\delta s\cos\theta)^{\cdot}\\ &= \left\{\left[\frac{(ds)^{\cdot}}{ds} + \frac{(\delta s)^{\cdot}}{\delta s}\right]\cos\theta - \theta^{\cdot}\sin\theta\right\} ds\,\delta s.\end{aligned} \tag{1.12}$$

Denoting the unit vectors of the directions PP' and PP'' by μ_k and ν_k, respectively, we have $dx_k = \mu_k\,ds$ and $\delta x_k = \nu_k\,\delta s$. Comparison of (1.10) with (1.12) and use of (1.11) therefore furnishes

$$\left[\frac{(ds)^{\cdot}}{ds} + \frac{(\delta s)^{\cdot}}{\delta s}\right]\cos\theta - \theta^{\cdot}\sin\theta = 2V_{jk}\mu_j\nu_k. \tag{1.13}$$

If we let P'' coincide with P', this relation reduces to

$$\frac{(ds)^{\cdot}}{ds} = V_{jk}\mu_j\mu_k, \tag{1.14}$$

The quotient of the rate of change $(ds)^{\cdot}$ of the length of a material line element PP' and its instantaneous length ds thus depends only on the direction but not on the length of this element. This quotient is called the *rate of extension* in the direction PP'. As is seen from (1.14), the rate of extension in the direction μ is the normal component (Chapter I, Section 7) of the symmetric tensor V_{jk} for this direction. In particular, the components V_{11}, V_{22}, V_{33} of this tensor are the rates of extension in the coordinate directions.

To arrive at a mechanical interpretation of the remaining components of the rate of deformation V_{jk}, choose PP'' perpendicular to PP'. According to (1.13), the instantaneously right angle between the material line elements PP' and PP'' decreases at the rate

$$-\theta^{\cdot} = 2V_{jk}\mu_j\nu_k. \tag{1.15}$$

In the engineering literature, this rate of decrease is usually called the shear rate for the directions μ and ν. Adoption of this terminology would cause a certain lack of balance: whereas the rate of extension in the x_1-direction would be V_{11}, the shear rate for the x_1- and x_2-directions would be $2V_{12} = 2V_{21}$. In the modern mathematical literature, the term shear rate is therefore used for *half* the rate of decrease of the instantaneously right angle formed by two material line elements. This terminology will be adopted in the following, that is, the tensor components $V_{12} = V_{21}$, $V_{23} = V_{32}$, $V_{31} = V_{13}$ will be called the *shear rates* for the three pairs of coordinate directions.

Let us now investigate the contribution dv_k^{**} of the symmetric part of the vector gradient $\partial_j v_k$ to the relative velocity (1.3). In the same sense in which the contribution dv_k^* can be attributed to the *instantaneous rotation* of the neighborhood of the typical particle P, the contribution dv_k^{**} will be attributed to the *instantaneous pure deformation* of this neighborhood.

To study this pure deformation, set $dx_j = \mu_j\, ds$ as above. It follows from (1.4) and (1.11) that

$$dv_k^{**} = V_{jk}\mu_j\, ds. \tag{1.16}$$

In the neighborhood of P, choose a particle P' so that PP' is a principal direction of the rate of deformation V_{jk}. That part dv_k^{**} of the relative velocity dv_k of P' with respect to P which is due to the instantaneous pure deformation then is directed along the line PP', that is, the instantaneous pure deformation does not change the direction of the material line element PP'. According to Section 7 of Chapter I, there exists at least one triple of orthogonal material directions emanating from P that are not altered by the instantaneous pure deformation. If the unit vectors μ_i^{I}, μ_i^{II}, μ_i^{III}, indicate directions of this kind, and V_{I}, V_{II}, V_{III} denote the corresponding principal values of the rate of deformation, we have by (I, 7.15)

$$V_{ij} = V_{\mathrm{I}}\mu_i^{\mathrm{I}}\mu_j^{\mathrm{I}} + V_{\mathrm{II}}\mu_i^{\mathrm{II}}\mu_j^{\mathrm{II}} + V_{\mathrm{III}}\mu_i^{\mathrm{III}}\mu_j^{\mathrm{III}}. \tag{1.17}$$

The quantities V_{I}, V_{II}, V_{III} are called the *principal rates of extension.* The rate of deformation is *plane* if one and only one of the three terms on the right side of (1.17) vanishes; it is *uniaxial* if two of these terms vanish. The general rate of deformation (1.17) can be conceived as resulting from the superposition of three uniaxial rates of deformation with orthogonal axes. In the instantaneous pure deformation, material line elements of the directions μ^{I}, μ^{II}, μ^{III} experience the corresponding principal rates of extension V_{I}, V_{II}, V_{III}, but no rotation.

Other results obtained in Chapter I, Section 7 and Chapter II, Sections 3, 4, 5 can likewise be restated in terms of the rate of deformation. Leaving the details to the reader, we restrict ourselves to the following remarks.

Considered as a function of the direction, the rate of extension is stationary in the neighborhood of a principal direction. The principal rates of extension are the roots of the characteristic equation

$$V^3 - \mathscr{V}_{(1)}V^2 - \mathscr{V}_{(2)}V - \mathscr{V}_{(3)} = 0, \tag{1.18}$$

in which

$$\left.\begin{aligned} \mathscr{V}_{(1)} &= V_{ii}, \\ \mathscr{V}_{(2)} &= \tfrac{1}{2}(V_{ij}V_{ji} - V_{ii}V_{jj}), \\ \mathscr{V}_{(3)} &= \tfrac{1}{6}\epsilon_{ijk}\epsilon_{pqr}V_{ip}V_{jq}V_{kr} \\ &= \tfrac{1}{6}(2V_{ij}V_{jk}V_{ki} - 3V_{ij}V_{ji}V_{kk} + V_{ii}V_{jj}V_{kk}) \end{aligned}\right\} \tag{1.19}$$

are the basic invariants of the rate of deformation.

In analogy to (II, 3.1) and (II, 3.2), the mean rate of extension is defined as

$$\mathscr{V} = \tfrac{1}{3}V_{kk}, \tag{1.20}$$

and the deviator of the rate of deformation as

$$V'_{ij} = V_{ij} - \mathscr{V}\delta_{ij}; \tag{1.21}$$

this deviator has the same principal directions as the rate of deformation, and its principal values are obtained by subtracting $\mathscr{V}$ from the principal rates of extension.

In Chapter II, Section 3, the traction transmitted across a typical surface element was decomposed into the normal and tangential tractions. In a similar manner, the quotient $d\overset{**}{v}_k/ds$ of the relative velocity (1.16) and the length ds will be written as the sum of two vectors, one of which has the direction of μ_k, while the other is perpendicular to this direction. The magnitude V_N of the first vector is the rate of extension in the direction μ. If the direction of the second vector is given by the unit vector ν_k, its magnitude

$$V_S = \nu_k \frac{d\overset{**}{v}_k}{ds} = V_{jk}\mu_j\nu_k \tag{1.22}$$

is the shear rate for the orthogonal directions μ and ν. The vectors $V_N\,\mu_k$ and $V_S\,\nu_k$ will be respectively called the *extension velocity* and the *shear velocity* for the direction μ.

From the analogy between this decomposition of $d\overset{**}{v}_k/ds$ and that of the surface traction discussed in Chapter II, Section 3, it follows that the magnitude V_S of the shear velocity is stationary in the neighborhood of the three directions specified by

$$\left.\begin{aligned} \mu_1 &= 0, \quad \mu_2^2 = \mu_3^2 = \tfrac{1}{2}, \\ \mu_1^2 &= \mu_2^2 = \tfrac{1}{2}, \quad \mu_3 = 0, \\ \mu_1^2 &= \tfrac{1}{2}, \quad \mu_2 = 0, \quad \mu_3^2 = \tfrac{1}{2}. \end{aligned}\right\} \tag{1.23}$$

These directions are called the *principal shear velocity directions;* the corresponding stationary magnitudes of the shear velocity are

$$\left.\begin{aligned} V_S &= \tfrac{1}{2}|V_{\mathrm{II}} - V_{\mathrm{III}}|, \\ V_S &= \tfrac{1}{2}|V_{\mathrm{I}} - V_{\mathrm{II}}|, \\ V_S &= \tfrac{1}{2}|V_{\mathrm{III}} - V_{\mathrm{I}}|; \end{aligned}\right\} \tag{1.24}$$

they are called *principal shear rates.*

Mohr's graphical representation of the state of stress can be adapted to the representation of the rate of deformation, and a similar remark applies to Cauchy's stress quadrics. Note that the geometrical representations so obtained are exclusively concerned with the instantaneous pure deformation and do not furnish any information concerning the instantaneous rotation. As will be shown in the next section, Mohr's graphical representation of a plane state of stress can be adapted to the graphical representation of a plane instantaneous motion in such a way that it furnishes both the angular velocity and the rate of extension of an arbitrary material line element in the plane of motion.

2. Plane instantaneous motion. The instantaneous motion of a continuum is called *uniaxial,* if there exists a rectangular Cartesian coordinate system in which the velocity field has the form

$$v_1 = v_1(x_1), \quad v_2 = v_3 = 0. \tag{2.1}$$

Since the shear rates V_{21} and V_{23} then vanish identically, the x_2-direction is a principal direction of the rate of deformation at each point of the field; the corresponding principal rate of extension is $V_{22} = 0$. Similar remarks apply to the x_3-direction. According to the definition given in Section 1, the rate of deformation thus is everywhere uniaxial, if the instantaneous motion is uniaxial.

The instantaneous motion is called *plane,* if it is not uniaxial, and if there exists a rectangular Cartesian coordinate system in which the velocity field has the form

$$v_1 = v_1(x_1, x_2), \quad v_2 = v_2(x_1, x_2), \quad v_3 = 0. \tag{2.2}$$

We leave it to the reader to show that the rate of deformation is everywhere plane, if the instantaneous motion is plane.

Consider material line elements that emanate from a particle P in the plane $x_3 = 0$ and lie in this plane. According to (1.6), the vorticity of the velocity field (2.2) has the components

$$w_1 = w_2 = 0, \quad w_3 = \tfrac{1}{2}(\partial_1 v_2 - \partial_2 v_1), \tag{2.3}$$

and the instantaneous rotation makes all considered line elements rotate with the angular velocity w_3 about an axis through P that is parallel to the x_3-axis. If w_3 is positive, the sense of this rotation is related to the positive

x_3-direction in the same manner in which the sense of rotation of a right-handed screw is related to its direction of progress.

To obtain the instantaneous relative motion of the neighborhood of P, we must superimpose the instantaneous pure deformation on the instantaneous rotation. To study the effect of the instantaneous pure deformation on the considered line elements, we use rectangular Cartesian coordinates x_1', x_2', $x_3' = x_3$ with axes in the principal directions of the rate of deformation at the particle P.

Let V_{I} and $V_{\text{II}} \neq V_{\text{I}}$ be the principal rates of extension in the x_1'- and x_2'-directions, and assume that the primed axes are so labelled that $V_{\text{I}} > V_{\text{II}}$.

In the first or second quadrant of the x_1', x_2'-plane, consider the direction μ that forms the angle φ with the positive x_1'-direction. Since its direction cosines are

$$\mu_1' = \cos\varphi, \quad \mu_2' = \sin\varphi, \quad \mu_3' = 0, \tag{2.4}$$

it follows from (1.14) that the rate of extension in the direction μ has the value

$$\begin{aligned} V_N &= V_{\text{I}} \cos^2\varphi + V_{\text{II}} \sin^2\varphi \\ &= \tfrac{1}{2}(V_{\text{I}} + V_{\text{II}}) + \tfrac{1}{2}(V_{\text{I}} - V_{\text{II}}) \cos 2\varphi. \end{aligned} \tag{2.5}$$

Since v_3' vanishes identically, the shear velocity for the direction μ falls into the x_1', x_2'-plane.

The quantity V_S in (1.22) is positive by definition, because the unit vector $\boldsymbol{\nu}$ was given the direction of the shear velocity for the direction μ. For the plane instantaneous motion considered here, the unit vector $\boldsymbol{\nu}$ will be chosen in the x_1', x_2'-plane and perpendicular to the unit vector $\boldsymbol{\mu}$ in such a manner that the directions of $\boldsymbol{\mu}$ and $\boldsymbol{\nu}$, and the positive x_3-direction form a right-handed system. Thus,

$$\nu_1' = -\mu_2' = -\sin\varphi, \quad \nu_2 = \mu_1' = \cos\varphi, \quad \nu_3' = 0. \tag{2.6}$$

The shear rate V_S computed from (1.22) may now be positive or negative. The value of V_S represents the contribution of the instantaneous pure deformation to the angular velocity of a material line element that emanates from P and has the direction μ. If V_S is positive, the sense of this rotation corresponds to the positive x_3-direction in the same manner in which the sense of rotation of a right-handed screw corresponds to its direction of progress. It follows from (2.4), (2.6), and (1.22) that

$$V_S = -\tfrac{1}{2}(V_{\text{I}} - V_{\text{II}}) \sin 2\varphi. \tag{2.7}$$

The total angular velocity Ω of the considered line element is obtained by adding to (2.7) the angular velocity w_3 of the instantaneous rotation of the neighborhood of P. Thus,

$$\Omega = w_3 - \tfrac{1}{2}(V_{\text{I}} - V_{\text{II}}) \sin 2\varphi, \tag{2.8}$$

where w_3 is given by (2.3).

To represent the relative motion of the particles in the neighborhood of P that lie in the plane $x_3 = 0$, introduce a *plane of relative velocities*, in which the point with the abscissa Ω and the ordinate V_N corresponds to the direction μ of the plane $x_3 = 0$. As μ varies, this point describes the circle with the parametric equations (2.5) and (2.8), in which φ is the angle formed by the positive x_1'-axis and the direction μ. This *circle of relative velocities* has the center B with the coordinates w_3, $(V_{\mathrm{I}} + V_{\mathrm{II}})/2$ and the radius $(V_{\mathrm{I}} - V_{\mathrm{II}})/2$ (see Figure 12). The highest point $X_1'^*$ of this circle corresponds to the x_1'-direction; its ordinate is the maximum rate of extension V_{I} in the plane of motion. The lowest point $X_2'^*$ of the circle corresponds to the x_2'-direction and its ordinate is the minimum rate of extension V_{II} in this plane. The common abscissa of the points $X_1'^*$ and $X_2'^*$ is the angular velocity w_3 of the instantaneous rotation.

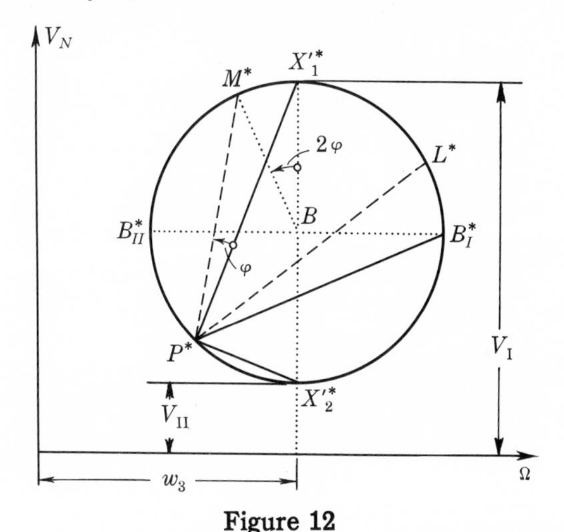

Figure 12

If M^* is the point on the circle of relative velocities that corresponds to the direction μ, the angle $X_1'^*BM^*$ equals 2φ. Let us draw a line of direction μ through M^* and a parallel to the x_1'-axis through $X_1'^*$; the intersection P^* of these lines lies on the circle of relative velocities, because the angle $X_1'^*P^*M^*$ equals the peripheral angle φ of the arc $X_1'^*M^*$. The point P^* will be called the *pole* of the circle of relative velocities. To find the point of this circle that corresponds to a given direction in the plane of motion, we only need to draw a line of this direction through the pole and determine its second intersection with the circle.

We finally investigate the rate of change of the angle between two material line elements in the plane of motion. Let the instantaneous directions of these line elements be denoted by λ and μ, and the corresponding points of the circle of relative velocities by L^* and M^* (Figure 12). The considered line elements are parallel to P^*L^* and P^*M^*, and their angular velocities are represented by the abscissas of L^* and M^*, respectively. In the situation illustrated by Figure 12, the material angle corresponding to $L^*P^*M^*$ increases at a rate that is represented by the difference of the abscissas of L^* and M^*.

Now, the difference of the abscissas of B_1^* and B_2^* is greater than that of any other pair of points on the circle of relative velocities. Accordingly, the material angle corresponding to $B_1^*P^*B_2^*$ increases at a greater rate than any other material angle in the plane of motion. Because of the factor 1/2 in the definition of the shear rate, this greatest rate of change of a material angle equals twice the principal shear rate in the plane of motion. The discussion that led to the expressions (1.24) for the principal shear rates was restricted to the rate of change of an instantaneously right angle. For plane instantaneous motion, it has now been shown that of *all* material angles in the plane of motion the *right* angle formed by material line elements in the principal shear directions changes most rapidly.

3. Conditions of integrability. The components $w_i(x)$ of the vorticity field and the components $V_{ij}(x) = V_{ji}(x)$ of the field of the rate of deformation represent a total of nine functions of position. Since these nine functions can be expressed in terms of the first derivatives of three functions, namely the components $v_i(x)$ of the velocity field, they are subject to certain integrability conditions. In establishing these conditions, we shall restrict the discussion to fields that are defined in a simply connected region.

Consider first the vorticity field $w_i(x)$. According to (1.5) and (I, 8.12), the divergence of the vorticity vanishes:

$$\partial_i w_i = 0. \tag{3.1}$$

We propose to show that any vector field $w_i(x)$ that satisfies (3.1) can be represented as the field of the curl of another vector field $v_i(x)$. Let $\eta(x) =$ constant and $\chi(x) =$ constant be the equations of two families of surfaces that are formed by the field lines of w_i, which will be called *vortex lines*. The surface $\eta(x) =$ constant passing through a typical point P of the vorticity field contains the vortex line through this point. The vorticity vector w_i at P is therefore tangential to the considered surface and hence normal to the gradient of η at P. By the same reasoning, w_i is seen to be normal to the gradient of χ at P, so that the vorticity w_i can be written as a suitable multiple of the vector product of the two gradients:

$$w_i = \varphi \epsilon_{ijk} \partial_j \eta \partial_k \chi; \tag{3.2}$$

in this relation, the vector product $\epsilon_{ijk}\partial_j\eta\partial_k\chi$ has the direction of w_i, and the scalar factor $\varphi(x)$ changes the magnitude of this vector product to that of w_i. In view of (3.1) and (3.2), we have

$$\epsilon_{ijk} \partial_i \varphi \partial_j \eta \partial_k \chi = 0; \tag{3.3}$$

indeed expressions such as $\epsilon_{ijk}(\partial_i\partial_j\eta)$ vanish, because the first factor is antisymmetric in i and j, whereas the second factor is symmetric in these subscripts. The left-hand side of (3.3) is the Jacobian of the functions φ, η, and χ; its vanishing shows that φ is a function of η and χ:

$$\varphi = \varphi(\eta, \chi). \tag{3.4}$$

Let us choose the function $\psi = \psi(\eta, \chi)$ in such a manner that

$$\frac{\partial\psi}{\partial\eta} = \varphi. \tag{3.5}$$

We then have

$$\partial_j\psi = \frac{\partial\psi}{\partial\eta}\,\partial_j\eta + \frac{\partial\psi}{\partial\chi}\,\partial_j\chi = \varphi\partial_j\eta + \frac{\partial\psi}{\partial\chi}\,\partial_j\chi. \tag{3.6}$$

Substituting $\varphi\partial_j\eta$ from (3.6) into (3.2), we obtain

$$w_i = \epsilon_{ijk}\partial_j\psi\partial_k\chi - \epsilon_{ijk}\frac{\partial\psi}{\partial\chi}\,\partial_j\chi\partial_k\chi = \epsilon_{ijk}\partial_j\psi\partial_k\chi. \tag{3.7}$$

Finally, setting

$$v_k = 2\psi\partial_k\chi \tag{3.8}$$

and using (3.7), we find

$$\tfrac{1}{2}\epsilon_{ijk}\partial_j v_k = \epsilon_{ijk}\partial_j\psi\partial_k\chi = w_i, \tag{3.9}$$

since $\epsilon_{ijk}\partial_j\partial_k\chi = 0$. The velocity field $\mathbf{v}$ defined by (3.8) thus admits the given divergence-free vector field $\mathbf{w}$ as vorticity field. It follows that the condition (3.1) is the only integrability condition for the vorticity field.

According to (3.8), the vector $\mathbf{v}$ is parallel to grad χ and therefore perpendicular to the vector $\mathbf{w}$ which, by (3.7), is the vector product of grad η and grad χ. For the given vorticity field $\mathbf{w}$, we have therefore constructed a velocity field $\mathbf{v}$ such that $\mathbf{v}$ and $\mathbf{w}$ are orthogonal, whereas for an arbitrary velocity field the vorticity is in general not orthogonal to the velocity. The velocity field $\mathbf{v}$ found above is by no means the only velocity field with the given vorticity $\mathbf{w}$. In fact, since the curl of a gradient field vanishes identically, other velocity fields of the prescribed vorticity can be obtained from (3.8) by the superposition of gradient fields.

To derive the integrability for the components of the rate of deformation V_{jk}, we start with the identity $\partial_q v_s = \partial_{(q}v_{s)} + \partial_{[q}v_{s]}$. According to (1.7) and (1.11), this can be written as

$$\partial_q v_s = V_{qs} + \epsilon_{qst}w_t. \tag{3.10}$$

For brevity, the tensor field represented by the right side of (3.10) will be denoted by T_{qs}. Since the fields considered here are supposed to be defined in a simply connected region, the nine components of the field T_{qs} can be obtained from the three components of the velocity field v_s by differentiation in accordance with (3.10), if and only if $\partial_p T_{qs} - \partial_q T_{ps} = 0$ or

$$\epsilon_{ipq}\partial_p T_{qs} = 0. \tag{3.11}$$

Replacing T_{qs} in (3.11) by the right-hand side of (3.10), we obtain

$$\epsilon_{ipq}\partial_p V_{qs} + \epsilon_{ipq}\epsilon_{qst}\partial_p w_t = 0. \tag{3.12}$$

According to (I, 6.3) and (I, 6.5), we have

$$\epsilon_{ipq}\epsilon_{qst}\partial_p w_t = \delta_{is}\partial_t w_t - \partial_s w_i. \tag{3.13}$$

Since the divergence of the vorticity field vanishes identically, substitution of (3.13) into (3.12) furnishes

$$\partial_s w_i = \epsilon_{ipq}\partial_p V_{qs}. \tag{3.14}$$

Applying once more the reasoning used in connection with (3.10), we obtain

$$\epsilon_{ipq}\epsilon_{jrs}\partial_{pr} V_{qs} = 0 \tag{3.15}$$

as the required integrability condition for the components of the rate of deformation. Aside from trivial transformations, only the condition (3.11), which is known to be necessary and sufficient, has been used in the derivation of the integrability condition (3.15). No special proof is therefore required for the sufficiency of this certainly necessary condition.

Replacing the dummy subscripts p, q, r, s by r, s, p, q, respectively, and using the symmetry of the operator ∂_{pr} and the tensor V_{qs}, one readily shows that (3.15) is symmetric in i and j and therefore represents six equations. These fall into two classes, representatives of which are furnished by the subscript pairs $i = j = 1$ and $i = 1, j = 2$:

$$\partial_{22}V_{33} + \partial_{33}V_{22} - 2\partial_{23}V_{23} = 0, \tag{3.16}$$

$$\partial_3(\partial_1 V_{23} + \partial_2 V_{31} - \partial_3 V_{12}) - \partial_{12}V_{33} = 0. \tag{3.17}$$

These equations and the four obtained from them by cyclic permutations of subscripts are called the *equations of compatibility* for the components of the rate of deformation.

When the instantaneous motion is plane (see (2.2)), the integrability conditions established above are greatly simplified. According to (2.3), the vorticity field then has the form

$$w_1 = w_2 = 0, \quad w_3 = w_3(x_1, x_2). \tag{3.18}$$

Since an arbitrary vector field of this form satisfies (3.1), the function $w_3(x_1, x_2)$ in (3.18) is not subject to any integrability condition. On the other hand, V_{11}, V_{22}, and V_{12}, the only nonvanishing components of the rate of deformation, are independent of x_3, so that (3.16) and (3.17) are identically fulfilled. Moreover, three of the four integrability conditions obtained from (3.16) and (3.17) by cyclic permutation of subscripts are also identically fulfilled, the only remaining condition of integrability being

$$\partial_{11}V_{22} + \partial_{22}V_{11} - 2\partial_{12}V_{12} = 0. \tag{3.19}$$

Returning to the tensor form (3.15) of the compatibility conditions, consider a symmetrical tensor field V_{ij} that is defined in a simply connected region in which it satisfies (3.15). Regarding V_{ij} as the rate of deformation of a continuum, we propose to show that the corresponding velocity field is determined to within the velocity field of a rigid-body motion. Indeed, if the distinct velocity fields $\overset{*}{v_i}$ and $\overset{**}{v_i}$ correspond to the same rate of deformation field, their difference $\bar{v}_i = \overset{*}{v_i} - \overset{**}{v_i}$ satisfies

$$\partial_i\bar{v}_j + \partial_j\bar{v}_i = 0. \tag{3.20}$$

Differentiating (3.20) with respect to x_k and multiplying the resulting equation by ϵ_{lkj}, we obtain

$$\partial_i(\epsilon_{lkj}\partial_k\bar{v}_j) = 0. \tag{3.21}$$

The field $\bar{v}_j$ thus has a constant curl. Since by (3.20) the first component $\partial_2\bar{v}_3 - \partial_3\bar{v}_2$ of this curl can be written as $2\partial_2\bar{v}_3$, it follows from (3.20) and (3.21) that all second derivatives of the velocity components with respect to the coordinates vanish. We thus have

$$\bar{v}_i = a_i + 2b_{ki}x_k, \tag{3.22}$$

where a_i is a constant vector and b_{ki} a constant tensor of the second order. Since substitution of (3.22) into (3.20) reveals that the tensor b_{ki} is antisymmetric, (I, 6.20) shows that (3.22) represents the velocity field of a rigid-body motion: a_i is the velocity vector at the coordinate origin and b_{ki} the dual tensor of the angular velocity vector.

4. Material rates of change.

The preceding sections of this chapter were concerned with the *instantaneous* velocity field $v_k(x)$. By specifying how this field varies with the time t, we obtain a complete description of the motion of a continuum. In

$$v_k = v_k(x, t) \tag{4.1}$$

the letter x stands again for the variables x_1, x_2, x_3. Partial differentiation with respect to time will be denoted by the operator ∂_0, and partial differentiation with respect to x_j by the operator ∂_j.

In computing the partial derivative $\partial_0 v_k$ at the point P and the instant t, we compare the velocities $v_k(x, t)$ and $v_k(x, t + dt)$ that are observed, at one and the same point of space, at the instants t and $t + dt$, respectively. Consequently, the derivative $\partial_0 v_k$ does not, as a rule, represent the acceleration a_k of the particle with the instantaneous position P. In determining this acceleration, we must take account of the infinitesimal displacement of the considered particle during the time dt. At the time t the particle has the position P with the coordinates x_j, and at the time $t + dt$ the position P' with the coordinates $x'_j = x_j + v_j\,dt$; its acceleration therefore follows from $a_k\,dt = v_k(x', t + dt) - v_k(x, t)$. Thus,

$$a_k = v_j \partial_j v_k + \partial_0 v_k. \tag{4.2}$$

In symbolic notation, this relation is written as

$$\mathbf{a} = (\mathbf{v}\cdot\text{grad})\,\mathbf{v} + \partial\mathbf{v}/\partial t. \tag{4.3}$$

The first term on the right-hand side of (4.2) or (4.3) may be interpreted as the contribution of the motion of the particle in the instantaneous velocity field, and the second term as the contribution of the time dependence of the velocity field. Accordingly, these terms are respectively called the *convective* and the *local* parts of the acceleration.

To derive a useful alternative expression for the acceleration, add the identity $0 = v_j \partial_k v_j - v_j \partial_k v_j$ to (4.2); thus

$$a_k = v_j(\partial_j v_k - \partial_k v_j) + v_j \partial_k v_j + \partial_0 v_k. \tag{4.4}$$

Writing the parenthesis as $2\partial_{[j}v_{k]}$ and the second term on the right side as $\partial_k(\frac{1}{2}v_j v_j)$, and using (1.7) and (I, 6.3), we obtain the relation

$$a_k = 2\epsilon_{kij} w_i v_j + \partial_k(\tfrac{1}{2}v_j v_j) + \partial_0 v_k, \tag{4.5}$$

in which the first term on the right-hand side is twice the vector product of the vorticity and the velocity. In symbolic notation, (4.5) assumes the form

$$\mathbf{a} = 2\mathbf{w} \times \mathbf{v} + \text{grad}\,(v^2/2) + \partial\mathbf{v}/\partial t. \tag{4.6}$$

Using the terminology introduced in connection with (1.10), we may speak of the acceleration a_k as the *material rate of change* $\dot{v}_k$ of the velocity v_k. The reasoning that led to the expression (4.2) for the material rate of change of the velocity is readily applied to other quantities. Consider, for instance, the time-dependent temperature field $\Theta = \Theta(x, t)$ of a continuum. The temperature of the typical particle changes at the rate given by the relation

$$\Theta^{\boldsymbol{\cdot}} = v_j \partial_j \Theta + \partial_0 \Theta, \tag{4.7}$$

in which the right-hand side is to be evaluated for the considered instant t and the instantaneous position x of the particle. In (4.7) the temperature Θ may be replaced by any other scalar property of the continuum. Similarly, the material rate of change of a tensorial property $T_{kl\cdots}(x, t)$ is found to be

$$\dot{T}_{kl\cdots} = v_j \partial_j T_{kl\cdots} + \partial_0 T_{kl\cdots}. \tag{4.8}$$

The material rates of change considered so far concern properties that are defined with reference to a specific particle. Not all important concepts of continuum mechanics can be defined in this manner. Thus, one may for instance speak of the *density* of the continuum *at a specific particle* but not of the *mass of this particle*, because the term particle refers to a point of the continuum and not to an element of volume.

A finite part of the continuum possesses the mass $m = \int \rho \, dV$, where $\rho = \rho(x, t)$ is the time-dependent density field and the integration is to be extended over the volume V that the considered part of the continuum occupies at the instant under consideration. The material rate of change of a volume integral of this type is to be defined in such a manner that the conservation of mass is expressed by the relation $m^{\cdot} = 0$.

Consider the volume integral

$$I = \int T_{kl\cdots} \, dV, \tag{4.9}$$

where $T_{kl\cdots}(x, t)$ denotes a tensorial property of the continuum and the integral is evaluated at the typical instant t, the integration being extended over that part of the continuum that at this instant occupies the regular

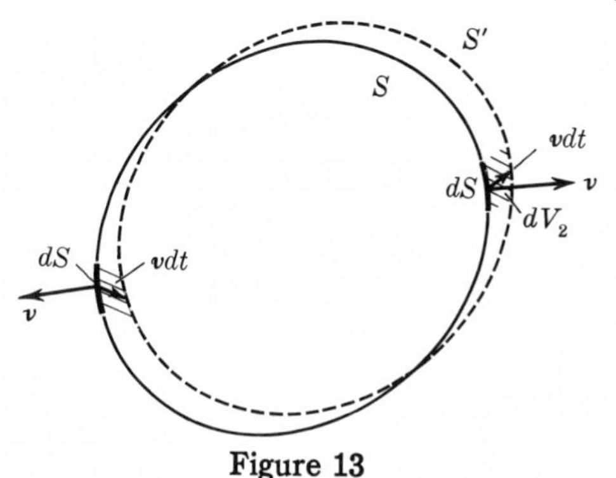

Figure 13

region V. The particle that has the coordinates x_j at the instant t will have the coordinates $x_j' = x_j + v_j \, dt$ at the time $t + dt$. Consider in particular the particles that at the instant t occupy the surface S of V; at the time $t + dt$ these particles occupy a neighboring surface S', which bounds the volume V' (Figure 13). The material rate of change $I^{\cdot}$ of the integral (4.9) is then defined by the relation

$$I^{\cdot} \, dt = \int T_{kl\cdots}(x', t + dt) \, dV' - \int T_{kl\cdots}(x, t) \, dV.$$

If dV_1 is an element of V' as well as V, it furnishes the contribution $\partial_0 T_{kl\cdots} \, dV_1$ to $I^{\cdot}$, where the partial derivative is to be taken at the time t and the position dV_1. The shaded volume element dV_2 in Figure 13 is swept out by the particles on the element dS of S as these undergo the displacement $v_j dt$; thus, dV_2 is an element of V' but not of V. If ν_j is the unit vector along the exterior normal of S, we have $dV_2 = v_j \nu_j \, dS \, dt$. The contribution of this volume element to $I^{\cdot}$ thus equals $T_{kl}\ldots v_j\nu_j\,dS$. This expression also represents the contribution of a volume element that is in V but not in V', for instance the element indicated at the lower left of Figure 13. Indeed, the scalar product $v_j\nu_j$ is negative for an element of this kind and this corresponds to the negative sign of the volume integral over V in the expression for $I^{\cdot}$. Summing up, we have

$$I^{\cdot} = \int T_{kl}\ldots v_j\nu_j\,dS + \int \partial_0 T_{kl}\ldots\,dV. \tag{4.10}$$

Transforming the first integral in (4.10) by means of Gauss' theorem and using (4.8), we find

$$\begin{aligned} I^{\cdot} &= \int [\partial_0 T_{kl}\ldots + \partial_j(v_j T_{kl}\ldots)]\,dV \\ &= \int [T^{\cdot}_{kl}\ldots + T_{kl}\ldots\partial_j v_j]\,dV. \end{aligned} \tag{4.11}$$

In many applications I is a property of the considered part of the continuum that remains constant during the motion of this part (conservation of mass or energy). We then have $I^{\cdot} = 0$, and if this relation is to hold for an arbitrary part of the continuum, the integrands in (4.11) must vanish identically.

As an example for the application of (4.11) consider the special case in which the tensor $T_{kl}\ldots$ is replaced by the scalar 1. The integral I then represents the instantaneous volume of the considered part of the continuum, and (4.11) furnishes

$$I^{\cdot} = \int \partial_j v_j\,dV. \tag{4.12}$$

Since this relation holds for an arbitrary part of the continuum, the expression $\partial_j v_j\,dV$ represents the rate of increase of the instantaneous volume dV of an element of the continuum. The divergence $\partial_j v_j$ is therefore called the *cubical rate of dilatation.*

As is seen from (4.11), the operations of forming the material derivative of an arbitrary tensorial property $T_{kl}\ldots$ and integrating over an arbitrary material volume V are commutative if and only if $\partial_j v_j$ vanishes identically, i.e., if and only if the instantaneous motion of the continuum is volume-preserving.

Let us now discuss the material rate of change of the line integral

$$J = \int c_i\,dL_i, \tag{4.13}$$

where $c_i = c_i(x, t)$ is a vectorial property of the continuum and the integration is extended at the instant t over those particles of the continuum which form the closed curve L with the directed line element dL_i. In the notation used in connection with (4.10) the material rate of change $J^{\cdot}$ of the integral (4.13) is given by

$$J^{\cdot}\, dt = \int c_k(x', t + dt)\, dL'_k - \int c_k(x, t)\, dL_k, \tag{4.14}$$

where dL'_i is the directed line element of the curve L' formed at the time $t + dt$ by the same particles that formed the curve L at the time t.

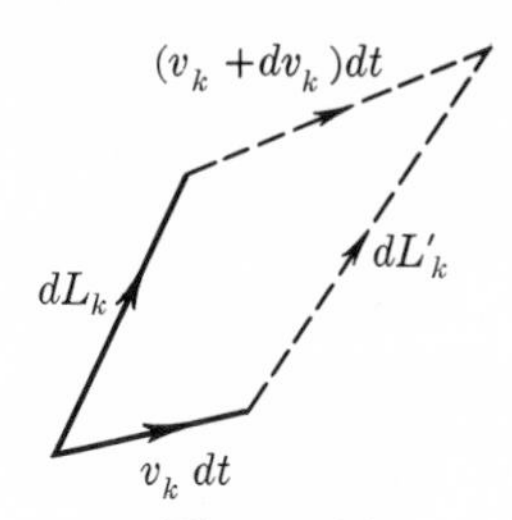

Figure 14

As is shown by Figure 14, during the interval dt the material line element dL_i changes by $(dL_k)^{\cdot}\, dt = dv_k\, dt$, where dv_k is given by (1.1). The line element dL'_k in (4.14) is therefore given by

$$dL'_k = dL_k + \partial_j v_k\, dL_j\, dt. \tag{4.15}$$

On the other hand,

$$c_k(x', t + dt) = c_k(x, t) + c_k^{\cdot}(x, t)\, dt. \tag{4.16}$$

The material rate of change of $c_k\, dL_k$ thus equals

$$\begin{aligned}(c_k\, dL_k)^{\cdot} &= c_k^{\cdot}\, dL_k + c_k \partial_j v_k\, dL_j \\ &= c_k^{\cdot}\, dL_k - v_k \partial_j c_k\, dL_j + \partial_j(c_k v_k)\, dL_j.\end{aligned} \tag{4.17}$$

When (4.17) is integrated along the closed curve L, the contribution of the last term in (4.17) vanishes because $c_k v_k$ has the same value at the start and end of the closed path of integration. Accordingly,

$$J^{\cdot} = \int c_k^{\cdot}\, dL_k - \int v_k \partial_j c_k\, dL_j. \tag{4.18}$$

If, in particular, we set $c_k = v_k$ in (4.18), the integral J is the circulation of the velocity vector, and the second integrand in (4.18) can be written as the gradient $\partial_j(\frac{1}{2} v_k v_k)$ so that the second integral in (4.18) vanishes. Thus

$$\left(\int v_k\, dL_k\right)^{\cdot} = \int v_k^{\cdot}\, dL_k, \tag{4.19}$$

where $v_k^{\cdot}$ is the acceleration a_k. This equation represents a special case in which the operations of forming the material derivative and integrating along a closed material curve are commutative. There exists, however, no general condition for the velocity field of a continuum that would ensure this kind of commutativity for an arbitrary vector field c_k and an arbitrary closed curve L. In this respect, the integral (4.13) along a closed material curve differs markedly from the integral (4.9) over a material volume.

As is seen from (4.19), the circulation of the velocity vector along a closed material curve does not change with time as long as the acceleration field is a gradient field.

PROBLEMS

1.1. Let the rates of extension for the coordinate directions have the common value a, and the shear rates the common value b. Establish a condition which the components of the unit vector $\boldsymbol{\nu}$ must fulfill if the rate of extension for the direction ν is to have the value a.

1.2. Prove the following proposition: at each particle of a deforming continuum there exists at least one material direction that is instantaneously stationary.

1.3. Let the instantaneous velocity field of a continuum be the gradient field of a scalar field $\varphi(x)$. Show that, at each particle, there exist at least three orthogonal directions of the kind considered in Problem 1.2.

1.4. Let the scalar λ and the orthogonal unit vectors $\boldsymbol{\mu}$ and $\boldsymbol{\nu}$ be independent of the coordinates x_i. The velocity field $v_i = \lambda x_j \mu_i \nu_j$ then represents simple shearing: material planes that are normal to $\boldsymbol{\nu}$ perform translations in the direction of $\boldsymbol{\mu}$ in such a manner that the relative velocity of any two of these planes is proportional to their distance. Determine the principal rates of extension and shear as well as the orientation of the principal axes of the rate of deformation with respect to the directions of $\boldsymbol{\mu}$ and $\boldsymbol{\nu}$.

1.5. Prove that a field of rate of deformation represents simple shearing (see Problem 1.4) if and only if its components V_{ij} are independent of the coordinates and the basic invariants $\mathscr{V}_{(1)}$ and $\mathscr{V}_{(3)}$ vanish.

1.6. Express the components of the rate of deformation in the cylindrical coordinates ρ, θ, ζ in terms of the velocity components v_ρ, v_θ, v_ζ and their derivatives with respect to ρ, θ, ζ. Solve the corresponding problem for spherical coordinates.

1.7. Let dx_i and δx_i be directed material line elements emanating from the typical particle P. They specify a material surface element whose area and orientation is given by the vector $dS_i = \epsilon_{ijk}\, dx_j\, \delta x_k$. Show that the material rate of change of dS_i is $(dS_i)^\cdot = \partial_j v_j\, dS_i - \partial_i v_j\, dS_j$.

2.1. Prove that the rate of deformation V_{ij} is uniaxial if and only if the basic invariants $\mathscr{V}_{(2)}$ and $\mathscr{V}_{(3)}$ vanish. Establish a necessary and sufficient condition for the rate of deformation to be plane.

2.2. At the typical particle of a continuum in plane motion consider all pairs of material line elements that lie in the plane of motion and form the angle α with each other. Using the circle of relative velocities, determine those pairs for which the material rate of change of the angle α is maximum or minimum.

2.3. At the typical particle P of a continuum in plane motion let w_3 be the angular velocity of the instantaneous rotation, and V_{I}, V_{II} the principal rates of extension in the plane of motion. Give a necessary and sufficient condition for the existence of two distinct material directions at P that lie in the plane of motion and are instantaneously stationary.

3.1. From a scalar field φ that is independent of x_3 derive a symmetric tensor field of the second order in accordance with $V_{ij} = \partial_i\varphi\partial_j\varphi$. Show that V_{ij} may be considered as the field of the rate of deformation of a continuum if the surface $x_3 = \varphi(x_1, x_2)$ is developable (i.e. the envelope of a one-parameter family of planes).

3.2. Show that the rate of deformation V_{ij} considered in Problem 3.1 is everywhere uniaxial, and determine the direction of the axis as well as the value of the nonvanishing principal rate of extension at the typical point of the field.

3.3. Considering a plane velocity field $v_1 = v_1(x_1, x_2)$, $v_2 = v_2(x_1, x_2)$, $v_3 = 0$ with vanishing divergence, denote the rate of extension in the x_1-direction by ϵ, the shear rate for the x_1- and x_2-directions by γ, and the angular velocity of the instantaneous rotation by ω. From (3.14) derive equations of compatibility for ϵ, γ, ω, and show that these have the same structure as the equations of equilibrium (II, 2.7) for a plane field of stress whose not identically vanishing components $T_{11} = \sigma + s$, $T_{22} = \sigma - s$, $T_{12} = \tau$ are independent of x_3, provided that body forces can be neglected and the variables σ, s, and τ are made to correspond to $-\omega$, γ ,and $-\epsilon$, respectively.

3.4. Prove the following proposition concerning the analogy in Problem 3.3: to the relative velocity of the end points of a material line element in the plane $x_3 = 0$ there corresponds the infinitesimal force transmitted across a rectangle that is perpendicular to the x_1, x_2-plane and has the line element as base and the unit of length as height.

4.1. Prove that in a rigid-body motion the negative divergence of the acceleration equals twice the square of the vorticity, while the curl of the acceleration equals twice the material rate of change of the vorticity.

4.2. Let v_i be the velocity and a_i the acceleration of a typical particle of a continuum and w_i the vorticity at this particle. Prove that

$$\partial_0\left(\int w_i\,dV\right) = \int (v_iw_j - w_iv_j)\nu_j\,dS - \tfrac{1}{2}\int \epsilon_{ijk}a_j\nu_k\,dS,$$

where V is a simply connected region of space, S its regular surface, and ν_i the unit vector along the exterior normal of S.

4.3. Using the relation in Problem 4.2, determine the material rate of change $\left(\int w_i \, dV\right)^{\cdot}$.

4.4. Writing the second rate of change of the scalar product of two material line elements as $(dx_k \, \delta x_k)^{\cdot\cdot} = 2A_{ij} \, dx_i \, \delta x_j$, show that

$$A_{ij} = \dot{V}_{ij} + \partial_i v_k V_{kj} + \partial_j v_k V_{ki},$$

where v_i is the velocity and V_{ij} the rate of deformation.

4.5. Considering a continuum with the velocity field $v_i(x, t)$, assume that its surface moves according to $F(x, t) = 0$. What differential equation must the function $F(x, t)$ satisfy in view of the fact that the surface of the continuum is a material surface?

4.6. Establish formulas for the material rate of change of a field vector in spherical and cylindrical coordinates. Apply these formulas to the velocity vector to obtain the expressions for the acceleration in these coordinates.

4.7. Let S be a simply connected, continuously curved part of a surface with the unit normal vector $\boldsymbol{\nu}$. Show that the material rate of change $\left(\int \mathbf{w} \cdot \boldsymbol{\nu} \, dS\right)^{\cdot}$ of the flux of vorticity through S equals one half of the flux $\int \boldsymbol{\nu} \cdot \operatorname{curl} \mathbf{a} \, dS$ of the curl of the acceleration $\mathbf{a}$.

CHAPTER IV

Fundamental Laws

1. Conservation of mass. The basic concepts of statics and kinematics of continua were presented in Chapters II and III, respectively. The present chapter is concerned with fundamental physical laws that apply to all continua.

At the typical instant t, a regular region V of space contains the mass

$$m = \int \rho \, dV, \tag{1.1}$$

where $\rho = \rho(x, t)$ is the density field of the continuum. *Conservation of mass* requires that $m^{\cdot} = 0$ for an arbitrarily chosen region V. According to the first line of (III, 4.11), this condition is expressed by the *equation of continuity*

$$\partial_0 \rho + \partial_j(\rho v_j) = 0, \tag{1.2}$$

while the second line of (III, 4.11) furnishes the alternative form

$$\rho^{\cdot} + \rho \partial_j v_j = 0. \tag{1.3}$$

Since $\rho \neq 0$, the last equation may also be written as

$$(\log \rho)^{\cdot} + \partial_j v_j = 0. \tag{1.4}$$

The following special cases of the equation of continuity are worth noting. In an *incompressible* medium, the density at each particle is independent of the time so that $\rho^{\cdot} = 0$. For an incompressible medium the equation of continuity (1.3) thus reduces to

$$\partial_j v_j = 0. \tag{1.5}$$

According to Section 3 of Chapter III, the velocity field $\mathbf{v}(x, t)$ of an incompressible continuum can therefore be written as the curl of a vector field $\mathbf{u}(x, t)$, which is called the *vector potential of* $\mathbf{v}$:

$$\mathbf{v} = \operatorname{curl} \mathbf{u}. \tag{1.6}$$

In deriving (1.6), we only assumed that the density at each particle is independent of time, but not that the density has the same value at all particles, i.e. that the continuum is *homogeneous*.

The motion of a continuum is called *steady*, if the velocity field and all other relevant fields in the continuum are independent of the time. For a steady motion, we therefore have $\partial_0 \rho = 0$, and the equation of continuity reduces to

$$\partial_j(\rho v_j) = 0. \tag{1.7}$$

For the *steady* motion of an *incompressible* continuum, it follows from (1.5) and (1.7) that

$$v_j \partial_j \rho = 0. \tag{1.8}$$

The motion of a continuum is called *irrotational* if the vorticity vanishes identically. According to Section 9 of Chapter I, the velocity field of an irrotational motion is the gradient field of a scalar field $\varphi(x, t)$:

$$v_j = \partial_j \varphi. \tag{1.9}$$

The function $\varphi(x, t)$ is called *velocity potential*, and motions of this kind are called *potential flows*. For a potential flow, the equation of continuity (1.3) takes the form

$$\rho^{\cdot} + \rho \Delta \varphi = 0. \tag{1.10}$$

In particular, for the potential flow of an *incompressible* continuum we have

$$\Delta \varphi = 0. \tag{1.11}$$

The equations of continuity (1.2) and (1.3) contain the values of the velocity components and the density as well as their first derivatives *at the considered point*. These equations can therefore be said to express the principle of conservation of mass *in the small*. It is occasionally useful to formulate this principle *in the large*. To this end, we return to (III, 4.10), in which we replace $T_{kl\cdots}$ by ρ and I by m. From $m^{\cdot} = 0$ it then follows that

$$\int \partial_0 \rho \, dV + \int \rho v_j \nu_j \, dS = 0. \tag{1.12}$$

The first integral in (1.12) represents the rate at which the mass in the fixed region V of space increases on account of the time-dependence of the velocity field; the second integral represents the rate at which this mass decreases on account of the flow across the surface S of V. Equation (1.12) thus states that any increase in the mass contained in V is necessarily due to the inflow of mass across S.

For steady motion, (1.12) reduces to

$$\int \rho v_j \nu_j \, dS = 0. \tag{1.13}$$

A typical application of this relation concerns the flow in a *stream filament*. By definition, the surface of a stream filament is formed by the stream lines through the points of an infinitesimal closed curve. Let dS' and dS'' be the areas of two normal cross sections of a stream filament. Assuming that the flow in the filament is directed from dS' toward dS'', denote the magnitudes of the velocity at these cross sections by v' and v'', respectively. When (1.13) is applied to the segment of the stream filament between the cross sections dS' and dS'', the normal velocity $v_j\nu_j$ is zero on the lateral surface and equals $-v'$ and v'' at the end surfaces. If the densities at dS' and dS'' are denoted by ρ' and ρ'', respectively, (1.13) yields

$$\rho' v' \, dS' = \rho'' v'' \, dS''. \tag{1.14}$$

For an incompressible continuum, the velocity in a stream filament thus is inversely proportional to the cross-sectional area.

2. Momentum theorem. At the typical instant t, a regular region V of space contains the momentum

$$Q_k = \int \rho v_k \, dV, \tag{2.1}$$

and the body and surface forces acting on the continuum in V have the resultant

$$R_k = \int \rho F_k \, dV + \int T_{lk}\nu_l \, dS, \tag{2.2}$$

where $F_k(x, t)$ denotes the field of specific body forces (other than inertia forces), $T_{lk}(x, t)$ the field of stress, and ν_l the unit vector along the exterior normal of the surface S of V. Applying Gauss' theorem to the second integral in (2.2), we obtain

$$R_k = \int (\rho F_k + \partial_l T_{lk}) \, dV \tag{2.3}$$

The *momentum theorem* states that $\dot{Q}_k = R_k$ for any choice of the region V. According to (III, 4.11), we therefore have

$$\partial_0(\rho v_k) + \partial_j(v_j \rho v_k) = \rho F_k + \partial_l T_{lk}. \tag{2.4}$$

The left side of this relation can be transformed as follows:

$$v_k[\partial_0 \rho + \partial_j(\rho v_j)] + \rho[\partial_0 v_k + v_j \partial_j v_k]. \tag{2.5}$$

The first bracket in (2.5) vanishes by the equation of continuity (1.2), while according to (III, 4.2) the second bracket represents the acceleration a_k. Equation (2.4) can therefore be written in the form

$$a_k = F_k + \frac{1}{\rho} \partial_l T_{lk}. \tag{2.6}$$

This *equation of motion*, which was here derived from the momentum theorem, could also be obtained from the equation of equilibrium (II, 2.7) by adding the specific inertia force $-a_k$ to the specific body force F_k.

Equation (2.6) can be said to express the momentum theorem *in the small.*

To formulate this theorem *in the large,* we write the material derivative of the integral (2.1) according to (III, 4.10) and set the result equal to the integral (2.2). We thus obtain

$$\int \partial_0(\rho v_k)\, dV_k = \int (T_{jk} - \rho v_j v_k)\nu_j\, dS + \int \rho F_k\, dV. \tag{2.7}$$

The left side of this relation represents the rate at which the momentum contained in the fixed region V increases because of the time-dependence of the density and velocity fields. On the right side of (2.7) the surface integral of $T_{jk}\nu_j$ represents the resultant of the surface forces that are transmitted at the considered instant onto the continuum in V. The surface integral of $-\rho v_k v_j \nu_j$ indicates the rate at which momentum flows across S into V, and the volume integral of ρF_k the resultant of the body forces acting on the continuum in V.

Let us apply (2.7) to the *steady flow in a stream filament.* In the notation introduced at the end of Section 1, we have

$$R_k = \rho'' v'' v_k''\, dS'' - \rho' v' v_k'\, dS', \tag{2.8}$$

where R_k is the resultant of the body and surface forces that instantaneously act on the continuum in the considered segment of the stream filament.

As a second example illustrating the use of (2.7), we consider the steady flow of a continuum past a rigid body, which is held at rest by suitable forces, and derive an expression for the force P_k that the continuum exerts on this body. Letting S' be the surface of the rigid body, and S'' a control surface that encloses S', apply (2.7) to the region V bounded by these surfaces. Since the motion is steady, the left-hand side of (2.7) vanishes. Moreover, the normal velocity $v_j\nu_j$ vanishes on S', and the resultant $\int T_{ij}\nu_j\, dS'$ of the surface forces transmitted in S' on the continuum equals $-P_k$. If P_k'' denotes the resultant of the surface forces transmitted across S'' on the continuum in V, the equation (2.7) yields

$$P_k = P_k'' + \int \rho F_k\, dV - \int \rho v_j v_k \nu_j\, dS''. \tag{2.9}$$

In the absence of body forces, it is often expedient to consider the limiting case in which S'' is a sphere of infinite diameter.

Another application of (2.7) is found in the theory of turbulence, where the velocity field is regarded as resulting from the superposition of two fields $v_k'(x, t)$ and $v_k''(x, t)$ that represent the smooth *mean motion* and the *turbulent fluctuations,* respectively. The statistical character of the latter is expressed by the following postulate: Volume or surface integrals of expressions that are of the first order in the turbulent velocity components v_k'' can be neglected in (2.7), provided that the smallest dimension of the domain of integration exceeds a certain length.

For an incompressible continuum, (2.7) can then be written in the form

$$\int \rho \partial_0 v_k' \, dV = \int (T_{ij} - \rho v_j'' v_k'') \nu_j \, dS - \int \rho v_j' v_k' \nu_j \, dS + \int \rho F_k \, dV. \quad (2.10)$$

Except for the second term of the first integrand on the right, this equation is the momentum theorem (2.7) written for the mean motion. The influence of the turbulent fluctuations on the mean motion is therefore represented by the *turbulent stresses*

$$T_{jk}'' = -\rho v_j'' v_k'', \quad (2.11)$$

which Reynolds † introduced into the theory of turbulence.

3. Moment of momentum theorem. At the typical instant t, the continuum contained in a regular region V of space has the moment of momentum (or whirl)

$$W_i = \int \epsilon_{ijk} x_j \rho v_k \, dV \quad (3.1)$$

with respect to the coordinate origin. On the other hand, the body and surface forces acting on this part of the continuum have the moment

$$M_i = \int \epsilon_{ijk} x_j \rho F_k \, dV + \int \epsilon_{ijk} x_j T_{lk} \nu_l \, dS \quad (3.2)$$

with respect to the origin. Because of the symmetry of the stress tensor, transformation of the last integral by means of Gauss' theorem yields

$$M_i = \int \epsilon_{ijk} x_j (\rho F_k + \partial_l T_{lk}) \, dV. \quad (3.3)$$

The *moment of momentum theorem* states that $W_i^{\cdot} = M_i$ for any choice of the region V. According to (III, 4.11) this means that

$$\epsilon_{ijk}[x_j \partial_0(\rho v_k) + \partial_l(v_l x_j \rho v_k) - x_j \rho F_k - x_j \partial_l T_{lk}] = 0. \quad (3.4)$$

The contribution of the second term in the bracket to the left side of (3.4) can be written as $\epsilon_{ijk} x_j \partial_l(\rho v_k v_l) + \epsilon_{ijk} \rho v_j v_k = \epsilon_{ijk} x_j \partial_l(\rho v_k v_l)$, and (2.4) shows that (3.4) is identically fulfilled. Accordingly, the moment of momentum theorem does not furnish any differential equation for the motion of a continuum. This is not surprising because the corresponding statical consideration in Section 2 of Chapter II furnished only (II, 2.8), i.e. the symmetry of the stress tensor, which has been used above.

With the aid of (III, 4.10), the moment of momentum theorem can be formulated *in the large* as follows:

$$\int \epsilon_{ijk} x_j \partial_0(\rho v_k) \, dV = \int \epsilon_{ijk} x_j (T_{kl} - \rho v_k v_l) \nu_l \, dS + \int \epsilon_{ijk} x_j \rho F_k \, dV. \quad (3.5)$$

† O. Reynolds, Philos. Transactions *174* (1883) 935.

In this form, it can, for instance, be used to determine the moment H_k of the force P_k in (2.9) with respect to the coordinate origin. With the notation from (2.9), we have

$$H_i = H_i'' + \int \epsilon_{ijk} x_j \rho F_k \, dV - \int \epsilon_{ijk} x_j \rho v_k v_l \nu_l \, dS'', \tag{3.6}$$

where H_i'' is the moment, with respect to the origin, of the surface forces transmitted across S'' onto the continuum in V. The force vector (2.9) and the moment vector (3.6) specify the line of action of the force that the continuum exerts on the rigid body.

4. Energy theorem. Whereas the preceding discussion had purely mechanical character, the interaction between mechanical and thermal processes will have to be taken into account in this section.

The energy that is contained in the regular volume V at the instant t is regarded as the sum of the *kinetic energy*

$$\mathscr{K} = \int \tfrac{1}{2} \rho v_k v_k \, dV \tag{4.1}$$

and the *internal energy*; the latter is written in the form

$$\mathscr{E} = \int \rho e \, dV, \tag{4.2}$$

where e is called the *specific internal energy*. Furthermore, a new vector, the *heat flux* $\mathbf{q}$, enters the equations; it is defined as follows. If dS is a surface element with the unit normal ν_k, the expression $q_k \nu_k \, dS$ is supposed to represent the rate at which energy is transmitted in nonmechanical manner across the surface element dS in the sense indicated by ν_k. If, for instance, all nonmechanical transfer of energy consists of heat conduction, we set

$$q_k = -J\lambda \partial_k \Theta, \tag{4.3}$$

where J denotes the mechanical equivalent of heat, λ the conductivity, and Θ the absolute temperature.

Returning to the general definition of q_k, we note that the continuum that is instantaneously contained in V loses energy in a nonmechanical manner at the rate

$$\mathscr{L} = \int q_k \nu_k \, dS = \int \partial_k q_k \, dV. \tag{4.4}$$

On the other hand, the power of the surface and body forces acting on this continuum equals

$$\begin{aligned}\mathscr{P} &= \int \rho F_k v_k \, dV + \int T_{lk} \nu_l v_k \, dS \\ &= \int [\rho F_k v_k + \partial_l (T_{lk} v_k)] \, dV. \end{aligned} \tag{4.5}$$

The *energy theorem* stipulates that $\mathscr{K}^{\bullet} + \mathscr{E}^{\bullet} = \mathscr{P} - \mathscr{L}$. According to (III, 4.11), we therefore have

$$(\tfrac{1}{2}v_k v_k + e)[\partial_0 \rho + \partial_j(\rho v_j)] + \rho[\partial_0 e + v_j \partial_j e] + v_k \rho[\partial_0 v_k + v_j \partial_j v_k]$$
$$= v_k[\rho F_k + \partial_l T_{lk}] + T_{lk}\partial_l v_k - \partial_k q_k. \quad (4.6)$$

In this equation, the first bracket on the left vanishes by (1.2), and the third bracket represents the acceleration a_k (see III, 4.2). Equation (2.6) shows that the third term on the left of (4.6) cancels the first on the right. Finally, the second term on the right side of (4.6) can be written as $T_{lk}\partial_{(l}v_{k)} = T_{kl}V_{kl}$ because of the symmetry of the stress tensor and the definition (III, 1.11) of the rate of deformation V_{kl}. Equation (4.6) thus reduces to

$$\rho(\partial_0 e + v_k \partial_k e) = T_{kl}V_{kl} - \partial_k q_k. \quad (4.7)$$

The contents of the parenthesis in (4.7) is the material rate of change $e^{\bullet}$ of the specific internal energy e.

If, in particular, all nonmechanical energy transfer consists of heat conduction, and the thermal conductivity is independent of position, (4.3) and (4.7) furnish

$$\rho(\partial_0 e + v_k \partial_k e) = T_{kl}V_{kl} + J\lambda \partial_{kk}\Theta \quad (4.8)$$

From (4.8), the usual equation of heat conduction in a continuum at rest is obtained by deleting the terms with v_k and V_{kl} and setting

$$e = Jc\Theta, \quad (4.9)$$

where c denotes the specific heat for vanishing rate of deformation.

In (4.7) and (4.8), the term $T_{kl}V_{kl}$ represents the power of the stresses on the rate of deformation. To derive a convenient alternative expression for this power, we use (II, 3.2) and (III, 1.21) in the forms

$$T_{kl} = T'_{kl} + \mathscr{T}\delta_{kl} \quad (4.10)$$

and

$$V_{kl} = V'_{kl} + \mathscr{V}\delta_{kl}. \quad (4.11)$$

Here, T'_{kl} is the stress deviator, $\mathscr{T}$ the mean normal stress, V'_{kl} the deviator of the rate of deformation, and $\mathscr{V}$ the mean rate of extension. Since $T'_{kl}\delta_{kl} = T'_{kk} = 0$ and $V'_{kl}\delta_{kl} = V'_{kk} = 0$, we have

$$T_{kl}V_{kl} = T'_{kl}V'_{kl} + 3\mathscr{T}\mathscr{V}. \quad (4.12)$$

5. Simple constitutive equations. Summing up the results obtained in the preceding sections of this chapter, we note that the following differential equations hold for the motion of *any* continuum:

1) the *equation of continuity* (1.2),

$$\partial_0 \rho + \partial_j(v_j) = 0; \quad (5.1)$$

2) the *equation of motion* (2.6), which takes the form

$$\rho(\partial_0 v_k + v_j \partial_j v_k) = \rho F_k + \partial_j T_{jk} \tag{5.2}$$

when a_k is substituted from (III, 4.2); and

3) the *energy equation*

$$\rho(\partial_0 e + v_j \partial_j e) = T_{jk} V_{jk} - \partial_j q_j. \tag{5.3}$$

In many problems of continuum mechanics, the effects of the interaction between mechanical and thermal processes are negligible, so that the discussion can be restricted to purely mechanical processes. Consider, for example, the slow plastic flow of a metallic test specimen. While the work of the deforming forces is transformed into heat, the high thermal conductivity will prevent the occurrence of large temperature differences. Any thermal stresses that may develop in the specimen will therefore be small in comparison to the stresses that produce the plastic flow. Even when thermo-mechanical effects are less irrelevant than in this example, they may have to be disregarded for the sake of mathematical simplicity. *When there is no statement to the contrary, it should therefore be understood in the following that the interaction between mechanical and thermal processes is to be disregarded.* From the mathematical point of view, this amounts to using only the equations of continuity and motion but not the energy equation and regarding the temperature (which may for instance affect the density) as specified by nonmechanical considerations.

The scalar equation (5.1) and the three components of the vector equation (5.2) form a system of four equations for ten unknown functions of time and position, namely the density ρ, the three velocity components v_j, and the six stress components T_{jk}. As this enumeration shows, six further equations between the ten unknowns are needed. A possible source of such equations is indicated by the remark that the equations of continuity and motion do not contain any information regarding the mechanical properties of the continuum under consideration because they hold for any continuum. These properties are specified by the *constitutive equation*; this is a tensor equation, which establishes a relation between statical and kinematical tensors, for instance the stress or the stress rate (to be defined in Section 1 of Chapter VIII), and the rate of deformation or the strain (to be defined in Section 3 of Chapter VIII and Sections 1 and 2 of Chapter IX). The coefficients in this tensor equation will, as a rule, depend on the temperature, but since the temperature field is usually regarded as known beforehand, this temperature-dependence does not introduce any new unknowns into our system of equations.

The remainder of this section is concerned with some arguments that are frequently used in the discussion of constitutive equations. To be specific, we consider relations between the stress tensor T_{ij} and the tensor of the rate of deformation V_{ij}, although the reasoning used in the following applies quite generally to relations between two symmetric tensors of the second order.

Assuming that the stress components are linear homogeneous functions of the components of the rate of deformation, we write

$$T_{ij} = C_{ijkl}V_{kl}, \tag{5.4}$$

where the coefficients C_{ijkl} represent properties of the continuum that may depend on the temperature but not on the stress or the rate of deformation. It follows from the symmetry of T_{ij} that

$$C_{ijkl} = C_{jikl}. \tag{5.5}$$

Moreover, because of the symmetry of V_{kl}, we do not restrict the generality of our discussion by stipulating that

$$C_{ijkl} = C_{ijlk}. \tag{5.6}$$

Now, the right side of (5.4) represents a symmetric tensor of the second order T_{ij} for any choice of the symmetric tensor V_{kl}; the coefficients C_{ijkl}, which are subject to the symmetry conditions (5.5) and (5.6), therefore are the components of a tensor of the fourth order.

In view of the *general* symmetry conditions (5.5) and (5.6), this tensor has at most $6 \times 6 = 36$ numerically distinct components instead of the $9 \times 9 = 81$ components of the general tensor of the fourth order. *Special* symmetry conditions, which reflect the structure of the continuum may further restrict the number of numerically distinct components of the tensor C_{ijkl} in (5.4). For instance, if the continuum possesses *transversal anisotropy* with respect to a given axis, the tensor C_{ijkl} has the same array of components in all coordinate systems that are obtained from each other by rotation about this axis or reflection on a plane that contains this axis or is normal to it.

The biggest reduction in the number of numerically distinct components of C_{ijkl} is obtained for an isotropic continuum. Here, the tensor C_{ijkl} has the same array of components in any right-handed or left-handed system of rectangular Cartesian coordinates. A tensor of this kind is called *isotropic* (see Problem 4.3 of Chapter I).

Since the unit tensor δ_{ij} is isotropic, the tensors

$$\delta_{ij}\delta_{kl} \quad \text{and} \quad \delta_{ik}\delta_{jl} + \delta_{il}\delta_{kj}, \tag{5.7}$$

which possess the symmetry properties (5.5) and (5.6), are isotropic. We propose to show that any isotropic tensor of the fourth order with these symmetry properties can be written as a linear combination of the tensors (5.7).

We begin with the remark that the coordinate axes may be labelled in an arbitrary order. Thus, a permutation of the indices 1, 2, 3 cannot affect the values of the components of an isotropic tensor. For example,

$$\left.\begin{aligned} C_{1122} &= C_{1133} = C_{2211} = C_{2233} = C_{3311} = C_{3322}, \\ C_{1212} &= C_{1313} = C_{2121} = C_{2323} = C_{3131} = C_{3232}. \end{aligned}\right\} \tag{5.8}$$

Next, we consider the transformation $x'_1 = -x_1$, $x'_2 = x_2$, $x'_3 = x_3$ for which the coefficients c_{ij} in (I, 2.4) have the following values: $c_{11} = -1$, $c_{22} = c_{33} = 1$, and $c_{ij} = 0$ for $i \neq j$. The transformation formula (I, 5.6) then shows that any component with an odd number of subscripts 1 changes sign under this reflection on the x_2, x_3-plane. Since isotropy requires that the value of such a component should not be changed by the considered reflection, it follows that any component with an odd number of indices 1 vanishes. The same remark applies to any component with an odd number of the other indices. For example,

$$C_{1222} = C_{1223} = C_{2212} = 0. \tag{5.9}$$

The conditions obtained so far reduce the maximum number of numerically distinct components of the tensor C_{ijkl} to three, C_{1111}, C_{1122}, and C_{1212} being representatives of the three types of components.

We finally consider the transformation $x'_j = (\delta_{ij} + d\theta\, \epsilon_{3ij})x_i$, which represents a rotation about the x_3-axis with the infinitesimal angle of rotation $d\theta$. With $c_{ij} = \delta_{ij} + d\theta\, \epsilon_{3ij}$, the transformation formula (I, 5.6) furnishes

$$C'_{pqrs} = C_{pqrs} + d\theta\{\epsilon_{3ip}C_{iqrs} + \epsilon_{3iq}C_{pirs} + \epsilon_{3ir}C_{pqis} + \epsilon_{3is}C_{pqri}\}, \tag{5.10}$$

where higher-order terms in $d\theta$ have been neglected. If the tensor C_{pqrs} is isotropic, $C'_{pqrs} = C_{pqrs}$ and the brace in (5.10) must vanish. With $p = 1$, $q = r = s = 2$, this condition furnishes the equation $-C_{2222} + C_{1122} + C_{1212} + C_{1221} = 0$. On account of (5.6), this equation reduces to

$$C_{2222} = C_{1122} + 2C_{1212}. \tag{5.11}$$

We leave it to the reader to show that all other choices of the indices p, q, r, s in (5.10) furnish either the same relation between the values of the three types of components or relations that are identically fulfilled because of the symmetry and isotropy conditions already obtained.

Since the transition from one rectangular Cartesian coordinate system to any other with the same origin can be performed by repeated infinitesimal rotations about coordinate axes followed, if necessary, by a reflection on a coordinate plane, the relations represented by (5.8), (5.9), and (5.11) are the only conditions imposed on the tensor C_{ijkl} by the isotropy of the continuum. To construct the array of components, we may therefore set $C_{1122} = \lambda$, $C_{1212} = \mu$, and hence $C_{2222} = \lambda + 2\mu$ according to (5.11), and use the symmetry conditions (5.5) and (5.6) as well as the isotropy conditions represented by (5.8) and (5.9) to obtain the values of all other components of C_{ijkl}. As is readily verified, the linear combination

$$C_{ijkl} = \lambda\delta_{ij}\delta_{kl} + \mu(\delta_{ik}\delta_{jl} + \delta_{il}\delta_{jk}) \tag{5.12}$$

of the isotropic tensors (5.7) furnishes precisely the same array of components. With this expression for C_{ijkl}, the constitutive equation (5.4) reduces to

$$T_{ij} = \lambda V_{kk}\delta_{ij} + 2\mu V_{ij}. \tag{5.13}$$

Contraction of (5.13) furnishes $T_{kk} = (3\lambda + 2\mu)V_{kk}$ or, in view of (II, 3.1) and (III, 1.20),

$$\mathscr{T} = (3\lambda + 2\mu)\mathscr{V}. \tag{5.14}$$

Combining this relation between the mean normal stress $\mathscr{T}$ and the mean rate of extension $\mathscr{V}$ with (5.13), we obtain the following relation between the stress deviator T'_{ij} and deviator V'_{ij} of the rate of deformation (see II, 3.2 and III, 1.21):

$$T'_{ij} = 2\mu V'_{ij}. \tag{5.15}$$

Together with the four equations represented by (5.1) and (5.2), the six components of the symmetric tensor equation (5.13) would form a system of ten equations for the ten unknown functions of time and position that were enumerated in the beginning of this section. Unfortunately, the constitutive equation (5.13) cannot be used to describe the mechanical behavior of a *viscous fluid*, because in a state of rest the rate of deformation and hence the stress tensor would vanish, whereas in a fluid at rest stress fields of the type considered in Section 6 of Chapter II are supposed to be possible. In the theory of viscous fluids, it is therefore customary to retain only (5.15), but replace (5.14) by the relation $\mathscr{T} = -p$, where $p(x, t)$ is the pressure field, which is supposed to be independent of the rate of deformation. In place of (5.13) one thus has the constitutive equation

$$\begin{aligned} T_{ij} &= -p\delta_{ij} + 2\mu V'_{ij} \\ &= -p\delta_{ij} + 2\mu V_{ij} - \tfrac{2}{3}\mu V_{kk}\delta_{ij}. \end{aligned} \tag{5.16}$$

In this equation, the *coefficient of viscosity* μ is the only constant characterizing the considered viscous fluid.

Since a new unknown function $p(x, t)$ has been introduced in (5.16) the system (5.1), (5.2), and (5.16) consists of ten equations for eleven unknowns. To achieve the necessary balance between the number of equations and the number of unknowns, an *equation of state* must be added, which as a rule involves the density ρ, the pressure p, and the temperature Θ. For example, the equation of state of an ideal gas has the form (II, 6.4).

To obtain a purely mechanical problem, we shall frequently use an equation of state that does not contain the temperature. Changes of state that obey an equation of state of this form are called *barotropic*. The following special barotropic changes of state are important: *isothermal* changes of state during which the temperature remains constant and *adiabatic* changes of state during which no heat flows into the system or out of it. The pressure in an ideal gas is proportional to the density for isothermal changes of state, and proportional to a power of density for adiabatic changes of state. A homogeneous incompressible fluid represents another special case of barotropic behavior, because the density is independent of time and position.

The constitutive equation (5.16) is usually named after Stokes.† If the viscosity effects are represented by terms that are linear in the components of the rate of deformation, one speaks of a *Newtonian fluid*, otherwise of a *non-Newtonian fluid.*

Setting $\mu = 0$ in (5.16), we obtain the constitutive equation of the *perfect fluid*

$$T_{ij} = -p\delta_{ij}; \tag{5.17}$$

as (5.16), this equation must be supplemented by an equation of state.

We finally mention a generalization of the constitutive equation (5.16) of the viscous fluid. The stress tensor (5.16) is the sum of the hydrostatic pressure $-p\delta_{ij}$ and a tensor of the form (5.13) with $\lambda = -2\mu/3$. This remark suggests the following generalization of (5.16):

$$T_{ij} = -p\delta_{ij} + \lambda V_{kk}\delta_{ij} + 2\mu V_{ij}, \tag{5.18}$$

where the *static pressure* p is to depend on density and temperature according to the equation of state, while λ and μ are independent of each other. According to (5.18), the negative mean normal stress has the value

$$-\tfrac{1}{3}T_{kk} = p - \tfrac{1}{3}(3\lambda + 2\mu)V_{kk}. \tag{5.19}$$

For arbitrary values of λ and μ, the negative mean normal stress and the static pressure coincide only if $V_{kk} = 0$, i.e., if the density ρ is stationary.

In the chapter on viscous fluids (VI), the constitutive equation (5.16) will be used exclusively. It is obtained from (5.18) by stipulating that the negative mean normal stress and the static pressure coincide in all circumstances.

PROBLEMS

1.1. What form does the equation of continuity (1.2) assume in cylindrical coordinates ρ, θ, ζ? (Denote the density by γ, to avoid confusion with the radius ρ.)

1.2. Specialize the equation obtained in Problem 1.1 as follows. Let the continuum be incompressible and the motion be steady and axially symmetrical ($v_\rho = v_\rho(\rho, \zeta)$, $v_\theta = 0$, $v_\zeta = v_\zeta(\rho, \zeta)$). Show that v_ρ and v_ζ may then be obtained from a (Stokesian) stream function $\psi(\rho, \zeta)$ according to

† G. G. Stokes, Trans. Cambridge Philos. Soc. *8* (1844–49) 287.

$v_\rho = \rho^{-1}\partial\psi/\partial\rho$, $v_\zeta = -\rho^{-1}\partial\psi/\partial\rho$. What differential equation must this stream function fulfill if the motion is to be irrotational?

1.3. Establish the differential equation for the velocity potential $\varphi = \varphi(\rho, \zeta)$ of a steady irrotational and axially symmetrical motion of an incompressible continuum.

1.4. Let a tensor field $T_{kl}\ldots(x, t)$ be defined in a continuum with the density field $\rho(x, t)$. Prove that

$$\left(\int \rho T_{kl}\ldots dV\right)^{\cdot} = \int \rho T^{\cdot}_{kl}\ldots dV.$$

2.1. In the plane of motion through a stream line c of a steady plane motion use the coordinates α, β of Problem 10.2 of Chapter I in the neighborhood of c. On account of the steady character of the motion, the acceleration a_k in the equations of motion (2.6) equals $v_j\partial_j v_k$. Write the equations of motion in the coordinates α, β.

2.2. In an *impulsive motion*, very great body and surface forces act on the continuum for a very short period of time τ. The integrals of typical body forces F_k or stresses T_{jk} over the duration τ of the impact will be denoted by F_k^* and T_{jk}^*, respectively. The starred quantities are called impulsive body force and impulsive stress. In treating impulsive motions, it is often convenient to let τ tend to zero, while F_k^* and T_{jk}^* are kept constant. In the resulting idealized description of the impulsive motion the typical particle experiences a discontinuous change v_j^* of its velocity v_j. Using the momentum theorem, establish a relation between the quantities v_j^*, F_j^* and T_{jk}^*.

2.3. A continuum that is subject to a time-dependent field of plane stress $t_{\underline{ij}}$ has the time-dependent plane velocity field $v_{\underline{i}}$. Show that the two equations of motion and the equation of continuity have the same structure as the three equations of equilibrium of a continuum with the stress field

$$T_{\underline{ij}} = t_{\underline{ij}} - \rho v_{\underline{i}} v_{\underline{j}},$$

$$T_{\underline{i}3} = -\rho v_{\underline{i}}, \quad T_{33} = -\rho,$$

if the operator ∂_0 in the first case is made to correspond to the operator ∂_3 in the second case.

4.1. The rate of change of the kinetic energy of a single particle of the mass m may be written as $\mathscr{K}^{\cdot} = mv_i a_i$, where v_i denotes the velocity and a_i the acceleration of the particle. Derive the corresponding formula for the material rate of change of the kinetic energy of a continuum that instantaneously occupies the regular region V of space.

4.2. The specific entropy s is defined in such a manner that the product of the absolute temperature Θ by the material rate of change $s^{\cdot}$ represents the rate $-\rho^{-1}\partial_k q_k$ at which energy is transmitted in a nonmechanical manner to the unit of mass. The specific free energy is defined by $\Phi = e - \Theta s$.

Show that the energy theorem (4.7) can be written in the form $\rho\Phi^{\cdot} + \rho s\Theta^{\cdot} = T_{kl}V_{kl}$.

5.1. Writing the solution of the constitutive equation (5.4) with respect to the rate of deformation in the form $V_{kl} = K_{klmn}T_{mn}$, show that

$$C_{ijkl}K_{klmn} = \tfrac{1}{2}(\delta_{im}\delta_{jn} + \delta_{in}\delta_{jm}) = K_{ijkl}C_{klmn}.$$

5.2. If a continuum possesses transversal anisotropy with respect to a given axis, the tensor C_{ijkl} has the same array of components in all coordinate systems that are obtained from each other by rotation about this axis or reflection on a plane that is normal to the axis or passes through it. Using the axis of anisotropy as the x_3-axis of a rectangular Cartesian coordinate system, investigate the general form of the tensor C_{ijkl}.

5.3. In the treatment of impulsive motions (see Problem 2.2) of a perfect fluid, the constitutive equation (5.17) is usually generalized by writing the impulsive stress as $T^*_{ij} = -p^*\delta_{ij}$, where p^* is the impulsive pressure. Show that in the impulsive motion of an incompressible perfect fluid the vorticity does not experience a discontinuous change if the impulsive body force F^*_i admits a potential.

5.4. Let a discontinuous change $v^*_i(x)$ of the velocity field of an incompressible perfect fluid be caused by an impulsive pressure field $p^*(x)$ in the absence of impulsive body forces. Show that $\partial_{ii}p^* = 0$.

5.5. The specific enthalpy h is defined as the sum of the specific internal energy e and the quotient of the pressure p and the density ρ. Show that for a perfect fluid the energy theorem (4.7) can be written as $h^{\cdot} = \rho^{-1}p^{\cdot} + \Theta s^{\cdot}$, where Θ is the absolute temperature and s the entropy (see Problem 4.2).

CHAPTER V

Perfect Fluids

1. Equation of motion and vortex theorems. With the use of (III, 4.5) and (IV, 5.17) the equation of motion (IV, 2.6) takes the form

$$2\epsilon_{kij}w_i v_j + \partial_k(\tfrac{1}{2}v_j v_j) + \partial_0 v_k = F_k - \frac{1}{\rho}\,\partial_k p. \tag{1.1}$$

In symbolic notation, this equation of motion of a perfect fluid reads

$$2\mathbf{w} \times \mathbf{v} + \operatorname{grad} v^2/2 + \partial\mathbf{v}/\partial t = \mathbf{F} - \frac{1}{\rho}\operatorname{grad} p, \tag{1.2}$$

where $\mathbf{v}$ denotes the velocity, $\mathbf{w}$ the vorticity (see III, 1.5), $\mathbf{F}$ the specific body force, ρ the density, and p the pressure.

In the majority of applications, $\mathbf{F}$ is independent of time and admits a *potential* $U(x)$ so that $\mathbf{F} = -\operatorname{grad} U$. If, moreover, the fluid is *barotropic*, i.e., if the density is a function $\rho(p)$ of the pressure, we shall find it convenient to introduce the function $P(p)$ defined by (II, 6.15). The equation of motion (1.2) then reduces to

$$2\mathbf{w} \times \mathbf{v} + \partial\mathbf{v}/\partial t = -\operatorname{grad}(U + P + \tfrac{1}{2}v^2). \tag{1.3}$$

Since $v^2/2$ is the kinetic energy per unit of mass, U can be regarded as the potential energy, and P as the pressure energy per unit of mass. Indeed, the reader will easily verify that P represents the work done on the unit of mass in barotropic compression from the reference pressure p_0 to the actual pressure p (see the definition II, 6.5 of P). The contents of the parenthesis in (1.3) will be called *total specific energy* and be denoted by G.

If gravity is the only body force to be considered, the potential is

$$U = gh, \tag{1.4}$$

where g is the acceleration of free fall and h the elevation above a reference level, e.g. sea level. Since the three terms in the parenthesis of (1.3) must have the same dimension, each of the quantities

$$h_p = P/g, \quad h_v = v^2/(2g) \tag{1.5}$$

has the dimension of a length; h_p is called *pressure head*, and h_v *velocity head*, and in this context the elevation h in (1.4) is called *geometrical head*. The velocity head h_v indicates the height of free fall that produces the final velocity v if the initial velocity was zero. We leave it to the reader to prove with the aid of (II, 6.7) that the pressure head h_p indicates the height of a column of the considered barotropic fluid that is in equilibrium when the lower end is exposed to the pressure p in (II, 6.15) and the upper end to the reference pressure p_0. The sum

$$H = h + h_p + h_v \tag{1.6}$$

is called the *total head*; with its introduction, the equation of motion (1.3) assumes the form

$$2\mathbf{w} \times \mathbf{v} + \partial\mathbf{v}/\partial t = -g \operatorname{grad} H, \tag{1.7}$$

which presupposes, of course, that gravity is the only body force acting on the fluid.

Sections 2 and 3 of this chapter will be respectively concerned with steady and irrotational flows; the remainder of this section will therefore be devoted to *unsteady vortex motions*. The divergence of the vorticity field $\mathbf{w}(x, t)$ vanishes identically (see I, 8.12). If the region V bounded by the regular surface S is contained in the region of definition of the velocity field, Gauss' theorem yields

$$\int \mathbf{w} \cdot \boldsymbol{\nu} \, dS = 0, \tag{1.8}$$

where $\boldsymbol{\nu}$ is the unit vector along the exterior normal of S. The expression $\mathbf{w} \cdot \boldsymbol{\nu} \, dS$ in (1.8) is called the *vorticity flux* across the surface element dS. Equation (1.8) thus states that the vorticity flux through the closed surface S vanishes.

The concept of the *vortex line* has already been mentioned in Chapter III, Section 1, where the vortex lines were defined as the field lines of the vorticity field. In analogy with the concept of the stream filament (see Chapter IV, Section 1), we now introduce the concept of the *vortex filament*. By definition, the surface of a vortex filament is formed by the vortex lines through the points of an infinitesimal closed curve. Let dS' and dS'' be the areas of neighboring normal sections of a vortex filament. Assuming that the vorticity is directed from dS' toward dS'', denote the magnitudes of the vorticity vectors at dS' and dS'' by w' and w'', respectively. When (1.8) is applied to the segment of the vortex filament between dS' and dS'', the vorticity flux across the lateral surface of the filament vanishes; thus,

$$w' \, dS' = w'' \, dS''. \tag{1.9}$$

Along a vortex filament, the magnitude of the vorticity vector varies inversely proportional to the cross-sectional area of the filament.

According to Stokes' theorem (I, 9.10), the left-hand side of (1.9) equals half the circulation of the velocity vector along the contour of dS', and the right-hand side of (1.9) can be interpreted in a similar manner. This equation therefore states that the circulation of the velocity vector along the contour of a section of a vortex filament is independent of the choice of the section. The constant value of this circulation is called the *strength* of the considered vortex filament. Note that according to this definition this strength is given by $2w\, dS$ if dS denotes the area of the normal cross section and w the magnitude of the vorticity vector at this section.

The vortex lines through the points of a curve that is not itself a vortex line form a *vortex surface.* According to this definition, the vorticity vector at an arbitrary point of a vortex surface is tangent to this surface, and the vorticity flux across a vortex surface vanishes. It therefore follows from Stokes' theorem that the circulation of the velocity vector along the contour of an arbitrary simply connected part of a vortex surface is zero. Conversely, if the circulation of the velocity vector along the contour of any simply connected part of a surface vanishes, this surface is a vortex surface, because the vortex flux across any element of this surface is zero.

The line of intersection of two vortex surfaces is a vortex line. Indeed, at any common point of the two vortex surfaces the vorticity vector is tangent to each surface and hence to their line of intersection.

The preceding theorems on vortex filaments and surfaces have purely *kinematical* content, since they are based on the definition of the vorticity vector, the vanishing of its divergence, and the theorems of Gauss and Stokes. We now propose to discuss vortex theorems of *dynamical* content, which are due to W. Thomson † (Lord Kelvin) and Helmholtz.‡ These theorems are concerned with a *barotropic perfect* fluid and assume that the body force is *conservative,* i.e. that it admits a single-valued potential. According to (1.3), the equation of motion can then be written as

$$\mathbf{a} = -\text{grad}\,(U + P), \tag{1.10}$$

where $\mathbf{a}$ is the acceleration (see III, 4.6). The scalar $-(U + P)$ may therefore be regarded as an *acceleration potential.* In view of (1.10), it follows from the remark made at the end of Section 4 of Chapter III that the *circulation of the velocity vector along a closed material curve in a barotropic perfect fluid under conservative body forces is independent of time.* As this theorem of W. Thomson shows, an instantaneously irrotational motion will remain irrotational under these conditions. Helmholtz' vortex theorems are readily derived from Thomson's theorem, as will now be shown.

At the typical instant t, let F and G be vortex surfaces, which intersect in the vortex line l. The fluid particles that lie on F (or G) at the instant t, form a neighboring surface F' (or G') at the instant $t + dt$, and the intersection l' of F' and G' consists of the same particles as the intersection l of F and G.

† W. Thomson, Philos. Trans. Roy. Soc. Edinburgh *25* (1869) 217.
‡ H. Helmholtz, Crelle's Journal *55* (1858) 25.

Because F is a vortex surface at the instant t, the circulation of the velocity vector along the contour of any simply connected part of F vanishes at this instant. Since the circulation of the velocity vector along any closed material curve does not change with time, the circulation along the contour of any simply connected part of F' vanishes at the time $t + dt$, i.e. F' is a vortex surface at the instant $t + dt$. The same remark applies to G'. It follows that the intersection l' of F' and G' is a vortex line at the instant $t + dt$. Since l and l' are consecutive positions of the same material line, *vortex lines are material lines.*

As the vortex lines, the vortex filaments are material configurations. Thomson's theorem shows that *the strength of a vortex filament does not change during the motion of the filament.* This result can be combined with the principle of conservation of mass as follows. Consider an element of a vortex filament that has the length dl and the cross-sectional area dS at the instant t, and the length dl' and the cross-sectional area dS' at the time $t + dt$, and denote the corresponding values of the density and the magnitude of the vorticity vector by ρ, ρ' and w, w'. The conservation of mass is expressed by $\rho\, dl\, dF = \rho'\, dl'\, dF'$, and the conservation of the strength of the vortex filament by $w\, dS = w'\, dS'$. It follows that

$$\frac{\rho}{w}\, dl = \frac{\rho'}{w'}\, dl'. \tag{1.11}$$

In the course of the motion, the length of an element of a vortex filament therefore varies in proportion to the quotient w/ρ. In particular, in an *incompressible* fluid the variable length of a material element of a vortex filament represents the variable magnitude of the vorticity vector.

2. Steady flow. The derivative $\partial \mathbf{v}/\partial t$ vanishes for steady flow. If the total specific energy, i.e. the contents of the parenthesis in (1.3), is denoted by G, the equation of motion for steady flow has the form

$$2\mathbf{v} \times \mathbf{w} = \operatorname{grad} G. \tag{2.1}$$

As this equation shows, the velocity vector and the vorticity vector at a typical point P are tangent to the surface G = constant through this point. The stream lines through the points of a vortex line therefore form a level surface of the total specific energy G. Since in steady flow the trajectories of the particles coincide with the stream lines, a vortex line that is regarded as a material line sweeps out a surface G = constant in the course of its motion.

To discuss the geometry of stream and vortex lines on a surface of constant total specific energy, let the full-line curves AA' and BB' in Figure 15 represent neighboring stream lines, and the dashed curves AB and $A'B'$ consecutive positions of a vortex line. Specifically, let the directed line

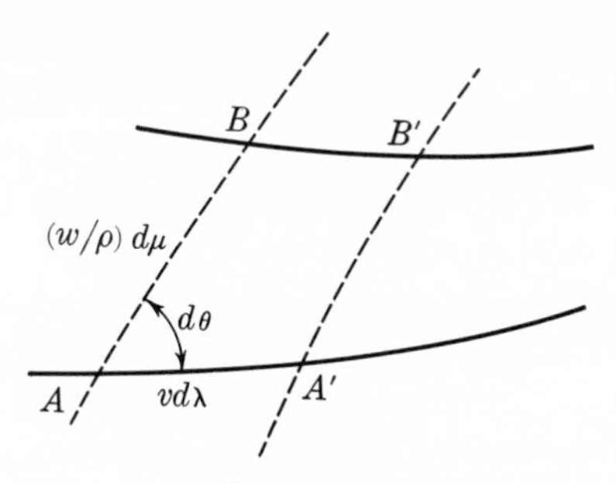

Figure 15

elements AA' and AB be obtained from the velocity at A and the quotient of the vorticity vector and the density at A by multiplication with the infinitesimal factors $d\lambda$ and $d\mu$, respectively. The first of these factors is obviously the infinitesimal interval of time during which the material vortex line moves from AB to $A'B'$; the second factor $d\mu$ does not admit such an intuitive interpretation.

Since the directed line element BB' is obtained from the velocity vector at B by multiplication with $d\lambda$, we have the following theorem: *the distance of neighboring vortex lines on a level surface of the total specific energy is proportional to the velocity component that is normal to the vorticity vector.*

According to the theorem proved at the end of the preceding section, the directed line element $A'B'$ can be obtained by dividing the vorticity vector at A' by the density at this point and multiplying the quotient by $d\mu$. The *distance of neighboring stream lines on a level surface of the total specific energy is therefore proportional to the quotient obtained by dividing the vorticity component that is normal to the velocity vector by the density.*

Let us imagine that a net of stream and vortex lines is drawn on the surface $G = c$ so that these theorems are everywhere valid with the same factors of proportionality $d\lambda$ and $d\mu$. In view of the physical significance of $d\lambda$, this means that the considered vortex lines are the consecutive positions of one and the same material line at instants that are separated by the constant time interval $d\lambda$.

On the neighboring surface $G = c + dc$, draw a similar net of stream and vortex lines starting with the lines through a point A^* in the neighborhood of A. Let $A^*B^*B^{*\prime}A^{*\prime}$ be the element of the surface $G = c + dc$ that corresponds to the element $ABB'A'$ of the surface $G = c$. If the normal distance of the point A^* from the surface $G = c$ is denoted by $d\nu$, it follows from (2.1) that

$$2vw \sin \theta = dc/d\nu, \tag{2.2}$$

where v and w are the magnitudes of the velocity and vorticity vectors, and θ is the angle between these vectors. The considered eight points are the corners of a cell with the volume $dV = (vw/\rho) \sin \theta \, d\lambda \, d\mu \, d\nu$; according to (2.2) this cell contains the mass

$$\rho \, dV = vw \sin \theta \, d\lambda \, d\mu \, d\nu = \tfrac{1}{2} \, d\lambda \, d\mu \, dc. \tag{2.3}$$

As this equation shows, all cells specified by the considered stream and vortex lines contain the same mass.

The vortex lines through the points of the quadrilateral $AA'A^{*\prime}A^*$ with the area $dS = v \sin \theta \, d\lambda \, d\nu$ bound a vortex filament with the strength

$$2w \, dS = 2vw \sin \theta \, d\lambda \, d\nu = d\lambda \, dc. \tag{2.4}$$

It follows from (2.4) that all vortex filaments specified by the considered vortex lines have the same strength. After the time interval $d\lambda$ each of these filaments occupies the original position of the preceding filament.

Of all these properties of the stream and vortex lines, the following one is used most frequently: *along a stream line, the total specific energy has a constant value.* This theorem is usually named after Daniel Bernoulli, and the constant value of the total specific energy is called Bernoulli's constant for this stream line. As the preceding discussion shows, this constant has the same value for all stream lines that are connected to a given stream line by vortex lines.

In conclusion, let us apply our results to a *plane* steady vortex motion. If the x_1, x_2-plane of a system of rectangular Cartesian coordinates coincides with the plane of motion, the vortex lines are parallel to the x_3-axis and form the generators of the cylindrical level surfaces of the total specific energy; the intersections of these cylinders with the planes x_3 = constant are the stream lines.

Since the stream lines through neighboring points of a vortex line have a constant distance from each other, the quotient w/ρ remains constant along a stream line and hence on a surface G = constant. Accordingly, w/ρ is a function of G; here w can be identified with w_3, the only vorticity component that does not vanish identically. In a plane steady flow of a homogeneous incompressible fluid, the vorticity thus has the same value at all points of a stream line.

3. Irrotational flow. According to (IV, 1.9) the velocity field of an irrotational motion can be represented as the gradient field of the velocity potential $\varphi(x, t)$:

$$\mathbf{v} = \operatorname{grad} \varphi. \tag{3.1}$$

Note that according to (3.1) a given velocity field determines the velocity potential only to within an arbitrary additive function of time. With (3.1), the equation of motion (1.3) reduces to

$$\operatorname{grad} \left(\frac{\partial \varphi}{\partial t} + U + P + \frac{v^2}{2} \right) = 0 \tag{3.2}$$

which shows that the contents of the parenthesis can at most depend on time. By an appropriate choice of the arbitrary additive function of time, we may therefore define the velocity potential in such a manner that

$$\frac{\partial \varphi}{\partial t} + U + P + \tfrac{1}{2}v^2 = 0. \tag{3.3}$$

In *acoustics* body forces such as the weight of the air are usually disregarded, and the discussion is restricted to small fluctuations of pressure and density about mean values p_0 and ρ_0 that are independent of time and position. The derivative of the function $p(\rho)$ for $\rho = \rho_0$ will be denoted by c^2:

$$\left(\frac{dp}{d\rho}\right)_{\rho=\rho_0} = c^2. \tag{3.4}$$

For the small fluctuations under consideration, we may use the following approximations:

$$\left.\begin{aligned} p - p_0 &= c^2(\rho - \rho_0), \\ P &= (p - p_0)/\rho_0. \end{aligned}\right\} \tag{3.5}$$

Since body forces are to be disregarded, the term U in (3.3) will be dropped. Moreover, it is customary in acoustics to treat P and v as small of the first order and therefore neglect the last term on the left of (3.3). Thus,

$$\partial_0 \varphi + P = 0. \tag{3.6}$$

With the aid of (3.5), the equation of continuity (IV, 1.2) can be written as follows:

$$\partial_0 P + v_j \partial_j P + (c^2 + P)\partial_j v_j = 0. \tag{3.7}$$

Extending our assumption regarding the order of magnitude of P and v, we drop the terms in (3.7) that contain both P and a component of the velocity. Writing velocity components as derivatives of the velocity potential, we obtain

$$\partial_0 P + c^2 \partial_{jj} \varphi = 0. \tag{3.8}$$

Elimination of the velocity potential between (3.6) and (3.8) finally leads to

$$\partial_{00} P = c^2 \partial_{jj} P. \tag{3.9}$$

An equation of the same form is found for φ, when P is eliminated between (3.6) and (3.8). The integration theory of the *wave equation* (3.9) is beyond the scope of this book.

To determine the mechanical meaning of the constant c in (3.9), we consider the special case when P depends only on one coordinate, say x_1. The corresponding form of the wave equation,

$$\partial_{00}P = c^2\partial_{11}P, \tag{3.10}$$

has the solution

$$P = f(x_1 + ct) + g(x_1 - ct), \tag{3.11}$$

where f and g are twice continuously differentiable but otherwise arbitrary functions. In view of the second equation (3.5), the first term on the right side of (3.11) represents a pressure wave that travels with the velocity c in the negative x_1-direction without changing its shape. A similar remark applies to the second term on the right of (3.11), except that the second pressure wave travels in the positive x_1-direction. The constant c therefore represents the *velocity of sound*, i.e. the velocity with which infinitesimal perturbations of pressure are propagated in a gas that is otherwise at rest.

The remainder of this section will be concerned with *steady potential flows*. It is then convenient to regard the velocity potential as independent of the time, but this precludes the use of (3.3), in which an additive function of time in the velocity potential has been chosen in a special manner. Returning to (3.2), we drop the first term in the parenthesis and integrate to obtain *Bernoulli's equation*

$$U + P + \frac{v^2}{2} = \text{constant}. \tag{3.12}$$

As has been shown in Section 2, an equation of this form holds along each stream line in a steady vortex motion, but to different stream lines correspond, in general, different values of Bernoulli's constant. In a steady potential flow, however, this constant has the same value throughout the field of flow.

As in acoustics, the body forces can be neglected in many fields of application. For example, in the computation of the aerodynamic forces acting on an airplane wing, the weight of air is disregarded. In the absence of body forces, (3.12) reduces to

$$P + \tfrac{1}{2}v^2 = \text{constant}. \tag{3.13}$$

Since P is by definition a function of the pressure, (3.13) furnishes the pressure p and hence the density ρ as functions of the magnitude v of the velocity.

To obtain a differential equation for the velocity potential of a steady irrotational flow of a barotropic perfect fluid, we return to the basic equations (IV, 5.1) and (IV, 5.2). On account of the constitutive equation (IV, 5.17) and the steady character of the flow, these equations reduce to

$$v_j\partial_j\rho + \rho\partial_j v_j = 0, \tag{3.14}$$

$$\rho v_j\partial_j v_k + \partial_k p = 0. \tag{3.15}$$

As we consider a barotropic fluid, we have

$$\partial_k p = \frac{dp}{d\rho}\,\partial_k \rho = c^2 \partial_k \rho, \tag{3.16}$$

where the velocity of sound

$$c = (dp/d\rho)^{1/2} \tag{3.17}$$

is not a constant as in acoustics, but corresponds to the local density ρ. According to Bernoulli's equation (3.13), this *local velocity of sound* is a function of the magnitude v of the velocity.

Substitution of (3.16) into (3.15) and multiplication of the resulting equation by v_k yields

$$\rho v_j v_k \partial_j v_k + c^2 v_k \partial_k \rho = 0. \tag{3.18}$$

Using (3.14), we may write the second term of (3.18) as $-c^2 \rho \partial_j v_j = -c^2 \rho \delta_{jk} \partial_j v_k$. This furnishes the *gas dynamical equation*

$$(c^2 \delta_{jk} - v_j v_k) \partial_j v_k = 0. \tag{3.19}$$

Writing the velocity in this equation as the gradient of the velocity potential, we finally obtain

$$(c^2 \delta_{jk} - \partial_j \varphi \partial_k \varphi) \partial_{jk} \varphi = 0. \tag{3.20}$$

In this non-linear partial differential equation of the second order for the velocity potential φ, the local velocity of sound is a function of the magnitude of grad φ.

To throw some light on the mathematical character of this equation, consider a plane flow of the form

$$v_1 = U + u_1, \quad v_2 = u_2, \quad v_3 = 0, \tag{3.21}$$

where the term U represents a uniform *main flow* in the positive x_1-direction, while u_1 and u_2 are small perturbations of the main flow. Substitution of (3.21) into (3.19), and deletion of all terms that are nonlinear in u_1, u_2, and their derivatives, furnishes the equation

$$\left(1 - \frac{U^2}{c^2}\right) \partial_1 u_1 + \partial_2 u_2 = 0. \tag{3.22}$$

Since u_1 and u_2 are treated as small in comparison to U, the local velocity of sound c is determined by the velocity U and therefore is constant. The quotient

$$M = U/c \tag{3.23}$$

is called the *Mach number* of the main flow.

Since we are concerned with irrotational flows, and the uniform main flow is irrotational, the field of the perturbation velocity with the components u_1, u_2, 0 must be irrotational, and therefore admit a velocity potential $\varphi(x_1, x_2)$, which will be called the *perturbation potential.* According to (3.23), this potential satisfies the relation

$$(1 - M^2)\partial_{11}\varphi + \partial_{22}\varphi = 0. \tag{3.24}$$

In the *subsonic range* $M < 1$, the coefficients of the two terms on the left side of (3.24) have the same sign, but in the *supersonic range* $M > 1$ they have opposite signs. Equation (3.24) thus is elliptic in the subsonic range, and hyperbolic in the supersonic range. In this simple example, the differential equation for the velocity potential is of the same type throughout the entire field of flow. As a rule, however, the solution of the differential equation (3.20) is greatly complicated by the fact that the field of flow consists of subsonic and supersonic regions, the boundaries of which are not known beforehand.

The remainder of this chapter will be concerned with the irrotational flow of a homogeneous incompressible fluid. Since the divergence of the velocity vector vanishes, the velocity potential satisfies the Laplace equation

$$\Delta\varphi = 0. \tag{3.25}$$

In Section 3 of Chapter III we concluded, from the vanishing of the divergence of the vorticity field, that the vorticity can be represented as the vector product of the gradients of two scalar fields, the level surfaces of which are formed by vortex lines. For the problem considered here, it follows by analogy from $\operatorname{div} \mathbf{v} = 0$ that the velocity can be written as

$$\mathbf{v} = \operatorname{grad} \varphi = \operatorname{grad} \psi \times \operatorname{grad} \chi, \tag{3.26}$$

where the level surfaces of the scalar fields $\psi(x)$ and $\chi(x)$ are formed by stream lines. As is shown by the proof in Section 3 of Chapter III, we have a good deal of freedom in the choice of these *stream surfaces.*

The plane of Figure 16 is normal to the velocity vector at the point A, the traces of the stream surfaces through A in the plane of the figure are denoted by ψ and χ, and the traces of neighboring stream surfaces by $\psi + d\psi$ and $\chi + d\chi$. If the normal distances of the latter surfaces from A are denoted by $d\mu$ and $d\nu$, respectively, the stream filament bounded by the four stream surfaces has the cross section

$$dS = d\mu\, d\nu/\sin\theta \tag{3.27}$$

at the point A; here θ is the angle shown in Figure 16. According to (3.26), the velocity at A has the magnitude

$$v = |\operatorname{grad} \psi|\, |\operatorname{grad} \chi| \sin\theta, \tag{3.28}$$

where

$$|\operatorname{grad} \psi| = d\psi/d\mu, \quad |\operatorname{grad} \chi| = d\chi/d\nu \tag{3.29}$$

are the magnitudes of the gradients of ψ and χ at A. It follows from (3.27),

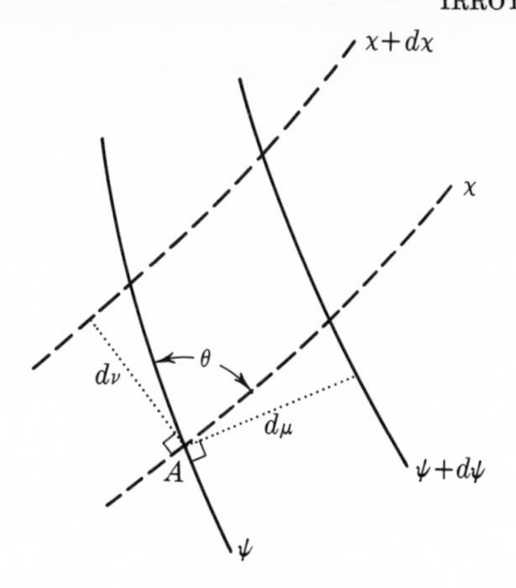

Figure 16

(3.28), and (3.29) that

$$\rho v \, dS = \rho \, d\psi \, d\chi. \tag{3.30}$$

The left side of this equation represents the rate at which mass flows through the typical cross section of the stream filament; it will be called the *mass flux* in the filament. If the difference $d\psi$ has the same value for any two neighboring stream surfaces ψ = constant, and if a similar statement applies to the difference $d\chi$, (3.30) shows that *all stream filaments bounded by neighboring stream surfaces have the same mass flux.*

Divide the considered stream filaments into cells by level surfaces of the velocity potential φ, in such a manner that the difference between the potentials on any two neighboring surfaces has the constant value $d\varphi$. If $d\lambda$ is the length of a typical cell in the direction of flow, we have

$$v = |\text{grad } \varphi| = d\varphi/d\lambda. \tag{3.31}$$

With the aid of (3.30) and (3.31), the kinetic energy contained in the cell can be written as

$$d\mathscr{K} = \tfrac{1}{2}v(\rho v \, dS) \, d\lambda = \frac{\rho}{2} \, d\varphi \, d\psi \, d\chi. \tag{3.32}$$

The considered stream and potential surfaces divide the flow field into cells all of which contain the same kinetic energy.

From (3.30) and (3.31), we finally obtain the relation

$$\frac{dS}{d\lambda} = \frac{d\psi \, d\chi}{d\varphi}. \tag{3.33}$$

For all considered cells, the quotient of cross section and length has the same value. These results as well as the geometrical results in Section 2 are due to von Mises.†

† R. v. Mises, *Theorie der Wasserräder*, Leipzig, 1908.

Let us now discuss the *plane* steady irrotational flow of an incompressible fluid. It is convenient to take the x_3-axis normal to the plane of flow, and to choose the function χ as $\chi = x_3$, which is admissible because the planes x_3 = constant are stream surfaces. As the other family of stream surfaces, we propose to choose the cylinders $\psi(x_1, x_2)$ = constant that have stream lines in the plane $x_3 = 0$ as directrices and parallels to the x_3-axis as generators. That this choice is legitimate can be seen as follows. Since grad χ is the unit vector with the positive x_3-direction, (3.26) takes the form

$$v_i = \partial_i \varphi = \epsilon_{ij3} \partial_j \psi. \tag{3.34}$$

Accordingly,

$$v_1 = \partial_1 \varphi = \partial_2 \psi, \quad v_2 = \partial_2 \varphi = -\partial_1 \psi. \tag{3.35}$$

If these relations are considered as simultaneous partial differential equations for ψ, the associated integrability condition furnishes the Laplace equation for φ, and (3.25) shows this to be satisfied.

The function $\psi(x_1, x_2)$ is called the *stream function*. For a given harmonic velocity potential $\varphi(x_1, x_2)$, (3.35) specifies the stream function $\psi(x_1, x_2)$ to within an unessential additive constant.

Equation (3.34) shows that the cylinders φ = constant and ψ = constant intersect orthogonally. Since the generators of these cylinders are normal to the planes χ = constant, the cells considered above are now rectangular parallelepipeds. Since $|d\chi|$ represents the length of one side of the rectangular cross section dS, (3.33) shows that for the choice $d\varphi = d\psi$ the stream lines and equipotential lines divide the plane of flow into infinitesimal *squares*. If we use the velocity potential φ and the stream function ψ as rectangular Cartesian coordinates in the *potential plane*, this net of squares in the plane of flow and the net of squares in the potential plane that corresponds to the same, equidistant values of φ and ψ define a conformal mapping of one of these planes onto the other. The *complex potential*

$$\Phi = \varphi + i\psi \tag{3.36}$$

therefore is an analytic function of the complex variable

$$z = x_1 + ix_2. \tag{3.37}$$

Analytically, this follows from the remark that the relations (3.35) between φ and ψ have the form of the Cauchy-Riemann equations between the real and imaginary parts of an analytic function of the complex variable (3.37). These equations are obtained by elimination of $\Phi' = d\Phi/dz$ between the relations

$$\partial_1 \Phi = \Phi' \partial_1 z = \Phi', \quad \partial_2 \Phi = \Phi' \partial_2 z = i\Phi' \tag{3.38}$$

and separation of the resulting equation into real and imaginary parts.

From the (3.35) and the first equation (3.38) it follows, that

$$\Phi' = \partial_1 \varphi + i\partial_1 \psi = v_1 - iv_2. \tag{3.39}$$

The *complex velocity*

$$w = v_1 - iv_2 \tag{3.40}$$

if therefore the derivative of the complex potential (3.36) with respect to the complex variable (3.37). If we use the quantities v_1 and $-v_2$ as rectangular Cartesian coordinates in the *hodograph plane*, the function $w = \Phi'(z)$ thus defines a conformal mapping of the plane of flow on the hodograph plane. Since, on the other hand, the function $\Phi = \Phi(z)$ defines a conformal mapping of the plane of flow on the potential plane, the sequence consisting of the first mapping and the inverse of the second provides a conformal mapping of the potential plane onto the hodograph plane. If the corresponding mapping function $w = w(\Phi)$ is known, the relation between Φ and z can be established by integrating the equation

$$dz = \frac{d\Phi}{w(\Phi)}, \tag{3.41}$$

which follows from $w = d\Phi/dz$.

As an example for the application of the complex representation of plane steady flows of an incompressible fluid, consider the efflux from the upper half-plane $x_2 > 0$ through the gap $-b \leq x_1 \leq b$ along the real axis (Figure 17a). In treating this problem, we shall neglect gravity and assume that the flow is solely due to an excess of pressure in the upper half-plane. At a great distance from the origin, the fluid in this half-plane is supposed to be at rest and under the constant pressure p'; the pressure in the exterior of the jet in the lower half-plane is supposed to have the constant value p''. In the absence of body forces and for an incompressible fluid, Bernoulli's equation (3.12) has the form $p + \rho v^2/2 =$ constant; applying this to the stream line ABC (Figure 17a), we find that the velocity has the constant value

$$v_0 = \sqrt{2(p' - p'')/\rho} \tag{3.42}$$

along the boundary of the jet. At a great distance from the origin, the boundaries of the jet will tend to be parallel to the x_2-axis, and the velocity will have the value (3.42) across the entire width CF of the jet (Figure 17a) and be parallel to the x_2-axis. Along CF we therefore have $v_1 = \partial_2\psi = 0$, $v_2 = -\partial_1\psi = -v_0$. If the asymptotic width of the jet is denoted by $2a$, the values of the stream function at F and C thus differ by $2av_0$.

The velocity field specifies the velocity potential and the stream functions only to within additive constants. Without loss of generality, we may therefore assign the value zero to the potential at the point B and also to the stream function on the stream line ABC. Because of the symmetry of the flow pattern with respect to the x_2-axis, the potential at the point E also has the value zero, and in view of the known difference between the values of the stream function at F and C, the stream function has the value $2av_0$ on the stream line DEF. Along the infinite stream line branch BA, the velocity potential decreases indefinitely, and along BC it increases indefinitely. The field of flow is therefore mapped on the infinite strip of the potential plane that is bounded by the lines $\psi = 0$ and $\psi = 2av_0$. In Figures 17a and b, corresponding points are labelled with the same letters. On the other hand, the boundaries BC and EF of the jet, on which the velocity has the constant magnitude v_0, are mapped on the arcs $B''C''$ and $E''F''$ of the circle in the hodograph plane (Figure 17c) that has the radius v_0 and is centered at the origin. Along each of the straight stream lines AB and DE, the velocity has a fixed direction while its magnitude increases from zero to v_0; the images of these stream lines in the hodograph plane therefore are the radii $A''B''$ and $D''E''$ of the circle mentioned above. In the hodograph plane, the flow field is thus mapped onto the interior of the semicircle shown in Figure 17c.

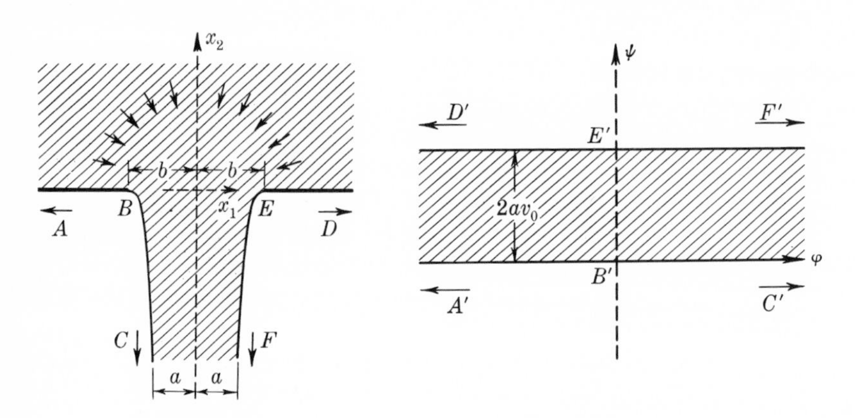

Figure 17a

Figure 17b

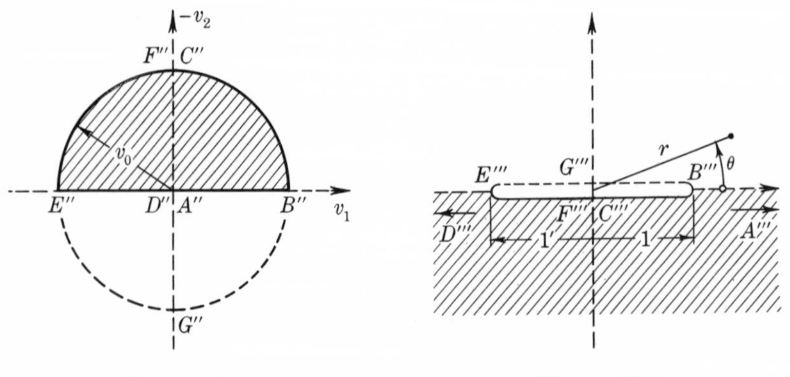

Figure 17c

Figure 17d

We must now map the strip in the potential plane (Figure 17b) conformally onto the semicircle in the hodograph plane (Figure 17c). To this end, we first map the strip of the Φ-plane by means of

$$\Phi^* = \exp\left(-\frac{\pi\Phi}{2av_0}\right) \tag{3.43}$$

onto the lower half of the auxiliary Φ^*-plane. Indeed, with $\Phi^* = re^{i\theta}$ (see Figure 17d), (3.43) furnishes

$$r = \exp\left(\frac{-\pi\varphi}{2av_0}\right), \qquad \theta = -\frac{\pi\psi}{2av_0}. \tag{3.44}$$

The strip in the Φ-plane, in which $-\infty \leq \varphi \leq \infty$ and $0 \leq \psi \leq 2av_0$, is therefore mapped into the lower Φ^*-plane, in which $0 \leq r \leq \infty$ and $0 \geq \theta \geq -\pi/2$. In particular, to the points B' and E' of the potential plane correspond the points $\Phi^* = \pm 1$, which have been labelled B''' and E''' in the Φ^*-plane.

We now add to the shaded regions of the w- and Φ^*-planes, which are to be mapped onto each other, their images by symmetry with respect to the real axes of their planes. In the w-plane, we thus obtain the interior of the circle with the radius v_0 around the origin. In the Φ^*-plane, the circumference $B''C''E''G''$ of this circle is mapped onto the boundary $B'''C'''E'''G'''$ of a slit along the real axis. The conformal mapping of the interior of the circle in the w-plane onto the exterior of the slit from $\Phi^* = -1$ to $\Phi^* = 1$ in the Φ^*-plane is well known; it is given by

$$\Phi^* = \frac{1}{2}\left(\frac{w}{v_0} + \frac{v_0}{w}\right). \tag{3.45}$$

Indeed, with $w = \rho e^{i\chi}$ it follows from (3.45) that the circle $\rho = v_0$, $0 \leq \chi \leq 2\pi$ is mapped onto the boundary $\Phi^* = \cos\chi$ of the slit. On the other hand, the radius $A''B''$ is mapped onto the part $A'''B'''$ of the positive real axis in the Φ^*-plane, on which $\infty \geq r \geq 1$, $\theta = 0$, and the radius $D''E''$ onto the part $D'''E'''$ of the negative real axis. In making the circuit $A''B''C''F''E''D''$ in the w-plane, one has the shaded semicircle in Figure 17c on the left, and in moving along the real axis of the Φ^*-plane in the corresponding sense $A'''B'''C'''F'''E'''D'''$, one has the lower Φ^*-plane, which is shaded in Figure 17d, on the left. It follows that the shaded regions correspond to each other in the mapping (3.45).

We leave it to the reader to use (3.43) and (3.45) to establish the relation between the complex velocity and the complex potential, and to determine the stream and equipotential lines in the z-plane by using this relation in (3.41). We shall, however, evaluate the *coefficient of contraction*, i.e. the ratio a/b of the asymptotic width a of the jet to the width b of the gap (Figure 17a).

The left boundary BC of the jet corresponds to the positive real axis of the Φ-plane. Along BC we have $\varphi \geq 0$ and $\psi = 0$; if the arc length measured from B is denoted by s, we have moreover $d\varphi/ds = v_0$ and hence $\varphi = sv_0$, because both φ and s vanish at B. It follows from (3.43) that

$$\Phi^* = \exp\left(-\frac{\pi s}{2a}\right) \tag{3.46}$$

along BC. Use of this value of Φ^* in (3.45) yields

$$w = v_0 \left\{\exp\left(-\frac{\pi s}{2a}\right) \pm i\left[1 - \exp\left(-\frac{\pi s}{2a}\right)\right]^{1/2}\right\}. \tag{3.47}$$

For $s \to \infty$, we have $w \to iv_0$. Accordingly, the upper sign must be taken in (3.47). Furthermore,

$$\frac{dx_1}{ds} = \frac{v_1}{v_0} \tag{3.48}$$

along the jet boundary BC. Equation (3.47) thus furnishes

$$\begin{aligned} x_1 &= -b + \int_0^s \exp\left(-\frac{\pi s}{2a}\right) ds \\ &= -b + \frac{2a}{\pi}\left\{1 - \exp\left(-\frac{\pi s}{2a}\right)\right\}, \end{aligned} \tag{3.49}$$

where the initial condition $x_1 = -b$ for $s = 0$ has been used. Since $x_1 \to a$ when $s \to \infty$, (3.49) yields the coefficient of contraction

$$\frac{a}{b} = \frac{\pi}{2 + \pi}. \tag{3.50}$$

PROBLEMS

1.1. Taking the curl of the equation of motion (1.3) and using the equation of continuity (IV, 1.3), show that, in a barotropic perfect fluid under conservative body forces, $(\rho^{-1}w_j)^\cdot = \rho^{-1}w_i\partial_i v_j$. Use this relation to prove (1.11).

1.2. Let $\mathbf{v}(x, t)$ be the velocity field of an incompressible continuum and $\mathbf{b}(x, t)$ a vectorial property of its particles. Prove that $\partial\mathbf{b}/\partial t + \text{curl}\,(\mathbf{b} \times \mathbf{v}) + \mathbf{v}\,\text{div}\,\mathbf{b} = 0$ is a necessary and sufficient condition for the $\mathbf{b}$-lines to be material lines, the line element of which varies in proportion to the intensity of $\mathbf{b}$.

1.3. Starting with (1.2) show in a manner similar to that used in Problem 1.1 that in a nonbarotropic perfect fluid under conservative body forces $(\rho^{-1}\mathbf{w})^{\cdot} = (\rho^{-1}\mathbf{w}\cdot\nabla)\mathbf{v} - \frac{1}{2}\rho^{-1} \operatorname{grad} \rho^{-1} \times \operatorname{grad} p$.

1.4. Prove that in a nonbarotropic perfect fluid under conservative body forces the rate of change of the circulation of the velocity vector along a closed material curve L is given by the integral $-\int (\operatorname{grad} \rho^{-1} \times \operatorname{grad} p)\boldsymbol{\nu}\, dS$, where the integration is extended over a surface S that lies within the fluid and is bounded by L. The direction of the unit normal vector $\boldsymbol{\nu}$ of S is to correspond to the sense of progression along L in the same way in which the sense of progression of a right-handed screw corresponds to its sense of rotation.

1.5. Using the solution of Problem III, 4.3 show that in a barotropic perfect fluid under conservative body forces $\left(\int w_i\, dV\right)^{\cdot} = \int v_i w_j \nu_j\, dS$.

1.6. In a nonbarotropic perfect fluid, consider the field vector $b_i = F_i - a_i$, where F_i is the specific body force and a_i the acceleration. Show that this vector is normal to its curl.

2.1. Specialize the equations of motion obtained in Problem 2.1 of Chapter IV for the plane steady flow of a barotropic perfect fluid.

2.2. Prove that in a plane steady flow of a barotropic fluid under conservative body forces the total specific energy G and the vorticity w are connected by the relation $\partial_i(w^{-1}\partial_i G) = 4w$.

3.1. The wave equation (3.10) describes the one-dimensional propagation of small disturbances in a barotropic gas that is otherwise at rest and is not subjected to any body forces. Abandoning the approximations made in the derivation of the wave equation, investigate the one-dimensional propagation of finite disturbances. Assume that the velocity field is of the form $v_1 = v(x, t)$, $v_2 = v_3 = 0$, and that pressure and density are independent of x_2 and x_3. Verify the equations

$$[\partial_0 + (v + c)\partial_1](V + v) = 0,$$

$$[\partial_0 + (v - c)\partial_2](V - v) = 0,$$

in which

$$c(\rho) = \left(\frac{dp}{d\rho}\right)^{1/2}, \quad V(\rho) = \int_{\rho_0}^{\rho} \frac{c(\rho)}{\rho}\, d\rho.$$

Show that V as well as v satisfy the wave equation if v can be neglected in comparison to c.

3.2. In a one-dimensional motion of the kind considered in Problem 3.1, let $x_1 = 0$ be a stationary plane of discontinuity, and suppose that pressure, density, and internal energy have constant values on each side of this plane. Using primes and double primes to distinguish the values of these quantities on the two sides of the plane of discontinuity, show that the conservation of mass, momentum, and energy, furnishes the following "shock conditions":

$$\rho' v' = \rho'' v''$$

$$p' + \rho' v'^2 = p'' + \rho'' v''^2$$

$$e' - e'' = \tfrac{1}{2}(p' + p'')\left(\frac{1}{\rho'} - \frac{1}{\rho''}\right).$$

3.3. For the plane steady flow of a barotropic perfect fluid, which is not subjected to any body forces, derive the condition of irrotationality and the gas-dynamical equation (3.19) in polar coordinates.

3.4. For the flow considered in Problem 3.3, use the velocity potential φ and the stream function ψ as orthogonal curvilinear coordinates ($v_1 = \partial_1\varphi = \rho^{-1}\partial_2\psi$, $v_2 = \partial_2\varphi = -\rho^{-1}\partial_1\psi$), and treat the density ρ, the magnitude v of the velocity, and the angle θ between the velocity vector and the positive x_1-direction as the dependent variables. Establish the condition of irrotationality and the gas-dynamical equation for these coordinates and dependent variables.

3.5. In the plane steady irrotational flow of an incompressible fluid, consider the cylindrical surface the directrix of which is a closed curve C in the plane of flow, while the generators are normal to the plane of flow. Show that the fluid contained in the unit length of this cylinder has the kinetic energy $(\rho/2)\int \varphi\, d\psi$, where ρ is the density, φ the velocity potential, and ψ the stream function, and the integration is extended over the closed curve C.

3.6. Show that the complex potential $\Phi = U(z + a^2 z^{-1})$ represents a plane flow about a circular cylinder with the radius a and generators that are normal to the plane of flow. Denoting the pressure at the stagnation point $z = -a$ by p_0, determine the variation of the pressure along the perimeter of the cylinder.

3.7. Investigate small surface waves on an infinite horizontal layer of fluid with the thickness h. Assume that the unsteady flow is irrotational and plane. In the vertical plane of flow, take the x_1-direction horizontal and the x_2-direction vertical and upward. The fluid is to be treated as perfect and incompressible, and gravity is supposed to be the only body force acting on the fluid. The free surface is at all times to consist of the same particles and to deviate but slightly from the plane $x_2 = 0$. Show that the motion admits a velocity potential $\varphi(x_1, x_2, t)$ which satisfies the Laplace equation. Show that the parenthesis in (3.2) can be set equal to zero, because the time dependent velocity field determines the velocity potential φ only to within an arbitrary additive function of time. Substitute the resulting expression for p into the condition that the material derivative $p^{\cdot}$ vanishes at the free surface. Neglecting all terms that are nonlinear in φ, and satisfying the condition $p^{\cdot} = 0$ at the plane $x_2 = 0$ instead of the free surface, derive the approximate boundary condition $\partial_{00}\varphi + g\partial_2\varphi = 0$ for $x_2 = 0$. The vertical velocity component v_2 must vanish at the bottom $x_2 = -h$. Discuss velocity potentials of the form $\varphi = f(x_2) \exp \beta(x_1 - ct)$, where β and c are constants.

CHAPTER VI

Viscous Fluids

1. Fundamental equations. Similarity. In deriving the fundamental equations of the theory of Newtonian fluids, we shall drop the simplifying assumption of barotropy and return to (IV, 5.1), (IV, 5.2) and (IV, 5.3). Considering a perfect gas, we write the equation of state in the form

$$p = J(c_p - c_v)\rho\Theta, \tag{1.1}$$

where J is the mechanical equivalent of heat, and c_p and c_v are the specific heats for constant pressure and volume, respectively. The specific internal energy is

$$e = Jc_v\Theta, \tag{1.2}$$

and the heat flux is given by (IV, 4.3). For mathematical simplicity, the specific heats c_p and c_v, the conductivity λ, and the coefficient of viscosity μ, will be treated as constants. Since, in fact, these quantities depend on the temperature, the equations that are to be derived will not apply to flow fields with large temperature differences. We finally assume that no body forces other than gravity need to be considered. If the positive x_3-direction is vertical and upward, we therefore have

$$F_k = -g\delta_{3k}. \tag{1.3}$$

With the use of the constitutive equation (IV, 5.16), equations (5.1), (5.2) and (5.3) of Chapter IV then assume the form

$$\partial_0\rho + \partial_j(\rho v_j) = 0, \tag{1.4}$$

$$\rho\partial_0 v_k + \rho v_j\partial_j v_k = -g\rho\delta_{3k} - \partial_k p + \mu(\partial_{jj}v_k + \tfrac{1}{3}\partial_{jk}v_j), \tag{1.5}$$

$$Jc_v\rho\partial_0\Theta + Jc_v\rho v_j\partial_j\Theta - J\lambda\partial_{jj}\Theta = -p\partial_j v_j + 4\mu\mathscr{V}'_{(2)}, \tag{1.6}$$

where $\mathscr{V}'_{(2)}$ is the second basic invariant of the deviator of the rate of deformation. In the derivation of (1.5), the rate of deformation in the constitutive equation was expressed in terms of the vector gradient of the velocity field (see III, 1.11), and the following transformation was used in the derivation of (1.6):

$$\begin{aligned} T_{jk}V_{jk} &= [-p\delta_{jk} + 2\mu(V_{jk} - \tfrac{1}{3}V_{ii}\delta_{jk})]V_{jk} \\ &= -pV_{jj} + 2\mu V'_{jk}(V'_{jk} + \tfrac{1}{3}V_{ii}\delta_{jk}) \\ &= -p\partial_j v_j + 2\mu V'_{jk}V'_{jk} = -p\partial_j v_j + 4\mathscr{V}'_{(2)}, \end{aligned} \tag{1.7}$$

where primes indicate deviators.

The scalar equations (1.1), (1.4), and (1.6), and the vector equation (1.5) constitute a system of six equations which contain six unknown functions of time and position, namely pressure, density, temperature, and three velocity components. Because of the nonlinear character of this system, the search for exact solutions representing unsteady three-dimensional flows is not likely to be rewarding, and problems with a smaller number of independent variables appear more promising. Before turning to problems of this kind, we use the general equations to derive conditions for the similarity of two flows. The typical application of these similarity conditions concerns the following question: to what extent can the performance of a projected installation be predicted from small scale experiments?

In comparing flow processes of different scales, we shall find it convenient to use *dimensionless* variables. To this end, we divide the coordinates by a characteristic length L of the problem, the time by a characteristic time T, and all velocities by a characteristic velocity U. For an airplane propeller, for instance, these characteristic quantities could be chosen as the radius, the time of revolution, and the axial velocity. Pressure, density, and temperature will be divided by the respective values p_0, ρ_0, and Θ_0 of these quantities at one and the same reference point; the reference quantities p_0, ρ_0, and Θ_0 therefore satisfy the equation of state (1.1). We thus obtain the dimensionless independent variables

$$x_j^* = x_j/L, \quad t^* = t/T \tag{1.8}$$

and the dimensionless dependent variables

$$v_j^* = v_j/U, \quad p^* = p/p_0, \quad \rho^* = \rho/\rho_0, \quad \Theta^* = \Theta/\Theta_0. \tag{1.9}$$

The operators ∂_j^* and ∂_0^* will be used to denote differentiation with respect to x_j^* and t^*, respectively.

With the use of these dimensionless variables, (1.1), (1.4), (1.5), and (1.6) assume the form

$$p^* = \rho^*\Theta^* \tag{1.10}$$

$$\frac{L}{TU}\,\partial_0^*\rho^* + \partial_j^*(\rho^* v_j^*) = 0, \tag{1.11}$$

$$\frac{L}{TU}\,\rho^*\partial_0^* v_k^* + \rho^* v_j^* \partial_j^* v_k^* = -\frac{gL}{U^2}\,\rho^*\delta_{3k} - \frac{p_0}{\rho_0 U^2}\,\partial_k^* p^* + \frac{\mu}{\rho_0 UL}\,(\partial_{jj}^* v_k^* + \tfrac{1}{3}\partial_{jk}^* v_j^*), \tag{1.12}$$

$$\frac{L}{TU}\,\rho^*\partial_0^*\Theta^* + \rho^* v_j^* \partial_j^*\Theta^* - \kappa\,\frac{\lambda}{c_p\rho_0 UL}\,\partial_{jj}^*\Theta^* = -\frac{p_0}{Jc_v\rho_0\Theta_0}\,p^*\partial_j^* v_j^* + 4\kappa\,\frac{\mu}{\rho_0 UL}\cdot\frac{U^2}{Jc_p\Theta_0}\,\mathscr{V}_{(2)}^{*\prime} \tag{1.13}$$

where κ denotes the ratio c_p/c_v of the specific heats, and $\mathscr{V}_{(2)}^{*\prime}$ depends on the components of $\partial_j^* v_k^*$ in the same manner as $\mathscr{V}'_{(2)}$ depends on those of $\partial_j v_k$.

For two flow processes to be represented by identical equations in the dimensionless variables, the dimensionless coefficients that do not contain any starred quantities must have the same values for the two processes. A detailed discussion of these *characteristic numbers* follows.

(i) $L/(TU)$ may be regarded as a *dimensionless frequency*. For the airplane propeller considered above, this characteristic number is inversely proportional to the *advance ratio* $U/(nD)$, where U is the axial velocity, n the number of revolutions per second, and D the diameter of the propeller. Our equations show that a characteristic number of this kind occurs only in problems of unsteady flow.

(ii) $p_0/(Jc_v\rho_0\Theta_0)$ in (1.13) can be transformed into $(c_p/c_v) - 1$ by the use of the equation of state (1.1). For similar flow processes, the ratio $\kappa = c_p/c_v$ of the specific heats must therefore have the same value. This condition is automatically fulfilled if the same fluid is used in both processes and the specific heats can be treated as constant in the considered temperature range.

(iii) $p_0/(\rho_0 U^2)$ in (1.12) can be transformed as follows. In computing the velocity of sound c, we suppose the changes of state to be adiabatic. Since p is then proportional to ρ^κ, we have

$$c^2 = \frac{dp}{d\rho} = \kappa \frac{p}{\rho} \tag{1.14}$$

and

$$\frac{p_0}{\rho_0 U^2} = \frac{c_0^2}{\kappa U^2}, \tag{1.15}$$

where c_0 is the velocity of sound at the reference point. In view of the stipulation made under (ii), the ratio U/c_0 must have the same value for similar flows. If the magnitude of the velocity at the reference point is chosen as the characteristic velocity U, the dimensionless number U/c_0 is the *Mach number* at this point; for similar flows, it must have the same value.

(iv) gL/U^2 in (1.12) is called the *Froude number*; it is a measure of the relative importance of potential and kinetic energy. For similar flows, the Froude number must have the same value.

(v) $\mu/(\rho_0 UL)$ in (1.12) and (1.13) can be interpreted in a similar manner as a measure of the relative importance of viscous dissipation and kinetic energy. The reciprocal value

$$Re = \frac{\rho_0 UL}{\mu} \tag{1.16}$$

is called the *Reynolds number*; for similar flows, it must have the same value.

(vi) The reciprocal value of $\lambda/(c_p\rho_0 UL)$ in (1.13) is called the *Péclet number:*

$$Pe = \frac{c_p\rho_0 UL}{\lambda}. \tag{1.17}$$

This dimensionless number may be written as the product of the Reynolds number (1.16) and the *Prandtl number*

$$Pr = \frac{c_p\mu}{\lambda}. \tag{1.18}$$

According to the kinetic theory of gases, the Prandtl number depends only on the ratio κ of the specific heats. The condition that the Péclet number should have the same value for similar flows, is therefore a consequence of the similarity conditions established under (ii) and (v).

(vii) $U^2/(Jc_p\Theta_0)$ in (1.13) may be interpreted as a measure of the relative importance of kinetic and internal energy. For similar flows, this characteristic number must have the same value. Since by (1.1) and (1.14)

$$\frac{U^2}{Jc_p\Theta_0} = (\kappa - 1)\frac{U^2}{c_0^2}, \tag{1.19}$$

this similarity condition is a consequence of those established under (ii) and (iii).

Summing up, we note that the dimensionless *differential equations* of two flows will be identical, if the similarity conditions established under (i) through (v) are fulfilled. For the flows to be similar, however, the dimensionless *boundary conditions* must also be identical.

If the field of flow is bounded by a rigid surface that is at rest or moves in a prescribed manner (for instance by the surface of a propeller with given angular and axial velocities), it follows from the geometric similarity of the two flows and the equality of the dimensionless frequencies that this similarity condition is fulfilled.

In other problems, however, the motion of the bounding surface is not prescribed in advance, but depends on the forces that the fluid exerts on this surface. For example, the flight of a projectile through air is influenced by the aerodynamic forces which it experiences. If this kind of boundary condition is expressed in the dimensionless variables (1.8) and (1.9), further characteristic numbers will arise which contain additional quantities, for instance the mass of the projectile. For similar flows, these characteristic numbers, too, must have the same values.

In addition to mechanical boundary conditions, thermal boundary conditions may have to be considered. If, for instance, the flow is guided by vanes that are kept at a constant temperature, the dimensionless temperature Θ^* of the vanes must have the same value in similar flows.

The similarity conditions that are expressed by the various dimensionless characteristic numbers are not necessarily compatible with each other. Suppose, for instance, that in an experiment each linear dimension of the projected installation is to be reduced to a quarter. If the same gas is to be used in the small scale experiment and the large scale installation, equality of the Froude numbers requires halving of the velocities, whereas equality of the Reynolds numbers demands quadrupling of the velocities. Since it is then impossible to fulfill all similarity conditions, one must single out those characteristic numbers that are of particular importance in the considered problem, and see to it that they have the same values in the two flows. For example, in the flow past an airplane wing the Archimedean buoyancy due to gravity is negligible in comparison to the aerodynamic lift; accordingly, the equality of the Froude numbers is not a relevant similarity condition for wind tunnel experiments concerning lift and drag of airplane wings.

2. Incompressible fluid: rigorous solutions. Consider an incompressible fluid of uniform density ρ and neglect all gravity effects. Equations (1.4) and (1.5) then assume the form

$$\partial_j v_j = 0, \tag{2.1}$$

$$\partial_0 v_k + v_j \partial_j v_k = -\frac{1}{\rho}\partial_k p + \frac{\mu}{\rho}\partial_{jj} v_k. \tag{2.2}$$

The quotient μ/ρ appearing in this equation is called the *kinematic coefficient of viscosity*.

The three equations indicated by (2.2) are called the *Navier-Stokes equations* of the incompressible viscous fluid. The system consisting of these equations and the equation of continuity (2.1) contains four unknown functions of time and position, namely the pressure and the three components of the velocity. Except for the last term in (2.2), these equations are identical with those for an incompressible *perfect* fluid that is not subjected to any body forces. The last term in (2.2) is therefore characteristic for the viscous fluid; since it contains the highest order derivatives in (2.2), more boundary conditions can be prescribed for the velocity components in a viscous fluid than for those in a perfect fluid. On account of the lack of viscosity, the particles of a perfect fluid can freely glide over a fixed wall, but the particles of a viscous fluid that are in contact with a wall are supposed to adhere to it. At a fixed wall in a perfect fluid only the velocity component normal to the wall has to vanish, but at a fixed wall in a viscous fluid all velocity components must vanish.

It is worth noting that any irrotational flow of an incompressible *perfect* fluid satisfies the Navier-Stokes equations. Indeed, a flow of this kind admits a velocity potential $\varphi(x, t)$ from which the velocity components follow according to $v_j = \partial_j \varphi$. Equation (2.1), which expresses the incompressibility and which has the same form for perfect and for viscous fluids, then furnishes $\partial_{jj}\varphi = 0$, and the only viscosity term in (2.2) vanishes. As a rule, however, these irrotational flows of an incompressible perfect fluid do not prove useful in the solution of problems concerning an incompressible viscous fluid, because the two types of fluid call for different boundary conditions.

The left-hand side of (2.2) represents the acceleration; according to (III, 4.6), this equation can therefore be written as follows:

$$2\mathbf{w} \times \mathbf{v} + \frac{\partial \mathbf{v}}{\partial t} = -\operatorname{grad}\left(\frac{p}{\rho} + \frac{v^2}{2}\right) + \frac{\mu}{\rho}\Delta\mathbf{v}. \tag{2.3}$$

Forming the curl of this equation, and using the third equation (I, 8.7) and the definition (III, 1.5) of $\mathbf{w}$ we obtain

$$\left[(\mathbf{v}\cdot\operatorname{grad})\,\mathbf{w} + \frac{\partial \mathbf{w}}{\partial t}\right] - (\mathbf{w}\cdot\operatorname{grad})\,\mathbf{v} = \frac{\mu}{\rho}\Delta\mathbf{w}. \tag{2.4}$$

According to (IV, 4.8), the bracket in (2.4) represents the material rate of change of the vorticity, which is therefore given by

$$\mathbf{w}^{\boldsymbol{\cdot}} = (\mathbf{w}\cdot\operatorname{grad})\,\mathbf{v} + \frac{\mu}{\rho}\Delta\mathbf{w}. \tag{2.5}$$

The first term on the right side of (2.5) can be interpreted as follows. To represent the instantaneous vorticity $\mathbf{w}$ at the typical particle P, we choose a fixed infinitesimal length ds and a neighboring particle P' in such a manner that the vector PP' equals $\mathbf{w}\,ds$. According to (III, 1.1), the relative velocity of P' with respect to P is given by $d\mathbf{v} = (\mathbf{w}\cdot\operatorname{grad})\,\mathbf{v}\,ds$. If the last term in (2.5) should vanish at all times, the reduced equation would indicate that the vorticity at the particle P continues to be represented by the quotient of the variable vector PP' and the fixed length ds. For an incompressible perfect fluid, this has already been proved at the end of Section 1 of Chapter V. It follows from (2.5) that this geometrical representation of the variable vorticity at the particle P remains valid for a viscous fluid provided that the vorticity components are at all times harmonic functions of position. When $\Delta\mathbf{w} \neq 0$, however, the vortex lines are, as a rule, no longer material lines.

For *plane flow*,

$$v_1 = v_1(x_1, x_2, t), \quad v_2 = v_2(x_1, x_2, t), \quad v_3 = 0, \tag{2.6}$$

the term $(\mathbf{w}\cdot\operatorname{grad})\,\mathbf{v}$ in (2.5) is zero, since w_3 is the only nonvanishing component of $\mathbf{w}$ and the velocity $\mathbf{v}$ does not depend on x_3. With $w_3 = \omega$, equation (2.5) therefore simplifies for plane flow as follows:

$$\omega^{\cdot} = \frac{\mu}{\rho} \partial_{\underline{ii}}\omega; \tag{2.7}$$

here underlined subscripts are restricted to the range 1, 2. Equation (2.7) is called the *vorticity transport equation*; it has the same structure as the special form of the energy equation that is obtained from (1.6) when one deals with the plane flow of an incompressible fluid in which the temperature field is independent of x_3, and neglects the heat generated by viscous friction, i.e. the last term in (1.6). In this manner, one obtains

$$\Theta^{\cdot} = \frac{\lambda}{c\rho} \partial_{\underline{ii}}\Theta, \tag{2.8}$$

where c denotes the specific heat of the incompressible fluid. Since the transport of heat represented by (2.8) is more readily visualized than the transport of vorticity represented by (2.7), the analogy between the two equations is often helpful.

In using this analogy, one must however keep in mind that for complete analogy between two processes not only the differential equations but also the boundary conditions must agree. It may be difficult to fulfill this condition rigorously. For example, a bounding wall of the fluid may readily be kept at a constant temperature Θ, but to enforce a constant vorticity ω along this wall is another matter. Despite this difficulty, the analogy between the two transport processes is useful.

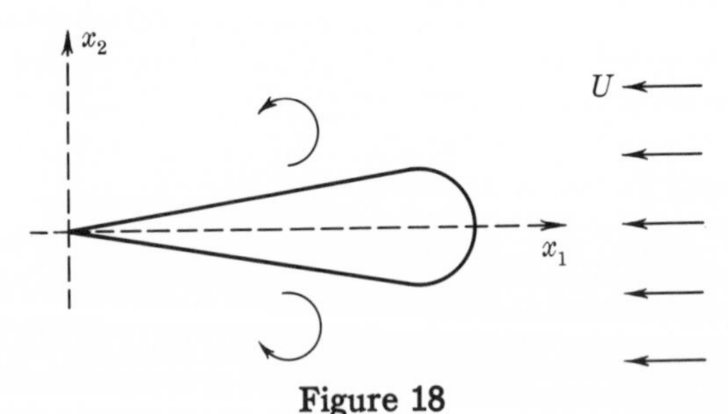

Figure 18

To illustrate this, let the fixed infinite cylinder of the streamlined cross section shown in Figure 18 be exposed to a uniform flow of a direction that is normal to the generators of the cylinder and parallel to its plane of symmetry. Since the viscous fluid adheres to the surface of the cylinder, the vorticity will be positive along the upper surface, and negative along the lower surface. Without knowing the velocity field, however, we cannot make a more precise statement regarding the values of the vorticity along these surfaces. In applying the thermal analogy, we must therefore consider a temperature difference between the upper and lower surfaces of the cylinder that is not specified in detail; the fluid temperature far upstream of the cylinder is somewhere between the temperatures at the two sides of the cylinder. For the steady flow under consideration, $\partial_0\Theta = 0$ and $\Theta^{\cdot}$ in (2.8) reduces to the convective term $v_{\underline{i}}\partial_{\underline{i}}\Theta$. Equation (2.8) represents the interaction between heat convection (left side) and conduction (right side). When the velocity U far upstream of the cylinder is sufficiently small, that is for small values of the Péclet number (1.17), heat convection will play a minor role compared to heat conduction. The fact that the wall temperatures of the cylinder differ from the fluid temperature upstream of the cylinder, will therefore be noticeable far above or below the cylinder. On the other hand, for sufficiently great values of U, i.e., for large Péclet numbers, heat convection will play a more important role than heat conduction, and the effect of the different wall temperatures will only be felt in thin layers along the upper and lower surfaces of the cylinder, and in a continuation of these layers along the half-plane $x_1 < 0$, $x_2 = 0$. The vorticity can be expected to follow a similar pattern. For large Reynolds numbers, in particular, the flow will be practically irrotational, except for thin layers along the two sides of the cylinder and their continuation along the half-plane $x_1 < 0$, $x_2 = 0$. In this irrotational *free flow* the viscosity does not play a significant role, and the equations of motion of a perfect fluid may be used. In the thin *boundary layer*, however, in which the vorticity does not vanish, the Navier-Stokes equations must be used. In this layer, the stream lines are practically parallel to the boundary of the cross section of the cylinder, and the magnitude of the velocity increases rapidly from the value zero at the surface of the cylinder to the value in the free flow. These remarks suggest certain simplifications in the Navier-Stokes equations for the boundary layer, which may render these equations amenable to mathematical treatment. The possibility of treating free flow and boundary layer flow separately, and the resulting simplification of the Navier-Stokes equations in the boundary layer were first pointed out by Prandtl.† Before turning to boundary layer theory, let us discuss some rigorous solutions of the Navier-Stokes equations.

In the search for rigorous solutions, consider *rectilinear flows* of the form

$$v_1 = v_2 = 0, \quad v_3 = v(x_1, x_2, t). \tag{2.9}$$

The equation of continuity (2.1) is identically fulfilled, and the first and second component of the vector equation (2.2) show that the pressure is independent of x_1 and x_2. The third component of (2.2) reduces to

$$\partial_0 v = -\frac{1}{\rho}\,\partial_3 p + \frac{\mu}{\rho}\,\partial_{\underline{i}\underline{i}} v, \tag{2.10}$$

where underlined subscripts are again restricted to the range 1, 2. Since v

† L. Prandtl, Proc. 3rd Internat. Congress Math. (Heidelberg, 1904) Leipzig, 1905, p. 484.

is independent of x_3, (2.10) shows that $\partial_3 p$ is also independent of x_3. As it has already been shown that the pressure is independent of x_3, we may set

$$-\partial_3 p = f(t) \tag{2.11}$$

in (2.10). The function $f(t)$ is called the *pressure gradient* of the rectilinear flow.

If, in particular, the pressure gradient vanishes, (2.10) assumes the form of the two-dimensional equation of heat conduction, the solutions of which can therefore be interpreted in terms of the rectilinear flows considered here. As example, we discuss the rectilinear oscillations of a fluid in the half-space $x_1 > 0$ that are caused by harmonic oscillations of the bounding wall $x_1 = 0$ in the x_3-direction. The corresponding thermal problem concerns the temperature fluctuations generated in a half-space by a periodic variation of the surface temperature. The solution of this problem is well known;† in terms of our flow problem it is given by

$$v(x, t) = v_0 e^{-ax_1} \cos(\omega t - ax_1), \tag{2.12}$$

where $a^2 = \omega\rho/(2\mu)$, while v_0 is the velocity amplitude of the wall and ω the circular frequency. According to (2.12) each fluid layer $x_1 =$ constant oscillates harmonically with the same frequency ω, but with an amplitude that decreases exponentially with x_1 and with the phase difference $-ax_1$. Layers with the distance $\lambda = 2\pi/a$ oscillate in phase, so that this distance may be interpreted as the wave length. On account of the infinite extension of the fluid, the only characteristic length in our problem is given by v_0/ω; the Reynolds number (1.16) must therefore be defined as

$$Re = \frac{\rho v_0^2}{\omega\mu}. \tag{2.13}$$

The dimensionless wave length

$$\lambda^* = \frac{\omega\lambda}{v_0} = 2\pi\frac{\omega}{v_0 a} = 2\pi\sqrt{\frac{2}{Re}} \tag{2.14}$$

thus is inversely proportional to the square root of the Reynolds number.

As a second example, consider a layer of fluid between infinite rigid plates in the planes $x_1 = 0$ and $x_1 = h$. Initially, let the fluid and the plates be at rest. At the time $t = 0$, let the plate $x_1 = 0$ start to move with the henceforth constant velocity v_0 in the x_3-direction, while the other plate is held fixed. The corresponding thermal problem concerns an infinite layer of the thickness h, that has initially a uniform temperature; at the time $t = 0$ one surface is suddenly exposed to a henceforth constant higher temperature, whereas the other surface is maintained at the original temperature. We

† See, for instance, H. S. Carslaw, *Introduction to the Mathematical Theory of the Conduction of Heat in Solids*, London, 1921, p. 47.

leave it to the reader to interpret the known solution of this problem in terms of the corresponding hydrodynamic problem.

Couette's viscosimeter uses a thin layer of fluid between two coaxial cylinders, the outer one of which rotates with a fixed angular velocity about the common axis, while the inner one is held fixed by a suitable torque. If the ratio between the mean radius of curvature of this fluid layer and its thickness is very large, the flow discussed above approximates the starting flow in a Couette viscosimeter. In the Couette experiment, the viscosity of the fluid is of course deduced from the asymptotic flow rather than the starting flow. For the flow between parallel plates considered above, the thermal analogy indicates that the asymptotic velocity varies linearly from $v = v_0$ at the moving plate to $v = 0$ at the fixed plate.

Other rigorous solutions of the type (2.9) correspond to the steady flow of an incompressible viscous fluid through a cylindrical pipe of arbitrary cross section. The left side of (2.10) vanishes in this case, but a constant pressure gradient $f(t) = c$ is needed to maintain the steady flow. Equation (2.10) thus takes on the form

$$\partial_{\underline{ii}} v = -c/\mu, \tag{2.15}$$

where $v = 0$ on the contour of the cross section of the pipe. Even when the shape of the cross section does not lend itself to an analytical treatment of this boundary value problem, one may visualize the solution by means of the following *soap film analogy*. Let a thin membrane, for instance a soap film, be stretched over a hole that is cut in the plane lid of a box and which has the shape of the cross section of the pipe, and let the principal stresses in the plane of the membrane have the common value T. If then an overpressure p, which is small in comparison to T, is generated inside the box, the small deflection v of the membrane satisfies (2.15), provided that the original plane of the membrane is taken as the x_1, x_2-plane and that c/μ is replaced by $p/(T\delta)$, where δ is the uniform thickness of the membrane. For a circular cross section, in particular, the velocity v at the distance r from the axis of the pipe is given by the equation

$$v(r) = \frac{c}{4\mu}(R^2 - r^2), \tag{2.16}$$

which is named after Poiseuille.† The average velocity in the pipe equals

$$v_0 = \frac{1}{\pi R^2}\int_0^R 2\pi r v(r)\,dr = \frac{cR^2}{8\mu}. \tag{2.17}$$

It is customary in hydraulics, to use the pipe diameter $D = 2R$ as the characteristic length, and $\rho v_0^2/2$ as the characteristic pressure. The dimen-

† J. L. M. Poiseuille, Comptes Rend. *11* (1840) 961, 1041; *12* (1841) 112.

sionless pressure gradient, which is usually denoted by λ, is called the *coefficient of resistance;* thus

$$\lambda = \frac{2cD}{\rho v_0^2}. \tag{2.18}$$

In an analogous manner, the Reynolds number is defined as

$$Re = \frac{\rho D v_0}{\mu}. \tag{2.19}$$

Eliminating c between (2.17) and (2.18) and using (2.19), we find

$$\lambda = 64/Re. \tag{2.20}$$

This formula agrees extremely well with experiments as long as the Reynolds number remains below a critical value of about 2000; for larger Reynolds numbers the flow ceases to be of the *laminar* type assumed in (2.9) and becomes *turbulent*. The velocity field can then be regarded as resulting from the superposition of turbulent fluctuations upon a smooth rectilinear mean motion. As has been shown in Section 2 of Chapter IV, the influence of these fluctuations on the mean motion can be treated by the introduction of turbulent stresses. On account of these additional stresses the mean motion no longer obeys the equations derived above.

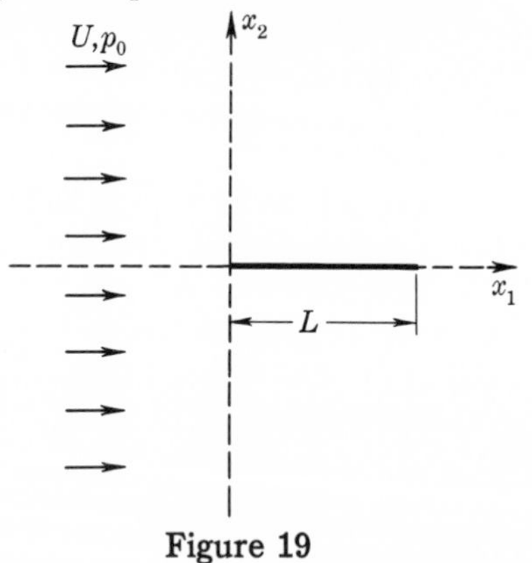

Figure 19

3. Incompressible fluid: boundary layer equations. To illustrate the simplifications that can be made in the Navier-Stokes equations for the boundary layer, consider the plane steady flow of an incompressible fluid of small viscosity past a plane plate of vanishing thickness. Choose $x_3 = 0$ as the plane of flow, and let the trace of the plate in this plane extend along the x_1-axis from $x_1 = 0$ to $x_1 = L$ (Figure 19). Far upstream from the plate, i.e. for $x_1 \to -\infty$, let the plane velocity field be given by

$$v_1 = U, \quad v_2 = 0. \tag{3.1}$$

In a perfect fluid, the particles of which can freely glide over the plate, the velocity components would everywhere have the values (3.1), but the particles of a viscous fluid that are in contact with the plate must adhere to it. The thermal analogy discussed in connection with Figure 18 shows that for a small viscosity, i.e. for a large Reynolds number, this condition influences the flow only in a thin boundary layer beyond which the flow is irrotational as in a perfect fluid. For our problem this free flow will be assumed to have the form (3.1).

The Navier-Stokes equations are valid in the boundary layer. We propose to write them in a dimensionless form, which expresses the fact that the thickness of the boundary layer and hence the velocity component v_2 in this layer tend toward zero for $Re \to \infty$. To this end, we introduce the dimensionless variables

$$\left.\begin{aligned} x_1^* &= x_1/L, \quad x_2^* = x_2 Re^{\alpha}/L, \\ v_1^* &= v_1/U, \quad v_2^* = v_2 Re^{\beta}/U, \quad p^* = (p - p_0)/(\rho U^2), \end{aligned}\right\} \tag{3.2}$$

where p_0 is the constant pressure for $x_1 = -\infty$ and the exponents α and β are positive. The definition of the dimensionless pressure is suggested by the remark that the superposition of a uniform pressure field has no influence on the flow of an incompressible fluid. Powers of the Reynolds number have been introduced in the definitions of the transversal coordinate x_2^* and the transversal velocity v_2^* in the boundary layer, so that these quantities have the same order of magnitude as x_1^* and v_1^* even when $Re \to \infty$. Applied to the plane steady flow considered here and written in the dimensionless variables (3.2), equations (2.1) and (2.2) become

$$\partial_1^* v_1^* + Re^{\alpha-\beta} \partial_2^* v_2^* = 0, \tag{3.3}$$

$$v_1^* \partial_1^* v_1^* + Re^{\alpha-\beta} v_2^* \partial_2^* v_1^* = -\partial_1^* p^* + Re^{-1}(\partial_{11}^* v_1^* + Re^{2\alpha} \partial_{22}^* v_1^*), \tag{3.4}$$

$$Re^{-\alpha-\beta} v_1^* \partial_1^* v_2^* + Re^{-2\beta} v_2^* \partial_2^* v_2^* = -\partial_2^* p^* + Re^{-1-\alpha-\beta}(\partial_{11}^* v_2^* + Re^{2\alpha} \partial_{22}^* v_2^*). \tag{3.5}$$

If the two terms in (3.3) are to remain of the same order of magnitude when $Re \to \infty$, we must have $\alpha = \beta$. If a viscosity term is to be retained in (3.4) when $Re \to \infty$, we must have $\alpha = \frac{1}{2}$. With $\alpha = \beta = \frac{1}{2}$, all terms in (3.5) except the pressure term disappear for $Re \to \infty$. The pressure in the boundary layer is therefore independent of x_2^*. Since the pressure in the free flow is constant for our problem, the pressure has the same value throughout the boundary layer. Equations (3.3) and (3.4) thus simplify as follows:

$$\partial_1^* v_1^* + \partial_2^* v_2^* = 0, \tag{3.6}$$

$$v_1^* \partial_1^* v_1^* + v_2^* \partial_2^* v_1^* = \partial_{22}^* v_1^*. \tag{3.7}$$

The definition of x_2^* shows that for $Re \to \infty$ the interface between boundary layer and free flow corresponds to $x_2^* = \infty$. For $0 < x_1^* \leq 1$, we have therefore the following boundary conditions for (3.6) and (3.7):

$$v_1^* = v_2^* = 0 \quad \text{for } x_2^* = 0, \tag{3.8}$$

$$v_1^* = 1 \quad \text{for } x_2^* = \infty. \tag{3.9}$$

While (3.6) and (3.7) represent considerable simplifications of the complete equations for the plane steady flow of a viscous fluid, the nonlinearity of (3.7) nevertheless creates great difficulties.

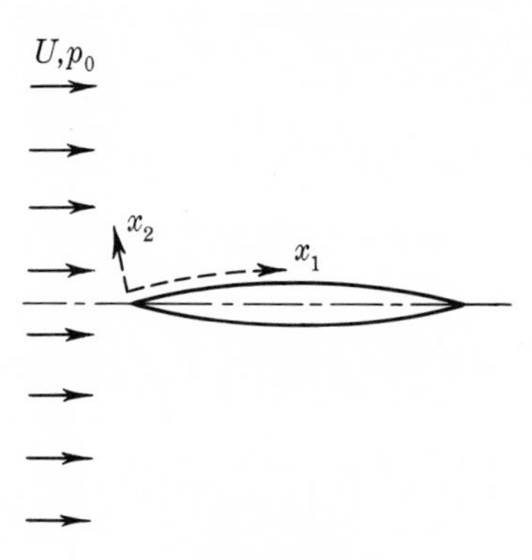

Figure 20

In an approximate way, the preceding discussion also applies to the flow along one side of a slightly curved slender profile (Figure 20), provided that x_1 is interpreted as the arc length measured along this side, and x_2 as the normal distance from it. In this flow, however, the pressure is no longer independent of x_1, and the function $p(x_1)$ must be obtained from the potential flow past the profile. Since in this potential flow the pressure $p(x_1)$ and the speed $v(x_1)$ along the profile are related by Bernoulli's equation, $(p/\rho) + v^2/2 =$ constant, we have $-\partial_1 p = \rho v \partial_1 v$. For the present problem, (3.7) must therefore be replaced by

$$v_1^* \partial_1^* v_1^* + v_2^* \partial_2^* v_1^* = v^* \partial_1^* v^* + \partial_{22}^* v_1^*, \tag{3.10}$$

whereas (3.6) can be used without change. In (3.10), the dimensionless velocity $v^* = v/U$ of the potential flow is a known function of x_1^*. For $0 < x_1^* \leq 1$, the boundary condition (3.8) applies to the present problem, whereas (3.9) must be replaced by

$$v_1^* = v^* \text{ for } x_2^* = \infty. \tag{3.11}$$

Let us return to (3.6) and (3.7) with the boundary conditions (3.8) and (3.9). The first equation suggests the introduction of a stream function

$\psi(x_1^*, x_2^*)$ from which the dimensionless velocity components are obtained as follows:

$$v_1^* = \partial_2^* \psi, \quad v_2^* = -\partial_1^* \psi. \tag{3.12}$$

Equation (3.6) is then identically fulfilled, while (3.7) assumes the form

$$\partial_2^* \psi \partial_{12}^* \psi - \partial_1^* \psi \partial_{22}^* \psi = \partial_{222}^* \psi. \tag{3.13}$$

Consider the transformation $\bar{x}_1^* = \alpha x_1^*$, $\bar{x}_2^* = \beta x_2^*$, $\bar{\psi} = \gamma \psi$, in which α, β, γ are constants. As is readily verified, the differential equation obtained from (3.13) for the function $\bar{\psi}(\bar{x}_1^*, \bar{x}_2^*)$ has the same form as (3.13), if we choose $\gamma = \alpha/\beta$. If a similar remark is to apply to the boundary condition following from (3.9), we must also have $\beta = \gamma$. With this choice, we have

$$\frac{\bar{x}_2^*}{\bar{x}_1^{*\frac{1}{2}}} = \frac{x_2^*}{x_1^{*\frac{1}{2}}}, \quad \frac{\bar{\psi}}{\bar{x}_1^{*\frac{1}{2}}} = \frac{\psi}{x_1^{*\frac{1}{2}}}. \tag{3.14}$$

These relations suggest that there are solutions of the form

$$\psi = x_1^{*\frac{1}{2}} f\left(\frac{x_2^*}{x_1^{*\frac{1}{2}}}\right). \tag{3.15}$$

Substitution of (3.15) into (3.13) yields the ordinary differential equation

$$2f''' + ff'' = 0. \tag{3.16}$$

For small values of $\xi = x_2^*/x_1^{*\frac{1}{2}}$, we propose to integrate this equation by a power series. Since the factor 2 of the first term in (3.16) would be awkward in the comparison of coefficients, we eliminate it by introducing $g = f/2$. The function g must then satisfy the differential equation

$$g''' + gg'' = 0 \tag{3.17}$$

and the boundary conditions

$$g = 0, \quad g' = 0 \quad \text{for } \xi = 0, \tag{3.18}$$

$$g' = \tfrac{1}{2} \quad \text{for } \xi = \infty, \tag{3.19}$$

which follow from (3.8) and (3.9).

The boundary conditions (3.18) show that the power series for g starts with the quadratic term; this will be written as $a\,\xi^2/2$. Comparison of coefficients shows that only powers of the form ξ^{3n+2} $(n = 0, 1, 2, \cdots)$ have nonvanishing coefficients. Following Blasius,† we set

$$\begin{aligned} g &= \sum_{n=0}^{\infty} (-1)^n \frac{c_n a^{n+1}}{(3n+2)!} \xi^{3n+2} \\ &= a^{\frac{1}{3}} \sum_{n=0}^{\infty} (-1)^n \frac{c_n}{(3n+2)!} (a^{\frac{1}{3}}\xi)^{3n+2}, \end{aligned} \tag{3.20}$$

where it follows from the assumed form of the quadratic term that $c_0 = 1$.

† H. Blasius, Zeitschrift f. Math. u. Phys. *56* (1908) 1.

Substituting (3.20) into the differential equation (3.17), we obtain the following values for the first four coefficients: $c_1 = 1$, $c_2 = 11$, $c_3 = 375$, $c_4 = 27897$.

The power series obtained in this manner satisfies the boundary conditions (3.18) regardless of the value of the parameter a. This value must now be determined from the boundary condition (3.19). To this end, we first set $a = 1$ and evaluate the power series (3.20) and the resulting series for g' and g'' for a value $\xi = \xi_1 > 0$ that is reasonably large but does not require the computation of an excessive number of terms. The values of $g(\xi_1)$, $g'(\xi_1)$, and $g''(\xi_1)$ obtained in this manner are then used to start a numerical integration of the differential equation (3.17), which is continued until the asymptotic value of g' for $\xi \to \infty$ can be estimated with sufficient accuracy. For the choice $a = 1$, this asymptotic value is found to be 1.655. To satisfy the boundary condition (3.19), the value of a must now be changed in such a manner that this asymptotic value is reduced to $\frac{1}{2}$. As can be seen from (3.13), the asymptotic values of g' for an arbitrary a and for $a = 1$ are related by

$$g' = a^{2/3}(g')_{a=1}. \tag{3.21}$$

The desired value of a is therefore found from

$$0.5 = 1.655a^{2/3} \tag{3.22}$$

as $a = 0.166$.

For the incompressible fluid considered here, the constitutive equation (IV, 5.16) furnishes the shearing stress at the plate $(0 < x_1^* \leq 1, x_2^* = 0)$ as follows:

$$T_{12} = \mu(\partial_1 v_2 + \partial_2 v_1) = \mu \partial_2 v_1. \tag{3.23}$$

In view of (3.2), we therefore have

$$\partial_2^* v_1^* = \frac{L}{\mu U Re^{1/2}} T_{12} = \left(\frac{L}{\mu\rho U^3}\right)^{1/2} T_{12}. \tag{3.24}$$

On the other hand, it follows from (3.12), (3.15), (3.20), and (3.2) that

$$\partial_2^* v_1^* = \partial_{22}^* \psi = x_1^{*-1/2} f'' = 2x_1^{*-1/2} g'' = 2(L/x_1)^{1/2} g'', \tag{3.25}$$

where g'' has the value a for $x_2^* = 0$. The shearing stress at the plate therefore equals

$$T_{12} = 2a(\mu\rho U^3/x_1)^{1/2}. \tag{3.26}$$

Since each of the two sides of the plate experiences this shearing stress, the total drag of the plate per unit length measured perpendicularly to the plane of flow is

$$D = 2\int_0^L T_{12} dx_1 = 8a(\mu\rho L U^3)^{1/2} = 1.328(\mu\rho L U^3)^{1/2}. \tag{3.27}$$

4. Incompressible fluid: non-Newtonian behavior. The constitutive equation (IV, 5.16), on which the preceding discussion of viscous flow was based, represents the stress tensor T as the sum of the isotropic tensor $-p\boldsymbol{\delta}$ and the stress deviator T' which is assumed to be proportional to the deviator V' of the rate of deformation. For the incompressible fluids that are to be considered in this section, V' is identical with the rate of deformation V, and Newtonian behavior is characterized by the relation

$$\mathsf{T}' = 2\mu\mathsf{V}. \tag{4.1}$$

The viscosity coefficient μ, which has so far been treated as a characteristic constant of the fluid, may in fact depend on the temperature, but it is essential for the linearity of the relation (4.1) that this coefficient is independent of the components of the rate of deformation.

If non-Newtonian behavior is to be discussed, the linear relation (4.1) must be replaced by a nonlinear one. A first step in this direction consists in letting μ in (4.1) depend not only on the temperature but also on the components of the rate of deformation. Being a scalar, μ cannot depend in an arbitrary manner on the components of V, but must be a function of expressions in these components that are themselves scalars. The basic invariants (III, 1.19) satisfy this requirement; to obtain other expressions of this kind, one might consider the basic invariants of the powers of V. The definition (I, 7.17) of the powers of a symmetric tensor and the definitions (III, 1.19) of the basic invariants of the rate of deformation show, however, that the scalar expressions obtained in this manner can be written as polynomials in the basic invariants of V.

To illustrate this, consider the second basic invariant of the square $\mathsf{Q} = \mathsf{V}^2$ of an arbitrary symmetric tensor V. According to (III, 1.19), we have

$$\begin{aligned} \mathscr{Q}_{(2)} &= \tfrac{1}{2}[\operatorname{tr} \mathsf{Q}^2 - (\operatorname{tr} \mathsf{Q})^2] \\ &= \tfrac{1}{2}[\operatorname{tr} \mathsf{V}^4 - (\operatorname{tr} \mathsf{V}^2)^2], \end{aligned} \tag{4.2}$$

where tr indicates the trace (see I, 7.20). According to (I, 7.19), V^4 in (4.2) can be written as a linear combination of $\boldsymbol{\delta}$, V, and V^2, with coefficients that are polynomials in the basic invariants of V. On the other hand, it follows from (I, 7.6) and (I, 7.8) that

$$\operatorname{tr} \mathsf{V} = \mathscr{V}_{(1)}, \quad \operatorname{tr} \mathsf{V}^2 = \mathscr{V}_{(1)}^2 + 2\mathscr{V}_{(2)}. \tag{4.3}$$

Equation (4.2) is therefore equivalent to

$$\begin{aligned} 2\mathscr{Q}_{(2)} = (\mathscr{V}_{(1)}^2 + \mathscr{V}_{(2)})(\mathscr{V}_{(1)}^2 + 2\mathscr{V}_{(2)}) + (\mathscr{V}_{(1)}\mathscr{V}_{(2)} + \mathscr{V}_{(3)})\mathscr{V}_{(1)} \\ + 3\mathscr{V}_{(1)}\mathscr{V}_{(3)} - (\mathscr{V}_{(1)}^2 + 2\mathscr{V}_{(2)})^2. \end{aligned} \tag{4.4}$$

In a similar manner, all basic invariants of the powers of V can be expressed in terms of $\mathscr{V}_{(1)}$, $\mathscr{V}_{(2)}$, and $\mathscr{V}_{(3)}$.

The following generalization of this result can be established: *Any single-valued function of the components of a symmetric tensor* V *that behaves as a scalar in the transition to another coordinate system can be written as a function of the basic invariants* $\mathcal{V}_{(1)}$, $\mathcal{V}_{(2)}$, *and* $\mathcal{V}_{(3)}$. We omit the proof of this theorem, which is beyond the scope of this book.

Whereas the preceding discussion applies to scalar functions of the components of an arbitrary symmetric tensor V, the rate of deformation V in the constitutive equation of an incompressible fluid is a deviator, so that $\mathcal{V}_{(1)} = 0$. The considered relation between the stress deviator T' and the rate of deformation V therefore has the form

$$\mathsf{T}' = 2\mu(\mathcal{V}_{(2)}, \mathcal{V}_{(3)})\mathsf{V}. \tag{4.5}$$

If the constitutive equation (4.5) is used, the equation of motion (2.2) must be replaced by

$$\partial_0 v_k + v_j \partial_j v_k = -\frac{1}{\rho}\partial_k p + \frac{1}{\rho}\partial_j(\mu \partial_j v_k), \tag{4.6}$$

where μ is a known function of the invariants $\mathcal{V}_{(2)}$ and $\mathcal{V}_{(3)}$, which in turn depend on the as yet unknown velocity field.

Let us apply (4.6) to the steady rectilinear flow in a cylindrical pipe of arbitrary cross section. We set

$$v_1 = v_2 = 0, \quad v_3 = 2\varphi(x_1, x_2), \tag{4.7}$$

where the factor 2 is to compensate for the awkward factor $\frac{1}{2}$ in the definition of the shear components of the rate of deformation V_{jk}. The velocity field (4.7) satisfies the equation of continuity (2.1), and the nonvanishing components of the rate of deformation are

$$V_{13} = V_{31} = \partial_1\varphi, \quad V_{23} = V_{32} = \partial_2\varphi. \tag{4.8}$$

According to (III, 1.19), we have

$$\mathcal{V}_{(1)} = 0, \quad \mathcal{V}_{(2)} = \partial_{\underline{j}}\varphi\partial_{\underline{j}}\varphi, \quad \mathcal{V}_{(3)} = 0, \tag{4.9}$$

where the underlined subscripts are restricted to the range 1, 2. The coefficient of viscosity μ is therefore a function of $(\operatorname{grad}\varphi)^2$.

The first two components of the equation of motion (4.6) show that the pressure is independent of x_1 and x_2; the third component reduces to

$$0 = -\partial_3 p + 2\partial_{\underline{i}}(\mu\partial_{\underline{i}}\varphi). \tag{4.10}$$

Since φ depends only on x_1 and x_2, whereas p is independent of these variables, each of the two terms in (4.10) is a constant. As in Section 2, the pressure gradient $-\partial_3 p$ will be denoted by c. Instead of the linear equation (2.15), we now must solve the nonlinear equation

$$\partial_{\underline{i}}(\mu\partial_{\underline{i}}\varphi) = -c/2, \tag{4.11}$$

with the boundary condition $\varphi = 0$ on the contour of the cross section. In

(4.11), the coefficient of viscosity μ is a known function of $\partial_j\varphi\partial_j\varphi$. For a general form of this function, the boundary value problem just formulated will have to be treated numerically, for instance by the relaxation method. If, however, the fluid is almost Newtonian, that is, if the viscosity only varies slightly with the rate of deformation, a method of successive approximations may be used in which the viscosity for the current approximation is computed from the velocity field of the preceding one, and the first approximation corresponds to Newtonian behavior.

The *quasi-linear* constitutive equation (4.5) has the following property in common with the linear constitutive equation (IV, 5.15) of the Newtonian fluid: if a certain component of $\mathbf{V}$ is zero, the corresponding component of $\mathbf{T}'$ also has the value zero. It is because of this property that the pressure in the rectilinear flow (2.9) is independent of x_1 and x_2 for the non-Newtonian fluid characterized by (4.5) as well as for the Newtonian fluid characterized by (IV, 5.15).

To obtain more general constitutive equations for *isotropic* incompressible non-Newtonian fluids, we write $\mathbf{T}'$ as a polynomial in $\mathbf{V}$ with coefficients that depend on $\mathscr{V}_{(2)}$ and $\mathscr{V}_{(3)}$. For this polynomial to represent a deviator, it must, as a rule, contain a suitable multiple of the unit tensor $\boldsymbol{\delta}$. Since, on the other hand, all powers of $\mathbf{V}^n$ with $n \geq 3$ can be written as linear combinations of $\boldsymbol{\delta}$, $\mathbf{V}$, and $\mathbf{V}^2$, we finally obtain

$$\mathbf{T}' = f(\mathscr{V}_{(2)}, \mathscr{V}_{(3)})\mathbf{V} + g(\mathscr{V}_{(2)}, \mathscr{V}_{(3)})[\mathbf{V}^2 - \tfrac{2}{3}\mathscr{V}_{(2)}\boldsymbol{\delta}]. \tag{4.12}$$

For the incompressible fluid considered here, $\mathbf{V}$ is a deviator; according to equation (I, 7.21), which applies to deviators, the tensor in the bracket in (4.12) has therefore a vanishing trace, and the right-hand side of (4.12) is a deviator. The argument leading to (4.12) was given by Reiner† and Prager ‡ in independent papers.

In applying the constitutive equation (4.12) to the steady rectilinear flow (4.7), we denote the tensor in the bracket in (4.12) by $\mathbf{W}$. As is readily verified,

$$\left.\begin{aligned} &W_{11} = \tfrac{1}{3}(\partial_1\varphi)^2 - \tfrac{2}{3}(\partial_2\varphi)^2, \quad W_{12} = \partial_1\varphi\partial_2\varphi, \quad W_{13} = 0,\\ &W_{22} = \tfrac{1}{3}(\partial_2\varphi)^2 - \tfrac{2}{3}(\partial_1\varphi)^2,\\ &W_{23} = 0, \quad W_{33} = \tfrac{1}{3}(\partial_1\varphi)^2 + \tfrac{1}{3}(\partial_2\varphi)^2. \end{aligned}\right\} \tag{4.13}$$

Despite the fact that most components of $\mathbf{V}$ are zero, no component of $\mathbf{T}'$ vanishes. This appearance of additional stress components in the nonlinear constitutive equation (4.12) represents an effect, which is usually named after Poynting,§ who first investigated this kind of effect in elastic solids.

† M. Reiner, American Journal of Mathematics *67* (1945) 350.
‡ W. Prager, Journal of Applied Physics *16* (1945) 837.
§ J. H. Poynting, Philosophical Magazine (6) *9* (1905) 393.

For the considered steady rectilinear flow, the equation of motion (2.2) now assumes the form

$$0 = \partial_k p + 2\partial_j(fV_{jk} + gW_{jk}). \tag{4.14}$$

On account of the Poynting effect, the first two components of the equation of motion no longer reduce to $\partial_1 p = 0$ and $\partial_2 p = 0$. Accordingly, (4.14) represents three differential equations for the two unknown functions p and φ. As Ericksen † has shown, these differential equations are, in general, not compatible, that is, in the absence of body forces, a non-Newtonian fluid is, as a rule, unable to perform the steady rectilinear motion (4.7). Important exceptions from this statement are the flow between parallel infinite plates and the flow in a cylindrical pipe with circular cross section.

To render the three components of the equation of motion (4.14) compatible, we must, in general, introduce a third unknown function, for instance the stream function $\psi(x_1, x_2)$ of a secondary flow in the plane of the cross section. Equations (4.7) must then be replaced by

$$v_1 = \partial_2\psi, \quad v_2 = -\partial_1\psi, \quad v_3 = 2\varphi. \tag{4.15}$$

For elliptical cross section and an almost Newtonian fluid, Green and Rivlin ‡ have discussed this secondary flow and shown that it corresponds to four vortices of alternating signs in the quadrants of the ellipse.

PROBLEMS

1.1. Let the scalar field $a(x, t)$ and the vector field $b_i(x, t)$ be defined in the simply connected regular region V, and suppose that the first field is continuously differentiable with respect to the coordinates and the time, while the second field is continuously differentiable with respect to the time and twice continuously differentiable with respect to the coordinates. Assume that the integral equations

$$\int b_i \partial_i A \, dV = 0$$

$$\int dt \int dV \, [b_i(\partial_0 B_i + b_j\partial_j B_i + c\partial_{jj} B_i) - B_j\partial_j a] - \int b_i B_i \, dV = 0$$

in which c is a given constant, are satisfied for any choice of the scalar field $A(x, t)$ and the vector field $B_i(x, t)$, provided that these fields fulfill the same continuity and differentiability conditions as a and b_i, respectively, and that the scalar A, the vector B_i, and the normal derivative $\partial B_i/\partial\nu$ vanish on the surface S of V. Prove that $b_i(x, t)$ can be regarded as the velocity

† J. L. Ericksen, Quarterly of Applied Mathematics *14* (1956) 318.

‡ A. E. Green and R. S. Rivlin, Quarterly of Applied Mathematics *14* (1956) 299.

$v_i(x, t)$ and $a(x, t)$ as the quotient of the pressure $p(x, t)$ and the constant density ρ of an incompressible viscous fluid which has the viscosity coefficient $c\rho$ and is not subject to body forces.

1.2. A closed rigid container, which is at rest, is completely filled with a moving incompressible viscous fluid which adheres to the container walls and is subject to conservative body forces. Prove that the material rate of change of the kinetic energy of the fluid equals $-4\mu \int w^2 \, dV$, where w is the magnitude of the vorticity vector.

1.3. Equation (1.10) does not contain a characteristic number. Prove that for an incompressible viscous fluid of the density ρ_0 the reference quantities L, T, U can be chosen in such a way that (1.11) and (1.12) also do not contain any characteristic numbers.

1.4. The term $\rho v_j \partial_j v_k$ in the equation of motion (1.5) is usually neglected in the discussion of the "slow" motion of a viscous fluid. Prove that in the absence of body forces the pressure in an incompressible viscous fluid in slow motion is a harmonic function of the coordinates.

1.5. Considering a slow plane flow of an incompressible viscous fluid in the x_1, x_2-plane, satisfy the equation of continuity (1.4) by the introduction of a stream function $\psi(x_1, x_2, t)$. Prove that the differential equation for $\Delta\psi$ has the same structure as the differential equation for the temperature in plane heat conduction with constant conductivity.

1.6. Consider the velocity field

$$v_i = U\left[\frac{3}{4}\frac{Rx_ix_3}{r^3}\left(\frac{R^2}{r^2} - 1\right) - \frac{1}{4}\,\delta_{i3}\frac{R}{r}\left(3 + \frac{R^2}{r^2}\right) + \delta_{i3}\right],$$

where R and U are constants and $r^2 = x_ix_i$. Show that this field represents the slow steady flow of an incompressible viscous fluid past a sphere of radius R, if the center of the sphere coincides with the origin and the velocity at great distance from the sphere has the magnitude U and the positive x_3-direction. Determine the resultant of the surface tractions exerted by the fluid on the sphere.

2.1. In the plane flow of an incompressible viscous fluid, consider the circulation of the velocity vector along a closed curve L that lies in the plane of motion. Show that the material rate of this circulation equals

$$2(\mu/\rho)\int (\partial\omega/\partial\nu)\, dL,$$

where $\partial\omega/\partial\nu$ denotes the rate of change of the vorticity ω in the direction of the exterior normal of L.

2.2. Use (2.7) to derive the differential equation of the stream function ψ of the plane flow of an incompressible viscous fluid.

2.3. In the x_1, x_2-plane, let the velocity field $v_1 = v_1(x_1, x_2, t)$, $v_2 = v_2(x_1, x_2, t)$, of a plane flow of an incompressible viscous fluid be defined for $x_1 \geq 0$ in such a manner that $v_i = 0$ for $x_1 = 0$. The following continuation of this field into the half-plane $x_1 < 0$ is proposed: if v_1, v_2 are the velocity components at the point x_1, x_2, the velocity components at the point $-x_1$, x_2 are to be v_1, $-v_2$. Prove that this continuation represents the velocity field of an incompressible viscous fluid if and only if in the half-plane $x_1 \geq 0$ the stream lines coincide with the lines of constant vorticity.

2.4. For $x_2 \geq 0$, the flow with the velocity components $v_1 = cx_1$, $v_2 = -cx_2$, $v_3 = 0$ with constant positive c may be interpreted as the plane irrotational flow of a perfect fluid against the infinite rigid wall $x_2 = 0$. In this flow, the fluid particles at the wall glide over the wall with the velocity $v_1 = cx_1$, but in the corresponding flow of an incompressible viscous fluid the fluid particles must adhere to the wall. Assume that the velocity field of the latter flow has the form $v_1 = cx_1\partial_2 f$, $v_2 = -cf$, where the function f depends only on x_2 and f and $\partial_2 f$ vanish for $x_2 = 0$. Use the vorticity transport equation to derive the differential equation for f, and show that the pressure on the wall is distributed according to $p = c\mu x_1^2 f'''(0)/(2\rho) + \text{constant}$.

2.5. Write the equations of continuity and motion (2.1) and (2.2) in cylindrical coordinates ρ, θ, ζ, and discuss solutions of the form $v_\rho = \rho^{-1}f(\theta)$, $v_\theta = v_\zeta = 0$. Establish the differential equation for $f(\theta)$.

3.1. Show that, upon return to the unstarred quantities in (3.2), the boundary layer equations (3.6) and (3.7) assume the form

$$\partial_1 v_1 + \partial_2 v_2 = 0, \quad v_1\partial_1 v_1 + v_2\partial_2 v_1 = (\mu/\rho)\partial_{22}v_1.$$

3.2. Derive the boundary layer equations for the unsteady flow along a plane wall, which performs a rectilinear translation in its plane. Except for the perturbation caused by the moving wall, the fluid is to be at rest. Establish the boundary conditions for a uniformly accelerating wall.

3.3. For an incompressible viscous fluid, the term $-\rho\partial_j v_j$ in (1.6) vanishes, and $c_v = c_p = c$. Adding the resulting equation to the system (2.1), (2.2), discuss the simplifications that can be made in the boundary layer along a heated stationary plane wall, when the Reynolds number tends to infinity while the Prandtl number remains finite.

3.4. The argument that led to the form (3.15) of the stream function in the boundary layer is to be applied to the unabbreviated differential equation for the stream function of an incompressible viscous fluid (see Problem 2.2).

4.1. Express the basic invariants of the cube of a symmetric tensor V_{ij} by those of V_{ij}.

4.2. Consider the steady rectilinear flow of an incompressible almost Newtonian fluid between parallel walls that are at rest, assuming that the viscosity is given by $\mu(1 + \epsilon\mathscr{V}_{(2)})$, where $\epsilon\mathscr{V}_{(2)} \ll 1$. Carry out two steps of the iterative procedure discussed in connection with (4.11).

4.3. Consider the steady rectilinear flow of a non-Newtonian fluid between parallel walls that are at rest. Show that, for this flow, equations (4.14) are compatible.

4.4. Using the constitutive equation (4.12) with constant values of f and g, discuss the steady rectilinear flow between parallel walls at rest.

4.5. Let the functions f and g in the constitutive equation (4.12) be homogeneous of the order $n - 1$ and $n - 2$, respectively. For this type of non-Newtonian liquid, let $v_i(x, t)$ and $T_{ij}(x, t)$ be the velocity and stress fields of a slow steady flow (see Problem 1.4). Show that the velocity field $cv_i(x, t)$ with constant positive c also represents a slow steady flow of this fluid, and that the corresponding stress field is given by $c^n T_{ij}(x, t)$.

CHAPTER VII

Visco-plastic and Perfectly Plastic Materials

1. Constitutive equation. If a nonvanishing shearing stress is transmitted across some surface element at a particle P of a continuum, the stress deviator at P is different from zero. In a Newtonian fluid, shearing stresses thus can only occur where the rate of deformation does not vanish. Consider, for example, the steady laminar flow of a Newtonian fluid in a cylindrical pipe of circular section. According to the momentum theorem (IV, 2.7) the pressure gradient in the direction of flow implies a shearing stress at the interior surface of the pipe. Thus, even an arbitrarily small pressure will cause some flow. This is confirmed by Poiseuille's equation (VI, 2.16) according to which the velocity is proportional to the pressure gradient.

The visco-plastic material considered in this chapter resembles the viscous fluid to some extent, but can sustain states of stress with nonvanishing deviator when in a state of rest. We first describe the mechanical behavior of this material under conditions of simple shear, when all components of the tensors of stress and rate of deformation except $T_{12} = T_{21}$ and $V_{12} = V_{21}$ vanish. As long as the absolute value of the shearing stress T_{12} remains below a certain constant K called *yield stress,* the material is supposed to be rigid, i.e., $V_{12} = 0$. If the absolute value of the shearing stress T_{12} exceeds the yield stress K, the shear rate V_{12} is supposed to have the same sign as T_{12} and an absolute value proportional to $|T_{12}| - K$. With the aid of a viscosity coefficient μ and the function

$$F = 1 - \frac{K}{|T_{12}|}, \tag{1.1}$$

this relation between shearing stress and shear rate can be written in the form

$$2\mu V_{12} = \begin{cases} 0 & \text{for } F < 0, \\ FT_{12} & \text{for } F \geq 0. \end{cases} \tag{1.2}$$

This constitutive equation for simple shear was first used by Bingham † after whom this visco-plastic material is named.

† E. C. Bingham, *Fluidity and Plasticity,* New York, 1922, p. 215.

For arbitrary states of stress, Hohenemser and Prager † generalized Bingham's relation as follows: In simple shear, the second invariant $\mathcal{T}'_{(2)}$ of the stress deviator equals the square of the shearing stress. This suggests the introduction of the *yield function*

$$F = 1 - \frac{K}{\mathcal{T}'^{1/2}_{(2)}} \tag{1.3}$$

which reduces to (1.1) for simple shear. Bingham's relation (1.2) for simple shear can then be regarded as a special case of the constitutive equation

$$2\mu V_{ij} = \begin{cases} 0 & \text{for } F < 0, \\ FT'_{ij} & \text{for } F \geq 0, \end{cases} \tag{1.4}$$

in which T'_{ij} denotes the stress deviator and F is given by (1.3). According to (1.4) the rate of deformation in this visco-plastic material is a deviator, i.e., the material is incompressible. When the yield function is negative, the material behaves in a rigid manner; positive values of the yield function imply finite rates of deformation. The states of stress for which $F = 0$ form the *yield limit* at which visco-plastic flow sets in or ceases, depending on the sense in which the yield limit is crossed.

Equation (1.3) by no means represents the only way of generalizing (1.1). Indeed, since $\mathcal{T}'_{(3)} = 0$ for simple shear the basic invariant $\mathcal{T}'_{(2)}$ in (1.3) could, for instance, be replaced by any function of $\mathcal{T}'_{(2)}$ and $\mathcal{T}'_{(3)}$ that reduces to $\mathcal{T}'_{(2)}$ when $\mathcal{T}'_{(3)} = 0$. If one does not insist on the exclusive use of analytic functions of the stress components, $\mathcal{T}'^{1/2}_{(2)}$ in (1.3) could also be replaced by the maximum shearing stress, i.e. one half of the largest difference between two principal stresses. We shall not pursue these possibilities, since the treatment of practically significant problems encounters considerable mathematical difficulties even if we use the simple constitutive equation (1.4) with the yield function (1.3).

To solve the second equation (1.4) with respect to the stress deviator, we multiply each side of this equation by itself and use (1.3) to obtain the relation

$$4\mu^2 \mathcal{V}_{(2)} = F^2 \mathcal{T}'_{(2)} = (\mathcal{T}'^{1/2}_{(2)} - K)^2, \tag{1.5}$$

in which $\mathcal{V}_{(2)}$ denotes the second basic invariant of the rate of deformation. It follows from (1.3) and (1.5) that

$$F = \frac{\mathcal{T}'^{1/2}_{(2)} - K}{\mathcal{T}'^{1/2}_{(2)}} = \frac{2\mu \mathcal{V}^{1/2}_{(2)}}{K + 2\mu \mathcal{V}^{1/2}_{(2)}}. \tag{1.6}$$

† K. Hohenemser and W. Prager, Zeitschrift f. angew. Math. u. Mech. *12* (1932) 216; see also W. Prager, *Mécanique des solides isotropes au delà du domaine plastique*, Paris, 1937, p. 27 and J. G. Oldroyd, Proc. Cambridge Philos. Soc. *43* (1947) 100.

The second equation (1.4) can therefore be written in the form

$$T'_{ij} = \left(2\mu + \frac{K}{\mathscr{V}^{1/2}_{(2)}}\right) V_{ij}, \tag{1.7}$$

which is of course to apply only if the rate of deformation does not vanish. For $V_{ij} = 0$, that is for rigid behavior of the material, the stress deviator is only subject to the condition $F \leq 0$; thus, $\mathscr{T}'_{(2)} \leq K^2$ when the material behaves in a rigid manner.

By setting $\mu = 0$ in the constitutive equation (1.7), we obtain the constitutive equation

$$T'_{ij} = \frac{K}{\mathscr{V}^{1/2}_{(2)}} V_{ij} \tag{1.8}$$

of the incompressible perfectly plastic material that was first considered by von Mises.† This constitutive equation, too, is only to be valid when the rate of deformation does not vanish. Multiplying each side of (1.8) by itself, we find that the stress deviator must satisfy the *yield condition of von Mises*,

$$\mathscr{T}'_{(2)} = K^2, \tag{1.9}$$

when the rate of deformation is different from zero. Accordingly, the constitutive equation (1.8) is to be supplemented by the requirement that $\mathscr{T}'_{(2)} \leq K^2$ for nonvanishing rate of deformation.

The constitutive equations of the visco-plastic and perfectly plastic materials have the same relation to each other as the constitutive equations of the viscous and perfect fluids. In a visco-plastic material of small viscosity the effects of viscosity are therefore likely to be restricted to boundary layers, just as in a viscous fluid of small viscosity. As will be seen in Section 3, various kinds of boundary layers may occur in a visco-plastic material.

2. Equation of motion. In the absence of body forces, the equation of continuity (IV, 5.1) and the equation of motion (IV, 5.2) assume the following form for an incompressible visco-plastic material with the constitutive equation (1.7):

$$\partial_j v_j = 0, \tag{2.1}$$

$$\rho \partial_0 v_k + \rho v_j \partial_j v_k = -\partial_k p + \mu \partial_{jj} v_k + K \partial_j (V_{jk} / \mathscr{V}^{1/2}_{(2)}). \tag{2.2}$$

The equation of motion (2.2) applies only where the rate of deformation does not vanish; it differs from the Navier-Stokes equation (VI, 2.2) only by the nonlinear, last term on the right-hand side. This term vanishes in a flow field in which the relation

$$V_{ij}(x,t) = \varphi(x,t) W_{ij}(t), \tag{2.3}$$

holds, $\varphi(x,t)$ being a positive scalar, and $W_{ij}(t)$ a symmetric deviator.

† R. von Mises, Göttinger Nachrichten, math. phys. Kl. (1913) 582.

Indeed, it follows from (2.3) that $V_{jk}/\mathscr{V}_{(2)}^{1/2} = W_{jk}/\mathscr{W}_{(2)}^{1/2}$ depends only on the time, so that the last term in (2.2) vanishes. Any motion of a Newtonian fluid, for which (2.3) is valid, thus can also be performed by the visco-plastic material considered here.

Examples of such motions are found among the rectilinear motions considered in Section 2 of Chapter VI. With

$$v_1 = v_2 = 0, \quad v_3 = v(x_1,t), \tag{2.4}$$

all components of the rate of deformation vanish except $v_{13} = v_{31} = \partial_1 v/2$. Accordingly, $\mathscr{V}_{(2)} = (\partial_1 v/2)^2$ and

$$\mathscr{V}_{(2)}^{1/2} = \tfrac{1}{2}|\partial_1 v|. \tag{2.5}$$

As in Section 2 of Chapter VI, it follows from the first and second component of (2.2) that the pressure in the rectilinear flow (2.4) is independent of x_1 and x_2. For $\partial_1 v \neq 0$, the third component of (2.2) reduces to

$$\rho\partial_0 v = -\partial_3 p + \mu\partial_{11} v + K\partial_1(\operatorname{sgn}\partial_1 v), \tag{2.6}$$

where $\operatorname{sgn}\partial_1 v$ has the value 1 for $\partial_1 v > 0$ and the value -1 for $\partial_1 v < 0$. Since v in (2.6) depends only on x_1 and t, and p only on x_3 and t, the pressure gradient $\partial_3 p$ can at most depend on the time.

If $\partial_1 v$ has the same sign throughout the field of flow and for all times, the last term in (2.6) vanishes, and this equation becomes identical with the Navier-Stokes equation for the rectilinear flow (2.4). As an example, consider the rectilinear flow that corresponds to the starting flow in a Couette viscosimeter. For a Newtonian fluid, this flow was briefly discussed in Section 2 of Chapter VI; in it the derivative $\partial_1 v$ is everywhere and at all times negative. The visco-plastic material considered here can flow in the same manner, but the absolute value of shearing stress in this material exceeds that of the corresponding shearing stress in a viscous fluid by K.

As an example of a flow of a visco-plastic material that differs from the corresponding flow of a viscous fluid, consider the steady rectilinear flow between parallel walls that are at rest. Denote the distance between the walls by h and the pressure gradient by c (Figure 21a).

To treat this flow, we write (2.6) in the form $-\partial_3 p + \partial_1 T_{13} = 0$ or $\partial_1 T_{13} = -c$. At $x_1 = h/2$, the shearing stress T_{13} vanishes by symmetry. Accordingly

$$T_{13} = \frac{c}{2}(h - 2x_1). \tag{2.7}$$

Starting from this equation, let us first determine the velocity distribution for a Newtonian fluid. According to (IV, 5.15) the shear rate corresponding to the shearing stress (2.7) is

$$V_{13} = \tfrac{1}{2}\partial_1 v = \frac{T_{13}}{2\mu} = \frac{c}{4\mu}(h - 2x_1). \tag{2.8}$$

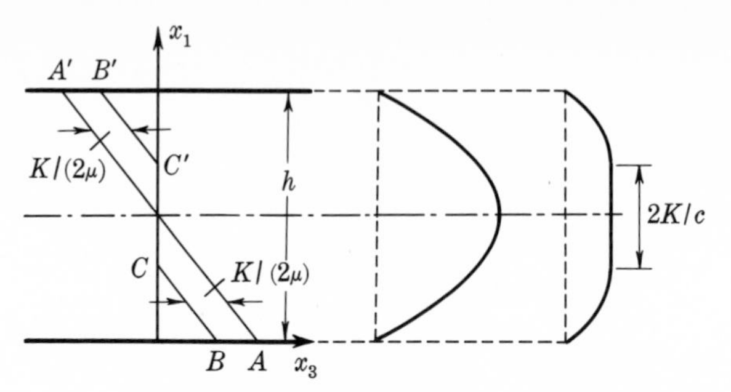

Figure 21a, b, c

In Figure 21a, this distribution of the shear rate over the width h of the channel is represented by the straight line AA'. From (2.8), there follows the differential equation

$$\partial_1 v = \frac{c}{2\mu}(h - 2x_1), \tag{2.9}$$

in which v depends only on x_1. Integration of this differential equation furnishes the velocity distribution,

$$v = \frac{c}{2\mu} x_1(h - x_1), \tag{2.10}$$

where the boundary condition $v(0) = 0$ has already been used. (The other boundary condition $v(h) = 0$ is automatically fulfilled, because the shearing stress (2.7) has been made to satisfy the symmetry condition $T_{13}(h/2) = 0$.) The parabolic velocity distribution (2.10) is shown in Figure 21b. According to (2.10), the average velocity equals

$$v_0 = \frac{ch^2}{12\mu}. \tag{2.11}$$

In the visco-plastic material, a positive shearing stress $T_{13} > K$ produces the shear rate $V_{13} = (T_{13} - K)/(2\mu)$ in accordance with (1.1) and (1.2). In Figure 21a, this distribution of the shear rate is represented by the line $BCC'B'$. For not too large values of x_1, equation (2.7) therefore furnishes

$$\partial_1 v = \frac{c}{2\mu}\left(h - 2x_1 - 2\frac{K}{c}\right) \tag{2.12}$$

This relation ceases to be valid where it furnishes $\partial_1 v = 0$, i.e. at

$$x_1 = \bar{x}_1 = \frac{h}{2} - \frac{K}{c}. \tag{2.13}$$

Integrating (2.12) under the initial condition $v(0) = 0$, we obtain the velocity distribution

$$v = \frac{c}{2\mu}\left\{x_1(h - x_1) - 2\frac{K}{c}x_1\right\} \quad \text{for } 0 \leq x_1 \leq \bar{x}_1. \tag{2.14}$$

As x_1 increases beyond $\bar{x}_1$, the shearing stress (2.7) drops below the yield stress K; the visco-plastic material therefore moves as a rigid body with the velocity

$$\bar{v} = \frac{c}{2\mu}\bar{x}_1^2, \tag{2.15}$$

which follows from (2.14) for $x_1 = \bar{x}_1$. By symmetry, this rigid layer extends only to $x_1 = h - \bar{x}_1$. Figure 21c shows a typical velocity distribution which corresponds to the same coefficient of viscosity and the same pressure gradient as the distribution in Figure 21b. The average velocity for the visco-plastic material is found to be

$$v_0 = \frac{ch^2}{12\mu}\left(1 - \frac{2K}{ch}\right)^2\left(1 + \frac{K}{ch}\right). \tag{2.16}$$

For $K = 0$, (2.16) reduces to (2.11). For $K \neq 0$, the average velocity (2.16) in the visco-plastic material is no longer proportional to the pressure gradient. Equation (2.16) applies only to values of the pressure gradient c, for which the constant of the first parenthesis in (2.16) is positive, i.e. to $c > 2K/h$; for $c < 2K/h$, there is no flow.

3. Boundary layer equations. In this section Oldroyd's † boundary layer equations for visco-plastic flow will be derived. For simplicity, the discussion will be restricted to plane steady flows without body forces. The development will closely follow that used in Section 3 of Chapter VI.

In addition to the Reynolds number

$$Re = \frac{\rho UL}{\mu} \tag{3.1}$$

which is a measure of the relative importance of kinetic energy and viscous dissipation, we now introduce another characteristic number, which compares plastic and viscous dissipation. This has been named after Bingham;‡ it is defined as follows:

$$Bi = \frac{KL}{\mu U}. \tag{3.2}$$

Depending on the relative order of magnitude of these characteristic

† J. G. Oldroyd, Proc. Cambridge Philos. Soc. *43* (1947) 383.

‡ See W. Prager, contribution to *Rheology*, edited by F. R. Eirich, New York, 1956, p. 95.

numbers, various types of boundary layer may arise. To treat these jointly, we introduce the dimensionless independent and dependent variables

$$\left.\begin{aligned} \overset{*}{x}_1 &= \frac{x_1}{L}, \quad \overset{*}{x}_2 = \frac{x_2}{\epsilon L}, \\ \overset{*}{v}_1 &= \frac{v_1}{U}, \quad \overset{*}{v}_2 = \frac{v_2}{\epsilon U}, \quad p^* = \frac{p - p_0}{p_0}. \end{aligned}\right\} \tag{3.3}$$

These dimensionless variables are defined in the same manner as those introduced in Section 3 of Chapter VI except that the powers of the Reynolds number used there are replaced by the reciprocal of a small positive number ϵ. The relation between ϵ and the characteristic numbers *Re* and *Bi* will not be specified at present. The same number ϵ has been used in the definitions of $\overset{*}{x}_2$ and $\overset{*}{v}_2$, because the dimensionless equation of continuity then has the same form as in Section 3 of Chapter VI, namely

$$\overset{*}{\partial}_1 \overset{*}{v}_1 + \overset{*}{\partial}_2 \overset{*}{v}_2 = 0. \tag{3.4}$$

The appropriate choice of the reference pressure p_0 will be discussed later.

Before establishing the dimensionless equations of motion, we express V_{jk} and $\mathscr{V}_{(2)}$ in the dimensionless variables. According to (3.4), we have $\overset{*}{\partial}_2 \overset{*}{v}_2 = -\overset{*}{\partial}_1 \overset{*}{v}_1$. The nonvanishing components of the rate of deformation are therefore given by

$$V_{jk} = \frac{1}{2}\frac{U}{L} \begin{bmatrix} 2\overset{*}{\partial}_1 \overset{*}{v}_1 & \dfrac{1}{\epsilon}\,\overset{*}{\partial}_2 \overset{*}{v}_1 + \epsilon \overset{*}{\partial}_1 \overset{*}{v}_2 \\ \dfrac{1}{\epsilon}\,\overset{*}{\partial}_2 \overset{*}{v}_1 + \epsilon \overset{*}{\partial}_1 \overset{*}{v}_2 & -2\overset{*}{\partial}_1 \overset{*}{v}_1 \end{bmatrix}$$

$$= \frac{1}{2\epsilon}\frac{U}{L}\,\overset{*}{\partial}_2 \overset{*}{v}_1 \begin{bmatrix} 2\epsilon \dfrac{\overset{*}{\partial}_1 \overset{*}{v}_1}{\overset{*}{\partial}_2 \overset{*}{v}_1} & 1 + \epsilon^2 \dfrac{\overset{*}{\partial}_1 \overset{*}{v}_2}{\overset{*}{\partial}_2 \overset{*}{v}_1} \\ 1 + \epsilon^2 \dfrac{\overset{*}{\partial}_1 \overset{*}{v}_2}{\overset{*}{\partial}_2 \overset{*}{v}_1} & -2\epsilon \dfrac{\overset{*}{\partial}_1 \overset{*}{v}_1}{\overset{*}{\partial}_2 \overset{*}{v}_1} \end{bmatrix} \tag{3.5}$$

To within higher order terms in ϵ, we therefore have

$$\mathscr{V}_{(2)} = \tfrac{1}{2} V_{jk} V_{jk}$$

$$= \frac{1}{4\epsilon^2}\frac{U^2}{L^2}\,(\overset{*}{\partial}_2 \overset{*}{v}_1)^2 \left\{ 1 + 4\epsilon^2 \left(\frac{\overset{*}{\partial}_1 \overset{*}{v}_1}{\overset{*}{\partial}_2 \overset{*}{v}_1} \right)^2 + 2\epsilon^2 \frac{\overset{*}{\partial}_1 \overset{*}{v}_2}{\overset{*}{\partial}_2 \overset{*}{v}_1} \right\}, \tag{3.6}$$

$$\frac{1}{\mathscr{V}_{(2)}^{1/2}} = 2\epsilon \frac{L}{U} \frac{1}{|\overset{*}{\partial}_2 \overset{*}{v}_1|} \left\{ 1 - 2\epsilon^2 \left(\frac{\overset{*}{\partial}_1 \overset{*}{v}_1}{\overset{*}{\partial}_2 \overset{*}{v}_1} \right)^2 - \epsilon^2 \frac{\overset{*}{\partial}_1 \overset{*}{v}_2}{\overset{*}{\partial}_2 \overset{*}{v}_1} \right\}, \tag{3.7}$$

and

$$\frac{V_{jk}}{\mathcal{V}_{(2)}^{1/2}} = \begin{bmatrix} 2\epsilon \dfrac{\partial_1^* v_1^*}{\partial_2^* v_1^*} & 1 - 2\epsilon^2 \left(\dfrac{\partial_1^* v_1^*}{\partial_2^* v_1^*}\right) \\ 1 - 2\epsilon^2 \left(\dfrac{\partial_1^* v_1^*}{\partial_2^* v_1^*}\right)^2 & -2\epsilon \dfrac{\partial_1^* v_1^*}{\partial_2^* v_1^*} \end{bmatrix} \operatorname{sgn} \partial_2^* v_1^*. \tag{3.8}$$

We are now ready to establish the dimensionless equations of motion for plane steady flow. If we assume $\partial_2^* v_1^*$ to be positive throughout the boundary layer and neglect higher order terms in ϵ, we obtain the following equations from (2.2):

$$\epsilon^2 Re(v_1^* \partial_1 v_1^* + v_2^* \partial_2^* v_1^*) = -\epsilon^2 \frac{p_0 L}{\mu U} \partial_1^* p^* + \partial_{22}^* v_1^*$$
$$+ 2\epsilon^3 Bi \left[\partial_1^* \left(\frac{\partial_1^* v_1^*}{\partial_2^* v_1^*}\right) - \partial_2^* \left(\frac{\partial_1^* v_1^*}{\partial_2^* v_1^*}\right)^2 \right], \tag{3.9}$$

$$0 = -\epsilon^2 \frac{p_0 L}{\mu U} \partial_2^* p^* + \epsilon^2 \partial_{22}^* v_2^* - 2\epsilon^3 Bi\, \partial_2^* \left(\frac{\partial_1^* v_1^*}{\partial_2^* v_1^*}\right). \tag{3.10}$$

In these equations, all inertia effects are represented by the left side of (3.9), and the viscous effects by the second terms of the right sides. The first terms on the right sides represent pressure effects, and the last terms plastic effects. The equations are written in such a manner that the pressure terms have identical coefficients.

As ϵ tends to zero, these equations will contain terms other than the viscous term in (3.9) only if Re and Bi grow indefinitely. We shall discuss two assumptions concerning the relative order of magnitude of these characteristic numbers; in each case, we shall choose the reference pressure p_0 in such a way that the pressure terms remain in the equations.

(i) If $Bi \ll Re^{3/2}$, the plastic terms may be neglected. The small quantity ϵ must then be identified with $Re^{-1/2}$, and the reference pressure must be chosen as $p_0 = \rho U^2$, so that the common coefficient of the pressure terms becomes $\epsilon^2 Re = 1$. The resulting equations of the *viscous boundary layer* have been discussed in Section 3 of Chapter VI. The associated free flow is governed by the equations that are obtained from (2.2) by restricting the discussion to plane steady flow and dropping the viscous and the plastic terms. These are, of course, the equations for the plane steady flow of a perfect fluid.

(ii) If $Re \ll Bi^{2/3}$, the inertia term in (3.9) may be neglected. The small quantity ϵ must then be identified with $Bi^{-1/3}$, and the reference pressure must be chosen as ϵK, so that the common coefficient of the pressure terms becomes $\epsilon^3 Bi = 1$. At first sight, the appearance of ϵ in the reference pressure may be surprising. As a matter of fact, the stipulateds of order magnitude of Bi and Re require not only a very small viscosity μ but also a very large yield stress K. As a consequence of this, the pressure differences observed in the flow are more likely to have the order of magnitude of ϵK than that of K. If the resulting equations of the *plastic boundary layer* are written in the original unstarred variables, they have the following form, if $\partial_2 v_1 > 0$:

$$\partial_1 p = \mu \partial_{22} v_1 + 2K \left[\partial_1 \left(\frac{\partial_1 v_1}{\partial_2 v_1} \right) - \partial_2 \left(\frac{\partial_1 v_1}{\partial_2 v_1} \right)^2 \right], \tag{3.11}$$

$$\partial_2 p = -2K \partial_2 \left(\frac{\partial_1 v_1}{\partial_2 v_2} \right). \tag{3.12}$$

The associated free flow is governed by the equations that are obtained from (2.2) by the restriction to plane steady flow and the neglect of inertia and viscosity terms. These equations are represented by

$$\partial_{\underline{k}} p = K \partial_{\underline{j}} \left(\frac{V_{\underline{jk}}}{\mathcal{V}_{(2)}^{1/2}} \right), \tag{3.13}$$

where the underlined subscripts have the range 1, 2.

If the considered plane steady flow is rectilinear and parallel to the x_1-direction, the equation of continuity furnishes $\partial_1 v_1 = 0$. As is readily seen, the boundary layer equations (3.11) and (3.12) are then identical with the rigorous equations of motion. In the flow shown in Figure 21c, the layers between the rigid central layer and the plate can therefore be regarded as boundary layers. Referring the reader to Oldroyd's paper for other examples of plastic boundary layers, we turn to the discussion of (3.13) for the free flow.

4. Plane plastic flow. Equation (3.13) was obtained by dropping the inertia and viscosity terms from the equations for the plane steady flow of a visco-plastic material. Equation (3.13) therefore describes plane quasi-static flows of perfectly plastic materials. Since body forces are not taken into account, (3.13) does indeed follow from the equation of equilibrium (II, 2.7), when the stress tensor is written as

$$T_{ij} = -p\delta_{ij} + K \frac{V_{ij}}{\mathcal{V}_{(2)}^{1/2}} \tag{4.1}$$

in accordance with (1.8). For the plane flow considered here, the mean pressure p is independent of x_3 and the matrix of the rate of deformation has the form

$$V_{ij} = \begin{bmatrix} \alpha & \beta & 0 \\ \beta & -\alpha & 0 \\ 0 & 0 & 0 \end{bmatrix}, \tag{4.2}$$

which reflects the incompressibility of the material. The quantities α and β are subject to the equation of compatibility

$$-\partial_{11}\alpha + \partial_{22}\alpha - 2\partial_{12}\beta = 0, \tag{4.3}$$

which follows from (III, 3.19).

Substitution of (4.2) into (4.1) yields

$$T_{ij} = \begin{bmatrix} -p + \dfrac{K\alpha}{(\alpha^2+\beta^2)^{1/2}} & \dfrac{K\beta}{(\alpha^2+\beta^2)^{1/2}} & 0 \\ \dfrac{K\beta}{(\alpha^2+\beta^2)^{1/2}} & -p - \dfrac{K\alpha}{(\alpha^2+\beta^2)^{1/2}} & 0 \\ 0 & 0 & -p \end{bmatrix}. \tag{4.4}$$

With

$$\frac{\alpha}{(\alpha^2+\beta^2)^{1/2}} = \sin 2\theta, \quad \frac{\beta}{(\alpha^2+\beta^2)^{1/2}} = -\cos 2\theta, \tag{4.5}$$

the stress tensor (4.4) can be written as follows

$$T_{ij} = \begin{bmatrix} -p + K\sin 2\theta & -K\cos 2\theta & 0 \\ -K\cos 2\theta & -p - K\sin 2\theta & 0 \\ 0 & 0 & -p \end{bmatrix}. \tag{4.6}$$

To discover the mechanical significance of the angle θ, consider Mohr's circle for surface elements that are parallel to the x_3-axis and pass through the typical point P of the x_1, x_2-plane. Three elements of this kind are indicated in Figure 22a: the element PX_1, the normal of which has the x_1-direction, and the elements PA_{I} and PA_{II}, for which the shearing stress T_S is respectively larger and smaller than for any other element through P.

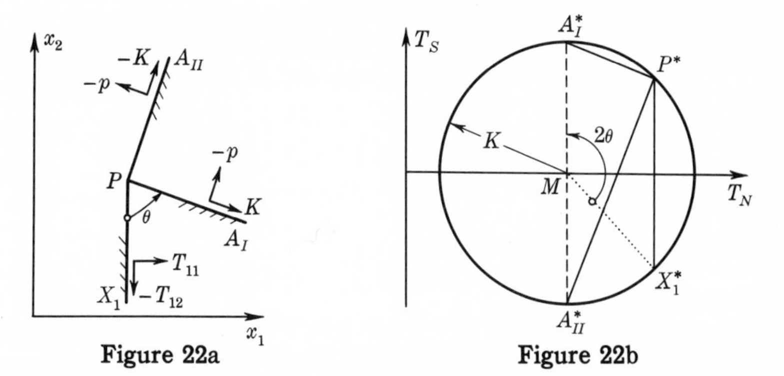

Figure 22a **Figure 22b**

The traces of the last two elements in the x_1, x_2-plane respectively define the first and second *shear direction* at P. A line that has the first shear direction at each of its points is called a first *shear line*, and the second shear lines are defined in an analogous manner. If positive directions have to be defined on the shear lines through P, this will be done so that the positive first and second shear directions are related to each other in the same manner as the positive x_1- and x_2-directions, respectively. In Figure 22a, let PA_{I} be the positive first shear direction and PA_{II} the positive second shear direction, and denote the angle X_1PA_{I} by θ.

According to (4.6) the Mohr circle for the point P has the center M with the coordinates $-p$, 0 and the radius K. In Figure 22b, let P^* be the pole of this circle, and X_1^*, A_{I}^*, and A_{II}^* the stress points for the three surface elements indicated in the figure. Since $P^*X_1^*$ is parallel to PX_1, and $P^*A_{\text{I}}^*$ is parallel to PA_{I}, the central angle of the arc $X_1^*P^*A_{\text{I}}^*$ has the value 2θ. The coordinates of X_1^* are therefore given by

$$T_N = T_{11} = -p + K \sin 2\theta, \quad T_S = -T_{12} = K \cos 2\theta. \tag{4.7}$$

Since these formulas agree with (4.6), the angle θ introduced in (4.5) may be interpreted as the angle between the negative x_2-direction and the positive first shear direction.

As is indicated by the ordinates of A_{I}^* and A_{II}^* in Figure 22b, the shearing stress T_S has the value K along a first shear line and the value $-K$ along a second shear line. The direction of the shearing stress transmitted along a first shear line is therefore obtained from the direction of the positive normal by a counterclockwise rotation of 90°. For the second shear lines, however, the transition from the direction of the positive normal to that of the shearing stress involves a clockwise rotation of 90°.

Substitution of the stress components (4.6) into the equations of equilibrium (II, 2.7) furnishes

$$\left.\begin{aligned} -\partial_1 p + 2K(\partial_1\theta \cos 2\theta + \partial_2\theta \sin 2\theta) &= 0, \\ -\partial_2 p + 2K(\partial_1\theta \sin 2\theta - \partial_2\theta \cos 2\theta) &= 0. \end{aligned}\right\} \tag{4.8}$$

To obtain a particular solution of these partial differential equations for the functions of position p and θ, assume that $\theta = \theta(x_2)$. Equations (4.8) then reduce to

$$\left.\begin{aligned} -\partial_1 p - K\partial_2(\cos 2\theta) &= 0, \\ -\partial_2 p - K\partial_1(\sin 2\theta) &= 0, \end{aligned}\right\} \tag{4.9}$$

and the elimination of p yields

$$\partial_{22}(\cos 2\theta) = 0. \tag{4.10}$$

We propose to discuss the particular solution corresponding to

$$\cos 2\theta = \frac{x_2}{h}, \quad \sin 2\theta = \left(1 - \frac{x_2^2}{h^2}\right)^{1/2}, \tag{4.11}$$

where h is a constant. The first equation (4.9) then furnishes

$$p = -K\frac{x_1}{h} + f(x_2), \tag{4.12}$$

while the second equation (4.9) gives

$$p = -K\left(1 - \frac{x_2^2}{h^2}\right)^{1/2} + g(x_1); \tag{4.13}$$

in these expressions for the pressure, f and g are arbitrary, continuous differentiable functions of x_2 and x_1, respectively. It follows from (4.12) and (4.13) that

$$p = p_0 - K\frac{x_1}{h} - K\left(1 - \frac{x_2^2}{h^2}\right)^{1/2}, \tag{4.14}$$

where p_0 is a constant. The nonvanishing stress components can now be obtained from (4.6); thus

$$\left.\begin{aligned} T_{11} &= -p_0 + K\left[\frac{x_1}{h} + 2\left(1 - \frac{x_2^2}{h^2}\right)^{1/2}\right], \\ T_{22} &= -p_0 + K\frac{x_1}{h}, \\ T_{12} &= -K\frac{x_2}{h}, \\ T_{33} &= -p_0 + K\left[\frac{x_1}{h} + \left(1 - \frac{x_2^2}{h^2}\right)^{1/2}\right]. \end{aligned}\right\} \tag{4.15}$$

To obtain a velocity field, that is compatible with this stress field, we set

$$\alpha = \left(1 - \frac{x_2^2}{h^2}\right)^{1/2}(\alpha^2 + \beta^2)^{1/2}, \quad \beta = -\frac{x_2}{h}(\alpha^2 + \beta^2)^{1/2} \tag{4.16}$$

in accordance with (4.5) and (4.11). Substituting these expressions for α and β into the equation of compatibility (4.3), we obtain a partial differential equation for $(\alpha^2 + \beta^2)^{1/2}$, which is, for example, satisfied by

$$(\alpha^2 + \beta^2)^{1/2} = \frac{c}{h}\left(1 - \frac{x_2^2}{h^2}\right)^{-1/2} \tag{4.17}$$

where c is a constant. A velocity field that corresponds to the relation (4.17) is found as follows. According to (4.2) and (III, 1.11), we have

$$\alpha = \partial_1 v_1 = -\partial_2 v_2, \quad \beta = \tfrac{1}{2}(\partial_1 v_2 + \partial_2 v_1). \tag{4.18}$$

Equations (4.16) and (4.17), on the other hand, yield

$$\alpha = \frac{c}{h}, \quad \beta = -\frac{cx_2}{h^2\left(1 - \frac{x_2^2}{h^2}\right)^{1/2}}. \tag{4.19}$$

Comparison of (4.18) and (4.19) furnishes differential equations for the velocity components. As is readily seen, the relations

$$v_1 = c\left[\frac{x_1}{h} + 2\left(1 - \frac{x_2^2}{h^2}\right)^{1/2}\right], \quad v_2 = -c\frac{x_2}{h} \tag{4.20}$$

constitute a particular solution of these differential equations.

On account of the square root in (4.15) and (4.20), the stress and velocity fields are restricted to the strip $-h \leq x \leq h$. On the boundaries $x_2 = -h$ and $x_2 = h$ of this strip, we have $T_{12} = K$, $v_2 = c$ and $T_{12} = -K$, $v_2 = -c$, respectively. The solution obtained above therefore represents the pressing of an infinite plastic layer of the thickness $2h$ between parallel rough rigid plates, provided that a plane state of flow is enforced by appropriate measures.† The shear line net associated with this solution can

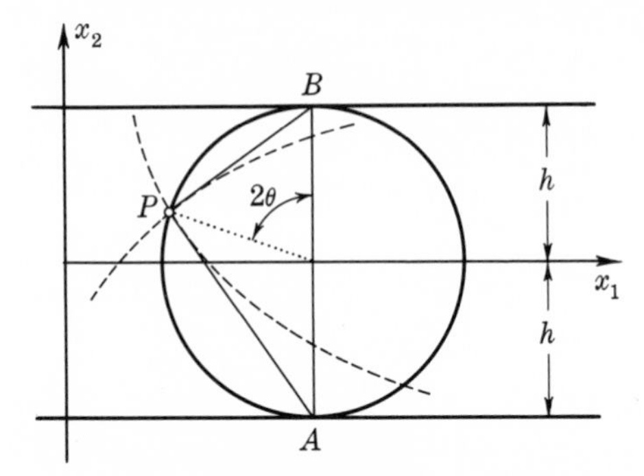

Figure 23

be determined as follows. In Figure 23, let P be a typical point of the stress field and x_2 its ordinate, which lies in the interval $(-h, h)$. Through P, draw the circle with the radius h, the center of which lies on the x_1-axis and has an abscissa that is not smaller than that of P. The line joining this center to P then forms the angle 2θ given by (4.11) with the positive x_2-direction. The line joining P to the lowest point of the circle therefore indicates the first shear direction at P. When the circle rolls on the line $x_2 = h$, the point P describes a cycloid, whose normal at P passes through the instantaneous center of rotation, i.e. the highest point of the circle. The tangent of this cycloid in P therefore has the first shear direction.

† L. Prandtl, Zeitschrift f. angew. Math. u. Mech. *3* (1923) 401.

Since this statement is valid for any position of the point P, the considered cycloid is a first shear line, and the other first shear lines are obtained from it by translation in the x_1-direction. Similarly, the cycloid described by P, when the considered shear line rolls on the line $x_2 = -h$, is a second shear line, and the other second shear lines are obtained from it by translation in the x_1-direction.

With $x_2 \to h$, the shear rate β in (4.19) grows indefinitely. An infinite shear rate is not in contradiction to the concept of the perfectly plastic material; in a visco-plastic material, however, such a shear rate would require infinite shearing stresses for any finite value of the viscosity coefficient μ. In our problem, the viscosity effects thus cannot be neglected in the neighborhood of the compressing plates, and the velocity field obtained above only represents the free flow outside a boundary layer, the investigation of which would however be beyond the scope of this book.

To conclude this chapter, we shall establish an important geometric property of the shear line nets in plane plastic flows (*Hencky-Prandtl nets* †). If the angle θ has the value $\pi/2$ at the considered point P, the operators ∂_1 and ∂_2 indicate differentiation in the first and the second shear line direction, respectively. Equations (4.8) then reduce to

$$\partial_1(p + 2K\theta) = 0, \quad \partial_2(p - 2K\theta) = 0. \tag{4.21}$$

As is shown by (4.21), the sum $p + 2K\theta$ remains constant along a first shear line, and the difference $p - 2K\theta$, along a second shear line. From this theorem, which is due to Hencky, the following geometric property of the shear lines can be derived. In Figure 24, let AB and CD be first

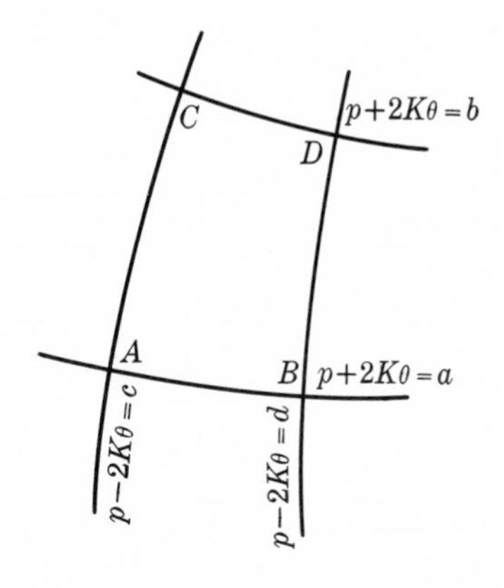

Figure 24

† H. Hencky, Zeitschrift f. angew. Math. u. Mech. *3* (1923) 241; L. Prandtl, *ibid.* 401. Results that contain those of Hencky and Prandtl as special cases are already found in J. Massau's classical work on soil mechanics (*Mémoire sur l'intégration graphique des équations aux dérivées partielles*, republished as Edition du Centenaire, Brussels, 1952).

shear line arcs on which the sum $p + 2K\theta$ has the constant values a and b, respectively. Similarly, let AC and BD be second shear line arcs with the constant values c and d of the difference $p - 2K\theta$. At A, we therefore have $p + 2K\theta = a$ and $p - 2K\theta = c$; it follows by subtraction that the angle θ at the point P has the value

$$\theta_A = \frac{a - c}{4K}. \tag{4.22}$$

One finds in a similar manner that

$$\theta_B = \frac{a - d}{4K}, \quad \theta_C = \frac{b - c}{4K}, \quad \theta_D = \frac{b - d}{4K}. \tag{4.23}$$

As is seen from (4.22) and (4.23),

$$\theta_C - \theta_A = \theta_D - \theta_B, \tag{4.24}$$

i.e. *the angle formed by the tangents of two first shear lines* (AB and CD) *in their points of intersection* (A and C or B and D) *with a second shear line* (AC or BD) *is independent of the choice of this shear line.* Since (4.24) can also be written in the form

$$\theta_D - \theta_C = \theta_B - \theta_A, \tag{4.25}$$

the words "first" and "second" may be interchanged in this statement. An important special case results when the shear line segment AC is rectilinear. It then follows that the shear line segment BD must also be rectilinear. A rectilinear shear line segment thus cannot occur singly: if one shear line has a rectilinear segment, the neighboring shear lines must also possess rectilinear segments.

Since the angle θ is constant along a straight shear line, (4.21) and (4.6) show that the pressure p and the state of stress are also constant along this line. A region in which the shear lines of both families are straight is therefore a region of constant stress.

PROBLEMS

1.1. Show that the typical component T'_{ij} of the stress deviator in the constitutive equation (1.7) is the derivative of the function $\Phi = 2(\mu\mathscr{V}_{(2)} + K\mathscr{V}^{1/2}_{(2)})$ with respect to the corresponding component V_{ij} of the rate of deformation, provided that the symmetric components V_{ij} and V_{ji} are formally treated as independent variables and the condition of incompressibility $V_{kk} = 0$ is only taken into account after the differentiation has been performed.

1.2. Let the stress deviator in a compressible viscous fluid be a linear combination of the deviators of the rate of deformation V and its square V^2, with coefficients that depend on the basic invariants of V. Show that the relation $T'_{ij} = \partial\Phi/\partial V_{ij}$ furnishes a constitutive equation of this kind, provided that Φ is a function of $\mathscr{V}_{(2)} + \frac{1}{3}\mathscr{V}^2_{(1)}$ and $\mathscr{V}_{(3)} + \frac{1}{3}\mathscr{V}_{(2)}\mathscr{V}_{(1)} + \frac{2}{27}\mathscr{V}^3_{(1)}$, and that the symmetric components V_{ij} and V_{ji} are formally treated as independent variables.

1.3. Assume that the fluid discussed in Problem 1.2 is incompressible. Show that Φ can then be written as a function of $\mathscr{V}_{(2)}$ and $\mathscr{V}_{(3)} + \frac{1}{3}\mathscr{V}_{(2)}\mathscr{V}_{(1)}$, provided that the condition of incompressibility, $\mathscr{V}_{(1)} = 0$, is only taken into account after the derivative $\partial\Phi/\partial V_{ij}$ has been formed.

1.4. The function Φ in Problem 1.1 is the sum of $\Phi_1 = 2\mu\mathscr{V}_{(2)}$ and $\Phi_2 = 2K\mathscr{V}^{1/2}_{(2)}$. These functions represent viscous and plastic behavior, respectively; Φ_1 is homogeneous of the second order in the components of V_{ij}, while Φ_2 is homogeneous of the first order in these components. Generalize these relations for an incompressible material by setting

$$\Phi_1 = 2\mu\left[\mathscr{V}_{(2)} + \frac{\alpha}{\mathscr{V}^2_{(2)}}\left(\mathscr{V}_{(3)} + \tfrac{1}{3}\mathscr{V}_{(2)}\mathscr{V}_{(1)}\right)^2\right],$$

$$\Phi_2 = 2K\left[\mathscr{V}^{1/2}_{(2)} + \frac{\beta}{\mathscr{V}_{(2)}}\left(\mathscr{V}_{(3)} + \tfrac{1}{3}\mathscr{V}_{(2)}\mathscr{V}_{(1)}\right)\right],$$

where α and β are constants. Determine the viscous and plastic stress deviators for the combined extension and shear specified by

$$V_{ij} = \begin{bmatrix} \epsilon & \gamma/2 & 0 \\ \gamma/2 & -\epsilon/2 & 0 \\ 0 & 0 & -\epsilon/2 \end{bmatrix}.$$

1.5. Show that for the material considered in Problem 1.4 the power of the stresses on the rate of deformation equals $2\Phi_1 + \Phi_2$.

1.6. Consider a uniform stress field in the perfectly plastic material with the constitutive equation (1.8). Letting the coordinate axes coincide with the principal axes of stress, investigate to what extent the principal components T'_{I}, T'_{II}, T'_{III} of the stress deviator determine the velocity field $v_i(x)$.

2.1. Discuss the rectilinear flow of the visco-plastic material characterized by (1.7) in a cylindrical pipe of circular cross section.

2.2. The space between coaxial cylinders of the radii a and $b > a$ is filled with a visco-plastic material characterized by (1.7). The exterior cylinder is at rest, while the interior cylinder has the constant axial velocity U and the pressure gradient vanishes. Determine the axial velocity v as a function of the distance r from the common axis of the cylinders.

3.1. For the flow indicated in Figure 21c, form the Bingham number Bi with h as the characteristic length and the average velocity v_0 as the characteristic velocity, and establish the relation between Bi and the dimensionless pressure gradient $c\,h/K$.

3.2. Prove that for the steady rectilinear flow $v_1 = v_1(x_2)$, $v_2 = v_3 = 0$ the boundary layer equations (3.11, 3.12) coincide with the unabbreviated equations of motion (2.2).

4.1. Show that in the plane quasi-static flow of a perfectly plastic material the rectangular Cartesian velocity components satisfy the equations

$$\partial_1 v_1 + \partial_2 v_2 = 0,$$

$$(\partial_1 v_1 - \partial_2 v_2) \cos 2\theta + (\partial_1 v_2 + \partial_2 v_1) \sin 2\theta = 0,$$

where θ is the angle introduced in (4.5).

4.2. The velocity components v_1, v_2 in the coordinate directions (see Problem 4.1) and the components $v_{\rm I}$, $v_{\rm II}$ in the shear directions are related by $v_1 = v_{\rm I} \sin\theta + v_{\rm II} \cos\theta$ and $v_2 = -v_{\rm I} \cos\theta + v_{\rm II} \sin\theta$. Prove that $\partial_{\rm I} v_{\rm I} - v_{\rm II} \partial_{\rm I} \theta = 0$ and $\partial_{\rm II} v_{\rm II} + v_{\rm I} \partial_{\rm II} \theta = 0$, where the operators $\partial_{\rm I}$ and $\partial_{\rm II}$ indicate differentiation in the first and second shear directions, respectively.

4.3. Show that the coordinate lines of a system of plane polar coordinates ρ, φ form a Hencky-Prandtl net. Assuming that the radii $\varphi = $ constant are the first shear lines, determine the most general velocity field v_ρ, v_φ in the ring sector $\rho_0 \leq \rho \leq \rho_1$, $0 \leq \varphi \leq \varphi_1$. Formulate boundary conditions on $\rho = \rho_0$ and $\varphi = 0$ that lead to a unique velocity field.

4.4. With reference to Problem 4.3, determine the most general stress field in the ring sector $\rho_0 \leq \rho \leq \rho_1$, $0 \leq \varphi \leq \varphi_1$.

4.5. Consider a thick-walled circular tube that is in a state of plane plastic flow under the action of a uniform exterior pressure p. Determine p as a function of the interior radius ρ_1, the exterior radius ρ_2, and the yield stress K. Discuss the instantaneous velocity field under the assumption that the radial velocity at the exterior surface of the tube has the constant value U.

4.6. Referring plane plastic flow to polar coordinates ρ, θ in the plane of flow, express the stresses $T_{\rho\rho}$, $T_{\theta\theta}$, and $T_{\rho\theta}$ in terms of the mean pressure p and the angle φ between the first shear direction at a typical point and the radius vector of this point. Establish the equations of equilibrium corresponding to (4.8).

4.7. Discuss the solutions of the equations established in Problem 4.6 for which φ depends only on θ.

4.8. With reference to Problem 4.7, determine the velocity field for the pressing of a plastic mass between rough rigid plates that form a small angle with each other. (Hint: As in the velocity field discussed in connection with Figure 23, the shear rate at the plates becomes infinite, i.e. the shear lines meet the plates tangentially or normally.)

4.9. Considering plane plastic flow, let the pressure p and the shear line angle θ be given along an arc c in the plane of flow. Assuming that this arc is nowhere tangential to a shear line, show how the fields $p(x)$ and $\theta(x)$ in the neighborhood of this arc can be constructed by an approximate graphical method based on the theorem stated in connection with (4.21).

CHAPTER VIII

Hypoelastic Materials; Classical Theory of Elasticity

1. Stress rate. The constitutive equations discussed in Chapters VI and VII relate the stress tensor to the tensor of the rate of deformation. To obtain constitutive equations of a more general type, we introduce a third tensor, which represents the *rate of stress.*

When the velocity field $v_i(x, t)$ and the stress field $T_{jk}(x, t)$ are given, the expression

$$T^{\cdot}_{jk} = v_i \partial_i T_{jk} + \partial_0 T_{jk}, \tag{1.1}$$

which has the form (III, 4.8), represents the material rate of change of the stress components with respect to a *fixed* coordinate system. The first term on the right side of (1.1) gives the *convective* part of this rate of change, and the second term, the *local* part.

As is shown by the following discussion, the tensor (1.1) cannot be used to represent the stress rate in constitutive equations. Consider, for instance, a prismatic rod in which a state of uniform axial stress is maintained by axial forces that are applied to the ends. When the rod and the forces acting on it undergo a rigid-body rotation with respect to the fixed coordinate system, the stress components with respect to this system change though, judged from the point of view of the moving material, the state of stress has remained constant. A stress-rate tensor that can be used in constitutive equations must of course be defined in such a manner that it vanishes in these circumstances; in addition to the convective and local terms in (1.1), its definition must therefore contain a *rotary* term. This term compensates for the fact that the stress components with respect to a fixed coordinate system x_i change, even when there is no change in the stress components with respect to a coordinate system x'_j that participates in the instantaneous rotation of the neighborhood of the considered particle.

Since we propose to study only this rotary term, we may disregard the translation of the typical particle P, and choose P as the common origin of the coordinate systems x_i and x'_j. At the typical instant t, these systems are coincident; the first is fixed, the second participates in the rotation of the neighborhood of P.

The infinitesimal coordinates dx'_j of a neighboring particle Q are not influenced by this rotation, whereas the coordinates dx_i of this particle change at the rate $dv_i = \epsilon_{ikj} w_k \, dx'_j = -\epsilon_{ijk} w_k \, dx'_j$, where w_k is the instantaneous vorticity vector at the particle P (see III, 1.8). At the instant $t + dt$, we therefore have

$$dx_i = dx'_i - \epsilon_{ijk} w_k \, dt \, dx'_j = (\delta_{ij} - \epsilon_{ijk} w_k \, dt) \, dx'_j. \tag{1.2}$$

Comparing (1.2) with (I, 2.8), we obtain the coefficients of the transformation $dx_i = c_{ij} \, dx'_j$ by which we can pass from the moving coordinates x'_j at the instant $t + dt$ to the fixed coordinates x_i; with the use of (III, 1.7), we find

$$c_{ij} = \delta_{ij} - \epsilon_{ijk} w_k \, dt = \delta_{ij} - \partial_{[i} v_{j]} \, dt. \tag{1.3}$$

To define the stress rate in a manner suitable for use in constitutive equations, we must compare the unprimed stress components at the particle P and the time t with the primed components at the time $t + dt$. Now, the unprimed stress components at the particle P and the time $t + dt$ are

$$T_{ij} + T^{\bullet}_{ij} \, dt, \tag{1.4}$$

where T_{ij} and $T^{\bullet}_{ij}$ are to be taken at the particle P and the time t. According to (I, 4.4) and (1.3), the primed components of the tensor (1.4) are

$$\begin{aligned} T'_{ij} &= c_{pi} c_{qj} (T_{pq} + T^{\bullet}_{pq} \, dt) \\ &= (\delta_{pi} - \partial_{[p} v_{i]} \, dt)(\delta_{qj} - \partial_{[q} v_{j]} \, dt)(T_{pq} + T^{\bullet}_{pq} \, dt). \end{aligned} \tag{1.5}$$

To within higher-order terms in dt, we therefore have

$$T'_{ij} = T_{ij} + \{ T^{\bullet}_{ij} - T_{iq} \partial_{[q} v_{j]} - T_{pj} \partial_{[p} v_{i]} \} \, dt, \tag{1.6}$$

where the left side is a typical primed component of the stress tensor at P and the time $t + dt$, whereas the first term on the right is the corresponding unprimed component at the time t. The contents of the brace in (1.6) therefore represent a suitable definition of the *stress* rate T^{∇}_{ij}. In view of the symmetry of the stress tensor, this definition can also be written in the form

$$T^{\nabla}_{ij} = T^{\bullet}_{ij} - T_{ip} \partial_{[p} v_{j]} - T_{jp} \partial_{[p} v_{i]}. \tag{1.7}$$

The definition (1.7) of the stress rate is due to Jaumann.† In the recent literature different definitions of the stress rate are frequently used. For

† G. Jaumann, Sitzungsberichte Akad. Wiss. Wien (IIa) *120* (1911) 385. This paper does not seem to be well known; the definition (1.7) has repeatedly been rederived (see, for instance, H. Fromm, Ingenieur-Archiv *4* (1933) 452; S. Zaremba, Mémorial des Sciences Mathématiques, No. 82, Paris, 1937; T. Y. Thomas, Journal Rat. Mech. Analysis *4* (1955); W. Noll, *ibid.* *4* (1955) 3; R. Hill, Journal Mech. Phys. Solids *7* (1959) 209.

example, Truesdell † uses the expression

$$T^{\bullet}_{ij} + T_{ij}\partial_p v_p - T_{ip}\partial_p v_j - T_{jp}\partial_p v_i \tag{1.8}$$

instead of the right side of (1.7), and Green ‡ the expression obtained from (1.8) by deletion of the second term; Cotter and Rivlin § also omit this term and change the signs of the last two terms while replacing each factor in these terms by its transpose. If the neighborhood of the considered particle moves as a rigid body, $\partial_i v_i$ and $\partial(_i v_j)$ vanish; the expressions of Truesdell, Green, and Cotter and Rivlin, then reduce to that of Jaumann.

The difference between Truesdell's expression (1.8) and the right side of (1.7) can be written as

$$T_{ij}V_{pp} - T_{ip}V_{pj} - T_{jp}V_{pi}, \tag{1.9}$$

where V_{ij} is the rate of deformation. As Oldroyd ‖ has observed, the difference between two acceptable definitions of the stress rate thus consists of terms that could anyhow appear in a constitutive equation that expresses the stress rate as a function of the stress and the rate of deformation. In a constitutive equation of this kind, the difference between the various definitions of the stress rate is not essential.

In the following, Jaumann's definition of the stress rate will be used exclusively, because it follows immediately from the stipulation that in a mechanically meaningful definition of the stress rate the stress components should be referred to a coordinate system that participates in the instantaneous rotation of the material. In addition to the rotary terms appearing in Jaumann's definition, the other definitions of the stress rate contain terms that would best be displayed explicitly in the constitutive equation.

The following remark indicates another advantage of Jaumann's definition. Let A_{pq} and B_{pq} be tensors that are defined at the typical particle P, and A^{∇}_{pq} and B^{∇}_{pq} their rates of change judged from the point of view of the moving material. It seems reasonable to stipulate that these rates of change should be defined in such a way that

$$(A_{pq}B_{pq})^{\bullet} = A^{\bullet}_{pq}B_{pq} + A_{pq}B^{\bullet}_{pq} = A^{\nabla}_{pq}B_{pq} + A_{pq}B^{\nabla}_{pq}. \tag{1.10}$$

As is readily verified, this condition is fulfilled by Jaumann's definition but not by the other definitions discussed above.¶

2. Hypoelastic materials. In this chapter and in Chapter X, three kinds of constitutive equation will be considered, which more or less correspond

† C. Truesdell, Journal Rat. Mech. Analysis *2* (1953) 604, Eq. (55b2).
‡ A. E. Green, Proc. Roy. Soc. (A) *234* (1956) 46.
§ B. A. Cotter and R. S. Rivlin, Quarterly Appl. Math. *13* (1955) 177.
‖ J. G. Oldroyd, Proc. Roy. Soc. (A) *200* (1950) 523.
¶ For further comments on the concept of stress rate see L. I. Sedov, Prikl. Mat. Mekh. *24* (1960) 393.

to the behavior that is commonly associated with the word "elastic." In the interest of a clear presentation of the mechanical relations, the discussion will be restricted to *isothermal* deformations.

For a material to qualify as elastic in any sense, it should satisfy the following minimal requirement: at a given state of stress, the components of the stress rate are homogeneous linear functions of the components of the rate of deformation; thus,

$$T^{\nabla}_{ij} = C_{ijkl}V_{kl}, \tag{2.1}$$

where the tensor C_{ijkl} depends, as a rule, on the stress tensor. A constitutive equation of this form was first discussed by Jaumann.† Truesdell ‡ has proposed the term "hypoelastic" for the materials characterized by (2.1). As will be seen in Section 3 and Sections 1 and 2 of Chapter X, the definition of hypoelastic behavior, which may at first seem farfetched, contains the usual definitions of elastic behavior for infinitesimal and finite deformations as special cases.

Let T_{ij} denote the instantaneous state of stress at the typical particle of a hypoelastic material, and assume that during the time element dt the neighborhood of P undergoes the rotation and deformation given by the infinitesimal displacements $du_i(x)$. If $v_i(x)$ is the corresponding velocity field, we have $du_i = v_i\,dt$. On account of (III, 1.11) and (1.7), the constitutive equation (2.1) furnishes the infinitesimal change of stress

$$\begin{aligned} dT_{ij} = \dot{T}_{ij}\,dt &= [T_{ip}\partial_{[p}v_{j]} + T_{jp}\partial_{[p}v_{i]} + C_{ijkl}\partial_{(k}v_{l)}]\,dt \\ &= T_{ip}\partial_{[p}du_{j]} + T_{jp}\partial_{[p}du_{i]} + C_{ijkl}\partial_{(k}du_{l)}, \end{aligned} \tag{2.2}$$

which is referred to fixed axes. This change of stress therefore depends only on the infinitesimal rotation and deformation, but not on the speed with which the rotation and deformation are performed. *Hypoelastic materials thus are inviscid.*

Equation (2.2) shows that the signs of all components of the infinitesimal change of stress are reversed if we reverse the signs of all components of the infinitesimal displacement without changing the initial state of stress. If we first subject the neighborhood of the typical particle to an infinitesimal rotation and deformation and then return this neighborhood to its original position and shape by a suitable additional rotation and deformation, the stress components will resume their initial values to within higher-order quantities. *Infinitesimal deformations in a hypoelastic material under initial stress thus are reversible.*

This reversibility and the absence of viscosity noted above partially justify the use of the term "elastic"; the prefix "hypo" is meant to indicate that the materials considered in this chapter and the *elastic* and *hyperelastic*

† G. Jaumann, Sitzungsberichte Akad. Wiss. Wien (IIa) *120* (1911) 385; see also *idem, Die Grundlagen der Bewegungslehre*, Leipzig, 1905.

‡ C. Truesdell, Journal Rat. Mech. Analysis *4* (1955) 83; note corrections, *ibid.* 1019.

materials to be discussed in Chapter X possess the hallmarks of elasticity in increasing measure.

Let us first assume that the tensor C_{ijkl} in the constitutive equation (2.1) is independent of the state of stress. For an isotropic material, it can then be shown as in Section 5 of Chapter IV that

$$C_{ijkl} = \lambda\delta_{ij}\delta_{kl} + \mu(\delta_{ik}\delta_{jl} + \delta_{il}\delta_{jk}) \tag{2.3}$$

(see IV, 5.12), where λ and μ are constants. In this special case, the tensor C_{ijkl} involves the unit tensor δ_{ij} and characteristic constants of the material so as to fulfill the symmetry conditions (IV, 5.5) and (IV, 5.6). In general, however, this tensor will also involve the stress tensor T_{ij} and its square $Q_{ij} = T_{ip}T_{pj}$. Higher powers of the stress tensor need not be considered in this connection, because they can be written as linear combinations of δ_{ij}, T_{ij}, and Q_{ij} (see, for instance, I, 7.18). The following discussion will be restricted to hypoelastic materials for which the components of C_{ijkl} are *linear* functions of the stress components. The tensor C_{ijkl} then is a linear combination of the five tensors:

$$\left.\begin{array}{l} \delta_{ij}\delta_{kl}, \quad \delta_{ik}\delta_{jl} + \delta_{il}\delta_{jk} \\ \delta_{ij}T_{kl}, \quad T_{ij}\delta_{kl}, \quad \delta_{ik}T_{jl} + \delta_{il}T_{jk} + \delta_{jk}T_{il} + \delta_{jl}T_{ik}, \end{array}\right\} \tag{2.4}$$

each of which possesses the symmetry properties stipulated by (IV, 5.5) and (IV, 5.6). The coefficients of the first two tensors (2.4) in this linear combination may linearly depend on the trace $\mathscr{T}_{(1)}$ of the stress tensor, but the coefficients of the last three tensors (2.4) must be constants. The resulting constitutive equation can be written as follows:

$$T_{ij}^{\triangle} = (\lambda V_{kk} + \lambda' T_{kk}V_{ll} + \lambda'' T_{kl}V_{kl})\delta_{ij} + 2(\mu + \mu' T_{kk})V_{ij} + 2\nu V_{kk}T_{ij} + 2\nu'(T_{ik}V_{kj} + T_{jk}V_{ki}). \tag{2.5}$$

The coefficients $\lambda, \lambda', \cdots, \nu'$ in (2.5) are characteristic constants of the material. Following Noll,† the materials with the constitutive equation (2.5) will be called *linear hypoelastic materials*.

A somewhat wider class of hypoelastic materials could be defined as follows: the tensor C_{ijkl} in (2.1) is assumed to be a linear combination of the five tensors (2.4) with coefficients that depend on the basic invariants of the stress tensor. The materials defined in this manner could be called *quasilinear hypoelastic materials*.

A theorem of Rivlin and Ericksen, ‡ the proof of which is outside the scope of this book, shows that for the *general isotropic hypoelastic material* the tensor C_{ijkl} in (2.1) is a linear combination of the five tensors (2.4) and

† W. Noll, Journal Rat. Mech. Analysis *4* (1955) 3.

‡ R. S. Rivlin and J. L. Ericksen, Journal Rat. Mech. Analysis *4* (1955) 323; see also R. S. Rivlin, *ibid.* 681 and A. J. M. Spencer and R. S. Rivlin, Archive Rat. Mech. Analysis *2* (1959) 306, 435.

the seven tensors

$$\left.\begin{array}{l}\delta_{ij}Q_{kl}, \quad Q_{ij}\delta_{kl}, \quad \delta_{ik}Q_{jl} + \delta_{il}Q_{jk} + \delta_{jk}Q_{il} + \delta_{jl}Q_{ik}, \\ T_{ij}T_{kl}, \quad T_{ij}Q_{kl}, \quad Q_{ij}T_{kl}, \quad Q_{ij}Q_{kl},\end{array}\right\} \tag{2.6}$$

with coefficients that depend on the basic invariants of the stress tensor.

To illustrate the use of the constitutive equation (2.5), consider the simple shearing with the velocity field

$$v_1 = 2cx_2, \quad v_2 = v_3 = 0, \tag{2.7}$$

where c is a constant. We have

$$\partial_{[2}v_{1]} = c = -\partial_{[1}v_{2]}, \quad V_{12} = V_{21} = c, \tag{2.8}$$

while all other components of $\partial_{[i}v_{j]}$ and V_{ij} vanish. If the stress field is assumed to be *homogeneous*, (1.7) and (2.5) furnish

$$\begin{aligned}
T_{11}^{\nabla} &= \partial_0 T_{11} - 2cT_{12} = 2c(\lambda'' + 2\nu')T_{12}, \\
T_{22}^{\nabla} &= \partial_0 T_{22} + 2cT_{12} = 2c(\lambda'' + 2\nu')T_{12}, \\
T_{33}^{\nabla} &= \partial_0 T_{33} = 2c\lambda'' T_{12}, \\
T_{12}^{\nabla} &= \partial_0 T_{12} + c(T_{11} - T_{22}) \\
&= 2c\mu + 2c\mu'(T_{11} + T_{22} + T_{33}) \\
&\qquad + 2c\nu'(T_{11} + T_{22}), \\
T_{13}^{\nabla} &= \partial_0 T_{13} - cT_{23} = 2c\nu' T_{23}, \\
T_{23}^{\nabla} &= \partial_0 T_{23} + cT_{13} = 2c\nu' T_{13}.
\end{aligned} \tag{2.9}$$

If we assume, for instance, that at the time $t = 0$ all stress components vanish, it follows from the fifth and the sixth equation that T_{13} and T_{23} vanish identically. Substitution of the first two equations into the time derivative of the fourth then furnishes

$$\partial_{00}T_{12} + 4c^2[1 - 2(\mu' + \nu')(\lambda'' + 2\nu') - \lambda''\mu']T_{12} = 0. \tag{2.10}$$

Depending on whether the sign of the contents of the bracket in (2.10) is positive or negative, the variation of the shearing stress T_{12} is given by a trigonometric or hyperbolic function of the time. Leaving it to the reader to discuss these cases in detail, we treat only the special case $\lambda'' = \mu' = 0$, $\nu' = \frac{1}{2}$, in which the bracket in (2.10) vanishes. Equations (2.9) and (2.10) then furnish the stress components:

$$\left.\begin{array}{ll}T_{11} = 4\mu c^2 t^2, & T_{22} = T_{33} = 0, \\ T_{12} = 2\mu ct, & T_{13} = T_{23} = 0.\end{array}\right\} \tag{2.11}$$

Let us consider directed material line elements that have the x_1- or x_2-

direction at the time $t = 0$. At the typical instant t, the originally right angle formed by them has decreased by

$$\theta = \text{arc tan } 2ct, \tag{2.12}$$

and, by (2.11), the nonvanishing stress components have the values

$$T_{11} = \mu \tan^2\theta, \quad T_{12} = \mu \tan\theta. \tag{2.13}$$

3. Hypoelastic materials in the neighborhood of the stress-free state. The relations established in the preceding section simplify considerably if the discussion is restricted to the neighborhood of the stress-free state. For an isotropic linear hypoelastic material the tensor C_{ijkl} is in general a linear combination of the tensors (2.4); some coefficients in this combination may still depend on the trace $\mathscr{T}_{(1)}$. At the stress-free state $T_{ij} = 0$, however, only the first two of the tensors (2.4) are different from zero and their coefficients must be constants. Accordingly, C_{ijkl} has the form (2.3) in which λ and μ are characteristic constants of the material. Furthermore, according to (1.1) and (1.8), the stress rate at the stress-free state $T_{ij} = 0$ is given by

$$T_{ij}^{\nabla} = \partial_0 T_{ij}. \tag{3.1}$$

In the homogeneous stress-free state, the constitutive equation (2.1) therefore reduces to

$$\partial_0 T_{ij} = \lambda V_{kk}\delta_{ij} + 2\mu V_{ij}. \tag{3.2}$$

To the infinitesimal displacements from the homogeneous stress-free state, $du_i(x) = v_i(x)\,dt$, thus correspond the infinitesimal stresses

$$dT_{ij} = \partial_0 T_{ij}\,dt = \lambda\,dU_{kk}\delta_{ij} + 2\mu\,dU_{ij}, \tag{3.3}$$

where

$$dU_{ij} = V_{ij}\,dt = \partial_{(i}v_{j)}\,dt = \partial_{(i}du_{j)} \tag{3.4}$$

is the infinitesimal deformation corresponding to the displacements $du_i(x)$. The mechanical meaning of the components of $dU_{ij} = V_{ij}\,dt$ follows from that of the components of V_{ij}. The components dU_{11}, dU_{22}, dU_{33} are called *unit extensions; dU_{11}*, for instance, is the quotient of the elongation and the original length of a material line element that is parallel to the x_1-axis. The components $dU_{12}, dU_{13}, dU_{23}$ are called *shears; dU_{12}*, for instance, is one half of the decrease of the originally right angle formed by material line elements with the positive x_1- or x_2-directions. As has been discussed in connection with (III, 4.12), the cubical rate of dilatation V_{jj} is the rate of increase of the volume of a material element of the continuum. Accordingly, $dU_{jj} = V_{jj}\,dt$ is the quotient of the volume increase and the original volume of a material element; this quotient is called the *cubical dilatation.*

For practical reasons, the deformations that can be tolerated in structures or machine parts are usually rather small. For example, a very small deflection of a beam may already cause undesirable cracks in a plaster ceiling, and an extremely small increase in the diameter of a turbine rotor may already bring this in contact with the housing and hence cause failure. In problems of this kind, the small finite displacements $u_i(x)$ from the homogeneous stress-free state are usually treated as infinitesimal. The *deformation* corresponding to these displacements is then defined as

$$U_{ij} = \partial_{(i}u_{j)} \tag{3.5}$$

in analogy with (3.4), and the associated state of stress as

$$T_{ij} = \lambda U_{kk}\delta_{ij} + 2\mu U_{ij} \tag{3.6}$$

in analogy with (3.3). The linear relation (3.6) between stress and deformation is called *Hooke's law,* though Hooke † only considered the special case of uniaxial stress; the constants λ and μ are called *Lamé's ‡ constants.*

To express the deformation in terms of the stress, form the contraction of (3.6), substitute the resulting value of U_{kk} into (3.6) and solve for U_{ij}; thus,

$$U_{ij} = \frac{1}{2\mu}\left(T_{ij} - \frac{\lambda}{3\lambda + 2\mu}T_{kk}\delta_{ij}\right). \tag{3.7}$$

Let us consider some special cases of (3.7) to familiarize ourselves with this equation. The uniaxial state of stress in which only T_{11} differs from zero is associated with the state of deformation in which

$$U_{11} = \frac{\lambda + \mu}{\mu(3\lambda + 2\mu)}T_{11}, \quad U_{22} = U_{33} = -\frac{\lambda}{2\mu(3\lambda + 2\mu)}T_{11}, \tag{3.8}$$

while all other components of the deformation vanish. The quotient of the uniaxial stress T_{11} and the corresponding unit extension U_{11} is called *Young's § modulus.* As is shown by (3.8), the unit extension U_{11} in the axial direction is accompanied by a unit contraction $-U_{22} = -U_{33}$ in each transverse direction; the quotient of the latter by the former is called *Poisson's ‖ ratio.* In the engineering literature, Young's modulus and Poisson's ratio are usually denoted by E and σ, respectively. According to (3.8),

$$E = \frac{\mu(3\lambda + 2\mu)}{\lambda + \mu}, \quad \sigma = \frac{\lambda}{2(\lambda + \mu)}. \tag{3.9}$$

† R. Hooke, *De potentia restitutiva,* London, 1678.

‡ G. Lamé, *Leçons sur la théorie mathématique de l'élasticité des corps solides,* Paris, 1852.

§ T. Young, *A Course of Lectures on Natural Philosophy and the Mechanical Arts,* London, 1807.

‖ S. D. Poisson, Mémoires Acad. Sci. (Paris) *8* (1829) 357.

The hydrostatic state of stress $T_{ij} = -p\delta_{ij}$ is associated with the state of deformation

$$U_{ij} = -\frac{p\delta_{ij}}{3\lambda + 2\mu}. \tag{3.10}$$

The quotient of the pressure p and the *cubical contraction* $-U_{jj}$ caused by it is called the *bulk modulus*; it is usually denoted by K. According to (3.10),

$$K = \lambda + \tfrac{2}{3}\mu. \tag{3.11}$$

Finally, to the state of simple shearing stress in which only $T_{12} = T_{21}$ differs from zero there corresponds the state of deformation in which

$$U_{12} = U_{21} = T_{12}/(2\mu), \tag{3.12}$$

while all other components of the deformation vanish. The quotient of the shearing stress T_{12} and the corresponding angle change $2U_{12}$ is called the *shear modulus* and denoted by G. According to (3.12),

$$G = \mu. \tag{3.13}$$

It is to be expected that hydrostatic pressure cannot cause an increase in volume. On the other hand, the volume decrease must remain finite. Consequently, the bulk modulus can only assume positive values. Similarly, it is to be expected that the shear caused by a state of simple shearing stress has the direction of this stress. The shear modulus must therefore be positive. Finally, for an incompressible material, K and hence λ must become infinite. These conditions furnish the following inequalities for the Lamé constants:

$$\infty \geq \lambda > -\tfrac{2}{3}\mu, \quad \infty > \mu > 0. \tag{3.14}$$

The corresponding inequalities for Young's modulus and Poisson's ratio are

$$0 < E \leq 3\mu, \quad -1 < \sigma \leq \tfrac{1}{2}. \tag{3.15}$$

(see 3.9). Accordingly, a state of simple tension cannot cause a contraction in the direction of the tensile stress, but our inequalities do not furnish a sign restriction for the change of the transverse dimensions.

4. Fundamental equations of elastostatics. All examples discussed in Section 3 concern homogeneous states of stress and deformation; the components of the displacement from the stress-free state thus are linear functions of the coordinates. The present section is concerned with more general displacement fields; as above, the displacements are treated as infinitesimal.

Considering a homogeneous body that consists of an isotropic hypoelastic material that occupies the regular volume V with the surface S in the stress-free state, we propose to study the following problem: given a displacement field $u_i(x)$ defined in V, what are the body forces and surface tractions that would have to act on the volume and surface elements of the body to make its deformed state a state of equilibrium?

Let the typical particle have the position P with the coordinates x_i in the homogeneous stress-free state and the position P' with the coordinates $x_i + u_i$ in the deformed state. The deformation U_{ij} of the neighborhood of this particle is given by (3.5) and the corresponding state of stress by (3.6). Strictly speaking, this is the stress at the point P', but since the displacements are treated as infinitesimal, this state of stress may be associated with the point P. According to (3.5) and (3.6), the stress field is given by

$$T_{ij} = \lambda \partial_k u_k \delta_{ij} + \mu(\partial_i u_j + \partial_j u_i). \tag{4.1}$$

To make the deformed state a state of equilibrium, we must apply the infinitesimal force

$$T_i^{(\nu)}\, dS = T_{ji}\nu_j\, dS = [\lambda \partial_j u_j \nu_i + \mu(\partial_i u_j + \partial_j u_i)\nu_j]\, dS \tag{4.2}$$

at the typical surface element dS with the unit normal vector ν_j (see II, 1.2, 2.9) and the infinitesimal force

$$\rho K_i\, dV = -\partial_j T_{ji}\, dV = -[(\lambda + \mu)\partial_{ij} u_j + \mu \partial_{jj} u_i]\, dV \tag{4.3}$$

at the typical volume element dV. Since the displacements are treated as infinitesimal, the density ρ in (4.3) may be interpreted as the uniform density ρ_0 in the homogeneous initial state.

The simplest problem of *elastostatics* may be regarded as the inverse of the problem just discussed: given the surface tractions $T_i^{(\nu)}$ and the specific body forces K_i, find displacements $u_i(x)$ that satisfy (4.2) and (4.3). We shall immediately treat a more general problem: whereas all three components of the specific body force K_i will be prescribed throughout V, it will not be required that all three components of the surface traction $T_i^{(\nu)}$ are given, but if certain components of $T_i^{(\nu)}$ should not be prescribed at a point of the surface S, then the corresponding components of u_i will be given at this point. A displacement field $u_i(x)$ is to be determined that satisfies (4.3) through V, while on the surface S the components of the displacement and those of the associated surface traction (4.2) assume the prescribed values. The following special cases of this boundary value problem are frequently encountered in the applications: (*a*) the surface traction $T_i^{(\nu)}$ is prescribed on the entire surface; (*b*) the displacement u_i is given on the entire surface; (*c*) the surface traction $T_i^{(\nu)}$ is given on the part S_1 of the surface, while the displacement u_i is prescribed on the remainder S_2.

It can be shown that the general boundary value problem formulated above admits a solution if the boundary values satisfy appropriate continuity conditions. This existence proof, however, is outside the scope of this book. Assuming that a solution exists, we shall investigate to what extent it is unique.

Let u_i^* and u_i^{**} be the displacement fields of two solutions, U_{ij}^* and U_{ij}^{**} the corresponding fields of deformation, and T_{ij}^* and T_{ij}^{**} the stress fields, and assume that the considered hypoelastic material is compressible, so that its bulk modulus (3.11) and hence Lamé's constant λ are finite.

If the component $T_1^{(\nu)}$ of the surface traction and the components u_2 and u_3 of the displacement are prescribed at the considered point of the surface, we have $T_{i1}^*\nu_i - T_{i1}^{**}\nu_i = 0$, $u_2^* - u_2^{**} = 0$, $u_3^* - u_3^{**} = 0$ at this point and hence

$$(T_{ij}^* - T_{ij}^{**})(u_j^* - u_j^{**})\nu_i = 0. \tag{4.4}$$

As a matter of fact, our boundary value problem is so formulated that (4.4) is valid at any point of the surface S. Accordingly,

$$\int (T_{ij}^* - T_{ij}^{**})(u_j^* - u_j^{**})\nu_i \, dS = 0. \tag{4.5}$$

Transformation of the left side of this equation by means of the theorem of Gauss yields

$$\int (\partial_i T_{ij}^* - \partial_i T_{ij}^{**})(u_j^* - u_j^{**}) \, dV + \int (T_{ij}^* - T_{ij}^{**})(\partial_i u_j^* - \partial_i u_j^{**}) \, dV = 0. \tag{4.6}$$

Since both stress fields satisfy the equation of equilibrium (II, 2.7) with the same body force K_i, the first parenthesis in the first integrand in (4.6) vanishes, and this equation reduces to

$$\int (T_{ij}^* - T_{ij}^{**})(\partial_i u_j^* - \partial_i u_j^{**}) \, dV = 0. \tag{4.7}$$

In view of the symmetry of the stress tensors, the integrand in (4.7) can also be written as

$$(T_{ij}^* - T_{ij}^{**})(\partial_{(i}u_{j)}^* - \partial_{(i}u_{j)}^{**}) = (T_{ij}^* - T_{ij}^{**})(U_{ij}^* - U_{ij}^{**}). \tag{4.8}$$

According to Hooke's law (3.6), the right side of (4.8) equals

$$\lambda(U_{ii}^* - U_{ii}^{**})(U_{jj}^* - U_{jj}^{**}) + 2\mu(U_{ij}^* - U_{ij}^{**})(U_{ij}^* - U_{ij}^{**}). \tag{4.9}$$

We introduce the abbreviation

$$A_{ij} = U_{ij}^* - U_{ij}^{**}, \tag{4.10}$$

and denote the deviator of this tensor by A'_{ij}. As in (II, 3.1) and (II, 3.2), we then have

$$A_{ij} = \tfrac{1}{3}A_{kk}\delta_{ij} + A'_{ij}. \tag{4.11}$$

Equation (4.8) can therefore be written as

$$(\lambda + \tfrac{2}{3}\mu)A_{ii}A_{jj} + 2\mu A'_{ij}A'_{ij}, \tag{4.12}$$

that is, as a sum of squares.

The coefficients in (4.12) are the positive bulk modulus (3.11) and the positive shear modulus (3.13). The sum of squares (4.12) is therefore non-negative; it can only vanish if $A_{ii} = 0$ and $A'_{ij} = 0$. It then follows from (4.11) that $A_{ij} = 0$, so that $U^*_{ij} = U^{**}_{ij}$.

The expression (4.12) was obtained by transforming the integrand in (4.7). This integrand thus is non-negative and vanishes only where $U^*_{ij} = U^{**}_{ij}$. For (4.7) to be satisfied, the non-negative integrand must vanish throughout V, i.e., the fields of deformation of the two solutions must coincide. Because λ is finite, it then follows from Hooke's law that the two solutions have identical stress fields. If the displacement fields should differ, their difference $u^*_i - u^{**}_i$ would have to represent a rigid-body displacement, since otherwise the fields of deformation U^*_{ij} and U^{**}_{ij} could not coincide (see the discussion at the end of Section 3 of Chapter III). If the boundary conditions involve only surface tractions, the displacement field is only determined to within a field that corresponds to a rigid-body displacement. On the other hand, the superposition of such a field is, as a rule, impossible, if the boundary conditions involve displacements, so that the displacement field then is, as a rule, uniquely determined.

It is worth noting that the integrand in (4.5) is the scalar product of $T^{(\nu)*}_i - T^{(\nu)**}_i$ and $u^*_i - u^{**}_i$ and hence independent of the choice of the coordinate directions. Without invalidating our uniqueness proof, we may therefore refer the surface traction and displacement at each surface point to rectangular axes defined at this point, prescribing for instance the component of the surface traction that is normal to the surface and the velocity components that are tangential to it.

A first form of the fundamental equations of elastostatics is furnished by the remark that (4.3) is valid for any element of the considered body; thus

$$\mu\partial_{jj}u_i + (\lambda + \mu)\partial_{ij}u_j + \rho K_i = 0. \tag{4.13}$$

The components of this vector equation form a system of three partial differential equations for the displacement components u_i.

In deriving a system of partial differential equations for the stress components, we start from the *equation of compatibility* for the components of the infinitesimal deformation. In analogy to (III, 3.15), this equation has the form

$$\epsilon_{ipq}\epsilon_{jrs}\partial_{pr}U_{qs} = 0. \tag{4.14}$$

Substituting (3.7) into (4.14) and using the third equation (I, 6.5), we obtain

$$\epsilon_{ipq}\epsilon_{jrs}\partial_{pr}T_{qs} + \frac{\lambda}{3\lambda + 2\mu}(\partial_{ij}T_{qq} - \delta_{ij}\partial_{pp}T_{qq}) = 0. \tag{4.15}$$

The components of this tensor equation of the second order form a system of six linear partial differential equations for the components of the symmetric stress tensor. A stress field that is defined in a simply connected regular domain must satisfy these six equations if it is to be derivable from a displacement field in accordance with (3.5) and (3.7). In addition, the stress field must of course fulfill the equations of equilibrium (II, 2.7).

Equation (4.15) can be regarded as an *equation of compatibility* for the stress components. An alternative equation that is more useful in the applications may be obtained as follows. Multiplying (4.14) by $\epsilon_{ikm}\epsilon_{jln}$, using the third equation (I, 6.5), and setting $m = n$, we find

$$\partial_{mm}U_{kl} + \partial_{kl}U_{mm} - \partial_{km}U_{ml} - \partial_{lm}U_{mk} = 0. \tag{4.16}$$

We now express the deformation in terms of the stress (see 3.7) and use the equation of equilibrium (II, 2.7) to replace, say, $\partial_{km}T_{ml}$ by $-\rho\partial_k K_l$; thus

$$\partial_{mm}T_{kl} + \frac{2(\lambda + \mu)}{3\lambda + 2\mu}\partial_{kl}T_{mm} - \frac{\lambda}{3\lambda + 2\mu}\partial_{mm}T_{nn}\delta_{kl} + \rho(\partial_k K_l + \partial_l K_k) = 0. \tag{4.17}$$

With $k = l$, this equation furnishes a relation between $\partial_{mm}T_{nn}$ and $\partial_m K_m$; if this is used to transform the third term in (4.17), the following relation is obtained:

$$\partial_{mm}T_{kl} + \frac{2(\lambda + \mu)}{3\lambda + 2\mu}\partial_{kl}T_{mm} + \rho(\partial_k K_l + \partial_l K_k) + \frac{\lambda}{\lambda + 2\mu}\rho\partial_m K_m\delta_{kl} = 0. \tag{4.18}$$

In addition to this equation, which is usually named after Beltrami † and Michell, ‡ the stress components must satisfy the equation of equilibrium (II, 2.7).

To conclude this section, we indicate the following special case. The derivative of (4.14) with respect to x_i shows that, in the absence of body forces, the cubical dilatation $\partial_i u_i$ is a harmonic function of the coordinates. Applying the Laplace operator ∂_{kk} to (4.13), we thus find that each displacement component is a biharmonic function. It then follows from (4.13) that each stress component is a biharmonic function of the coordinates.

5. Torsion of cylindrical bars. As example for the solution of an elastostatic problem, consider the torsion of a cylindrical bar of arbitrary simply connected cross section. In the stress-free initial state, let the generators of the cylindrical surface of the bar be parallel to the x_3-axis and terminal cross sections lie in the planes $x_3 = 0$ and $x_3 = l$. On the surface of the bar, let surface tractions and displacements be prescribed as follows: all three components of the surface traction are to vanish on the cylindrical

† E. Beltrami, Rendiconti Ac. Lincei (5) *1* (1892) 141.
‡ J. H. Michell, Proc. London Math. Soc. *31* (1899–1900) 100.

surface, but only the component T_{33} is to vanish on the terminal cross sections; on the cross section $x_3 = 0$ the displacement components u_1 and u_2 are to vanish, and on the cross section $x_3 = l$ these displacement components are to have the values $u_1 = -\theta l x_2$ and $u_2 = \theta l x_1$, where θ is an infinitesimal constant.

Since these boundary conditions do not contain any information concerning the values of u_3 on the terminal cross sections, it is entirely possible that these sections are no longer plane in the deformed state of the bar. If the axial displacements u_3 are disregarded, the boundary conditions for u_1 and u_2 demand that the cross section $x_3 = 0$ remains at rest, whereas the cross section $x_3 = l$ performs a counterclockwise rotation about the x_3-axis, the infinitesimal angle of rotation being θl. The quantity θ is called the *specific angle of twist*.

This boundary value problem is obviously of the type discussed in Section 4. If a solution exists at all, its fields of stress and deformation are therefore unique. Since the boundary conditions for displacements do not involve u_3, the displacement field is only determined to within a translation in the x_3-direction.

As was first pointed out by Saint Venant,† boundary value problems of this kind can often be solved in the following manner. Tentative expressions for the displacement components are considered that satisfy the boundary conditions for displacements while containing a sufficient number of arbitrary functions of position. Using the fundamental equations of elastostatics, one then tries to determine these functions in such a way that all boundary conditions of the problem are fulfilled. In the torsion problem, one may for instance consider the following tentative expressions for the displacement components:

$$u_1 = -\theta x_2 x_3, \quad u_2 = \theta x_1 x_3, \quad u_3 = \varphi(x_1, x_2), \tag{5.1}$$

which satisfy the boundary conditions for u_1 and u_2 on the terminal cross sections. The function $\varphi(x_1, x_2)$, which remains to be determined, represents an identical warping of all cross sections.

According to (3.5), the deformation associated with the displacement (5.1) is given by

$$\left.\begin{aligned} U_{11} &= U_{22} = U_{33} = 0, \quad U_{12} = 0, \\ U_{13} &= \tfrac{1}{2}(\partial_1\varphi - \theta x_2), \quad U_{23} = \tfrac{1}{2}(\partial_2\varphi + \theta x_1). \end{aligned}\right\} \tag{5.2}$$

Hooke's law (3.6) then furnishes the stress components

$$\left.\begin{aligned} T_{11} &= T_{22} = T_{33} = 0, \quad T_{12} = 0, \\ T_{13} &= \mu(\partial_1\varphi - \theta x_2), \quad T_{23} = \mu(\partial_2\varphi + \theta x_1). \end{aligned}\right\} \tag{5.3}$$

† B. de Saint Venant, Mémoires présentés par divers savants à l'Ac. Sci. math. et phys. *14* (1856) 233.

As is seen from (5.3), the boundary conditions for the stress component T_{33} on the terminal cross sections are fulfilled. The unit vector ν_i along the exterior normal of the cylindrical surface of the bar has the third component $\nu_3 = 0$. According to (5.3), the surface traction $T_i^{(\nu)} = \nu_i T_{ij}$ at the typical point of this surface therefore has vanishing first and second components, and its third component will vanish too if

$$\nu_1 \partial_1 \varphi + \nu_2 \partial_2 \varphi = -\theta(x_1 \nu_2 - x_2 \nu_1). \tag{5.4}$$

The left side of (5.4) is the derivative $\partial\varphi/\partial\nu$ of the function $\varphi(x_1, x_2)$ in the direction of the exterior normal of the boundary of a typical cross section. The condition that the cylindrical surface of the bar should be free from surface tractions is therefore fulfilled if the *warping function* $\varphi(x_1, x_2)$ is chosen so that its normal derivative on the boundary of the cross section assumes the values prescribed by (5.4). It remains to be seen whether there exists a warping function that will not only satisfy this boundary condition but also the fundamental equation (4.13).

Since body forces are to be disregarded and (5.2) shows that the cubical dilatation $\partial_i u_i$ vanishes, (4.13) reduces for the torsion problem to the statement that each displacement component is a harmonic function of the coordinates. According to (5.1), this condition, which is already fulfilled as far as u_1 and u_2 are concerned, furnishes the equation

$$\partial_{\underline{jj}} \varphi = 0 \tag{5.5}$$

for the warping function, underlined subscripts having the range 1, 2. The warping function $\varphi(x_1, x_2)$ must therefore be harmonic in the entire cross section while its normal derivative on the boundary of the cross section must assume the values prescribed by (5.4). As is well known, this boundary value problem of the Neumann type admits a solution if the integral of the normal derivative $\partial\varphi/\partial\nu$ extended over the boundary of the considered region vanishes. We leave it to the reader to show that this condition is fulfilled. To within an additive constant, the solution of the Neumann problem then is unique, i.e. the displacement field (5.1) is uniquely determined to within an axial translation. It then follows from the uniqueness considerations in Section 4, that our elastostatic boundary value problem does not admit a displacement field of a form that differs from (5.1). Once the Neumann problem for the warping function φ has been solved, the deformations and stresses in the twisted bar are readily obtained from (5.2) and (5.3).

In the preceding discussion of the torsion problem, the displacement components have been treated as the principal unknowns. In the following, the stress components will be regarded as the principal unknowns, and it will be tentatively assumed that only T_{13} and T_{23} differ from zero. The boundary condition that T_{33} should vanish on the terminal cross section is already fulfilled by this assumption. Since body forces are to be disregarded, the first two components of the equation of equilibrium (II, 2.7) are identically fulfilled, whereas the third component reduces to

$$\partial_1 T_{13} + \partial_2 T_{23} = 0. \tag{5.6}$$

As has been pointed out by Prandtl,† this equation suggests the introduction of a *stress function* $\psi(x_1, x_2)$ from which the nonvanishing stress components are obtained as follows:

$$T_{13} = \partial_2 \psi, \quad T_{23} = -\partial_1 \psi. \tag{5.7}$$

In this way, the equation of equilibrium (5.6) is satisfied for any choice of the stress function.

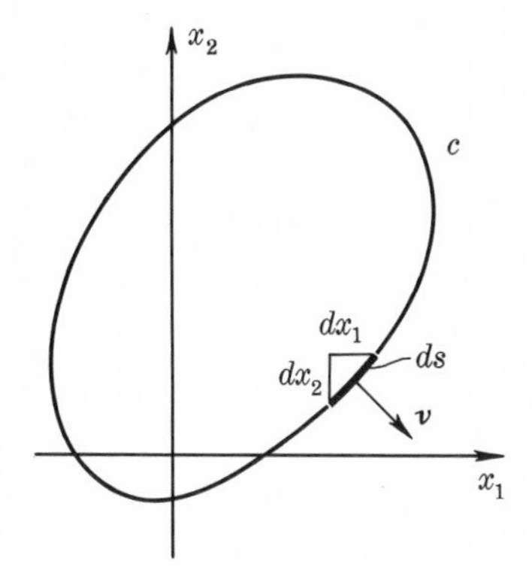

Figure 25

Let the curve c in Figure 25 be the boundary of the cross section of the bar. On this curve, choose the positive sense in such a way that it corresponds to the sense of rotation of a right-handed screw that progresses in the positive x_3-direction. Denote the length of a typical directed line element of c by ds and the projections of this element on the coordinate axes by dx_1 and dx_2. Consider an element of the cylindrical surface of the bar that has this line element as trace in the cross-sectional plane. The normal vector $\boldsymbol{\nu}$ of this surface element then has the components

$$\nu_1 = dx_2/ds, \quad \nu_2 = -dx_1/ds, \quad \nu_3 = 0. \tag{5.8}$$

The surface traction $T_j^{(\nu)} = T_{ij}\nu_j$ is to vanish. Since all stress components except those in (5.7) vanish, this condition furnishes $\nu_1 T_{13} + \nu_2 T_{23} = 0$ or, by (5.7) and (5.8),

$$\partial_1 \psi \, dx_1 + \partial_2 \psi \, dx_2 = 0. \tag{5.9}$$

As is seen from this equation, the rate of change of ψ in the direction of the tangent of c vanishes. The stress function thus is constant on the boundary

† L. Prandtl, Physikalische Zeitschrift *4* (1903) 758.

of the simply connected cross section. Since the stress field determines the stress function only to within an arbitrary additive constant, no loss of generality is involved in setting

$$\psi = 0 \tag{5.10}$$

on the boundary of the cross section. It remains to be seen whether a stress function satisfying this boundary condition can be chosen in such a way that the fundamental equation (4.17) is fulfilled.

Since only T_{13} and T_{23} differ from zero, we have $T_{kk} = 0$. In the absence of body forces, (4.17) therefore requires that T_{13} and T_{23} are harmonic functions of x_1 and x_2. By (5.7), we therefore have $\partial_{1jj}\psi = 0$, $\partial_{2jj}\psi = 0$, that is,

$$\partial_{jj}\psi = \text{constant}. \tag{5.11}$$

In this second way of treating the torsion problem, only the boundary conditions involving stresses have so far been considered. We now turn to the boundary conditions on displacements. Since all stress components except T_{13} and T_{23} have been assumed to be zero, it follows from (3.7) that U_{11}, U_{22}, U_{33}, and U_{12} vanish identically. According to (3.5), we have, therefore,

$$\partial_1 u_1 = \partial_2 u_2 = \partial_3 u_3 = \partial_1 u_2 + \partial_2 u_1 = 0. \tag{5.12}$$

These relations and the boundary conditions for u_1 and u_2 on the terminal cross sections $x_3 = 0$ and $x_3 = l$ then show that the displacement field is of the form (5.1). Substitution of the corresponding stresses (5.3) into (5.11) furnishes the value $-2\mu\theta$ for the constant on the right side of this equation. In the simply connected cross section, the stress function must therefore satisfy the differential equation

$$\partial_{jj}\psi = -2\mu\theta, \tag{5.13}$$

while on the boundary of the cross section it must satisfy the condition (5.10). As is well known, this boundary value problem possesses a unique solution.

We finally determine the resultant R_i of the surface tractions that act on the terminal cross section $x_3 = l$. In doing this, we could express the stresses in terms of either the warping function (see 5.3) or the stress function (see 5.7). We choose the second way. Because $T_{33} = 0$, it follows from (5.7) that

$$R_i = \int \epsilon_{3ij}\partial_j\psi \, dA, \tag{5.14}$$

where dA denotes the surface element of the cross section and ϵ_{hij} is the ϵ-tensor introduced in Section 6 of Chapter I. Transformation of (5.14) by means of the theorem of Gauss, and use of the boundary condition (5.10) furnish

$$R_i = 0. \tag{5.15}$$

Thus, the surface tractions acting on the terminal cross section $x_3 = l$ either form an equilibrium system or are equivalent to a couple. Since the nonvanishing components of the surface traction are acting in this cross section, only the third component of the moment vector M_i of this couple could be different from zero. As in (5.14), the force at the typical element dA of the cross section is given by $\epsilon_{3ij}\partial_j\psi\, dA$; according to (I, 6.15) and the third equation (I, 6.5) we have

$$\begin{aligned} M_3 &= \int \epsilon_{3hi}x_h\epsilon_{3ij}\partial_j\psi\, dA \\ &= \int (\delta_{3j}\delta_{h3} - \delta_{33}\delta_{hj})x_h\partial_j\psi\, dA \\ &= -\int x_j\partial_j\psi\, dA = -\int [\partial_j(x_j\psi) - 2\psi]\, dA. \end{aligned} \tag{5.16}$$

Transforming (5.16) by the theorem of Gauss and using the boundary condition (5.10), we obtain the *torque*

$$M_3 = 2\int \psi\, dA. \tag{5.17}$$

As example we consider a bar of elliptical cross section. Letting

$$\frac{x_1^2}{a^2} + \frac{x_2^2}{b^2} - 1 = 0 \tag{5.18}$$

be the equation of the cylindrical surface of the bar, we tentatively write the stress function in the form

$$\psi = c\left(1 - \frac{x_1^2}{a^2} - \frac{x_2^2}{b^2}\right), \tag{5.19}$$

which satisfies the boundary condition (5.10). Substitution of (5.19) into (5.13) furnishes

$$c = \frac{a^2b^2\mu\theta}{a^2 + b^2}. \tag{5.20}$$

According to (5.17), the torque is given by

$$M_3 = 2\frac{a^2b^2\mu\theta}{a^2 + b^2}\left[\int dA - \frac{1}{a^2}\int x_1^2\, dA - \frac{1}{b^2}\int x_2^2\, dA\right], \tag{5.21}$$

where the three integrals respectively represent the area of the cross section, and its moments of inertia with respect to the x_2-axis and the x_1-axis. Substitution of the well-known expressions for these quantities into (5.21) yields

$$M_3 = \frac{\pi a^3b^3\mu\theta}{a^2 + b^2}. \tag{5.22}$$

Consequently, the *torsional rigidity* $D = M_3/\theta$ has the value

$$D = \frac{\pi a^3 b^3 \mu}{a^2 + b^2}. \tag{5.23}$$

According to (5.7), the nonvanishing stress components are

$$T_{13} = -\frac{2a^2\mu\theta}{a^2 + b^2}x_2, \quad T_{23} = \frac{2b^2\mu\theta}{a^2 + b^2}x_1. \tag{5.24}$$

From (5.24) and (5.3), it finally follows that, to within an irrelevant additive constant, the warping function $\varphi(x_1, x_2)$ is given by

$$\varphi = -\frac{a^2 - b^2}{a^2 + b^2}\theta x_1 x_2. \tag{5.25}$$

6. Extremum principles. In this section, we shall return to the general boundary value problem discussed in Section 4 and establish extremum principles for its solution. As in Section 4, the specific body force is to be given throughout the volume V of the considered body; on the surface S certain components of the surface traction $T_i^{(\nu)}$ and the complementary components of the displacement u_i are to be prescribed. Boundary conditions will be called *statical* or *kinematical* depending on whether they involve components of the surface traction or the surface displacement.

Since the extremum principles that are to be established are most readily expressed in terms of energy, we begin by deriving expressions for the work done in deforming an elastic solid. The equivalent of this work is stored as the elastic energy $\mathscr{E}$ in the deformed solid. If a volume element dV is deformed with the velocity V_{ij} while it is under the stress T_{ij}, the instantaneous power of the stress components equals $T_{ij}V_{ij}dV$ (see 4.7). For the infinitesimal deformations considered here, we have the relation $V_{ij} = dU_{ij}/dt$, in which dU_{ij} denotes the additional deformation during the time element dt. The work done during this time element in the entire body is, therefore,

$$d\mathscr{E} = \int T_{ij}\, dU_{ij}\, dV. \tag{6.1}$$

When the stress T_{ij} in (6.1) is expressed according to Hooke's law (3.6) in terms of the deformation U_{ij}, the following relation is obtained:

$$\begin{aligned} \mathscr{E} &= \int dV \int_0^U (\lambda U_{kk}\delta_{ij} + 2\mu U_{ij})\, dU_{ij} \\ &= \int \tfrac{1}{2}(\lambda U_{ii}U_{jj} + 2\mu U_{ij}U_{ij})\, dV. \end{aligned} \tag{6.2}$$

On the other hand, we may express the deformation increment dU_{ij} in

(6.1) in terms of the stress increment dT_{ij} by using (3.7) to find

$$\mathscr{E} = \int dV \int_0^T \frac{1}{2\mu} T_{ij} \left(dT_{ij} - \frac{\lambda}{3\lambda + 2\mu} dT_{kk}\delta_{ij} \right)$$

$$= \int \frac{1}{4\mu} \left(T_{ij}T_{ij} - \frac{\lambda}{3\lambda + 2\mu} T_{ii}T_{jj} \right) dV. \tag{6.3}$$

In the following, the right side of (6.2) will be denoted by $\mathscr{E}_U$ and that of (6.3) by $\mathscr{E}_T$. For convenient reference, these expressions will be called *strain energy* and *stress energy*, respectively.

By their mechanical meaning, $\mathscr{E}_U$ and $\mathscr{E}_T$ are *positive definite* functions of their arguments, i.e., each of these functions assumes a positive value when at least one of its arguments differs from zero, and vanishes only when all of its arguments are zero. The positive definite character of these functions can be established independent of their mechanical meaning by the use of the definitions (6.2), (6.3) and the inequalities (3.14). We leave this proof to the reader, referring him to the discussion of (4.12).

Let U_{ij} and U_{ij}^* be two fields of deformation that are not identical. It follows then from the positive definite character of $\mathscr{E}_U$ that the strain energy computed from the difference $U_{ij}^* - U_{ij}$ satisfies

$$\mathscr{E}_U(U_{ij}^* - U_{ij})$$

$$= \int \tfrac{1}{2}[\lambda(U_{ii}^* - U_{ii})(U_{jj}^* - U_{jj}) + 2\mu(U_{ij}^* - U_{ij})(U_{ij}^* - U_{ij})]\, dV > 0. \tag{6.4}$$

Let T_{ij} and T_{ij}^* be the stress fields that follow from the deformation fields U_{ij} and U_{ij}^* by Hooke's law (3.6). According to (6.2), we may then write (6.4) in the form

$$\mathscr{E}_U^* - \mathscr{E}_U > \int (U_{ij}^* - U_{ij}) T_{ij}\, dV, \tag{6.5}$$

where $\mathscr{E}_U$ is the strain energy corresponding to U_{ij} and $\mathscr{E}_U^*$ that corresponding to U_{ij}^*. We leave it to the reader to establish the relation

$$\mathscr{E}_T^* - \mathscr{E}_T > \int (T_{ij}^* - T_{ij}) U_{ij}\, dV, \tag{6.6}$$

in which $\mathscr{E}_T$ and $\mathscr{E}_T^*$ are similarly defined.

Turning now to the general boundary value problem of elastostatics that has been reviewed at the beginning of this chapter, we assume that this problem admits a solution. As has been shown in Section 4, this solution is essentially unique. Let u_i, U_{ij}, and T_{ij} be the corresponding fields of displacement, deformation and stress. Furthermore, let u_i^* be a displacement field that fulfills the kinematical boundary conditions and is not identical with u_i, denote the associated field of deformation by U^*_{ij}, and assume that it is not identical with U_{ij}.

Since the stress field T_{ij} of the solution satisfies the equation of equilibrium (4.3), we have

$$\int \rho K_j(u_j^* - u_j)\, dV + \int \nu_i T_{ij}(u_j^* - u_j)\, dS = \int T_{ij}\partial_i(u_j^* - u_j)\, dV$$

$$= \int T_{ij}(U^*_{ij} - U_{ij})\, dV, \qquad (6.7)$$

where the symmetry of the stress tensor is used in the transition to the last integral. It follows from (6.5) and (6.7) that

$$\mathscr{E}^*_U - \mathscr{E}_U > \int \rho K_j(u_j^* - u_j)\, dV + \int \nu_i T_{ij}(u_j^* - u_j)\, dS. \qquad (6.8)$$

Since u_j^* as well as u_j satisfy the kinematical boundary conditions, the difference $u_j^* - u_j$ vanishes at the typical point P of the surface S for those components that appear in the kinematical boundary conditions. The complementary components of $\nu_i T_{ij}$ are the components of the surface traction $T_j^{(\nu)}$ that are prescribed at P. The last integral in (6.7) can therefore be written as

$$\int [T_j^{(\nu)}(u_j^* - u_j)]'\, dS, \qquad (6.9)$$

where the prime indicates that the summation indicated by the dummy subscript j extends over those components that appear in the statical boundary conditions at the considered point of the surface.

The inequality (6.8) thus is equivalent to

$$\mathscr{E}^*_U - \int [T_j^{(\nu)} u_j^*]'\, dS - \int \rho K_j u_j^*\, dV$$

$$> \mathscr{E}_U - \int [T_j^{(\nu)} u_j]'\, dS - \int \rho K_j u_j\, dV, \qquad (6.10)$$

i.e., *the difference between the strain energy and the virtual work of the body forces and prescribed surface tractions on the displacements assumes a smaller value for the displacement field of the solution than for any other displacement field that satisfies the kinematical boundary conditions.*

We leave it to the reader to establish the inequality

$$\int [\nu_i T_{ij} u_j]''\, dS - \mathscr{E}_T > \int [\nu_i T^{**}_{ij} u_j]''\, dS - \mathscr{E}^{**}_T, \qquad (6.11)$$

in a similar way. Here T_{ij} denotes the stress field of the solution and T^{**}_{ij} any other field of stress that satisfies the equation of equilibrium (II, 2.7) with the given body forces and furnishes the prescribed components of the surface traction; $\mathscr{E}_T$ and $\mathscr{E}^{**}_T$ are the corresponding values of the stress energy, and the double prime indicates that only those components should be used that appear in the kinematical boundary conditions at the considered point of the surface.

The inequality (6.11) expresses the following extremum principle: *The difference between the virtual work of the surface tractions on the prescribed surface displacements and the stress energy assumes a larger value for the stress field of the solution than for any other stress field that is in equilibrium with the given body forces and satisfies the statical boundary conditions.*

The inequalities (6.10) and (6.11) can be transformed as follows. The definitions (6.2) and (6.3) show that

$$\mathscr{E}_U + \mathscr{E}_T = \int dV \int (T_{ij}\, dU_{ij} + U_{ij}\, dT_{ij}) = \int T_{ij} U_{ij}\, dV. \tag{6.12}$$

On account of the symmetry of the stress tensor, the solution of the considered boundary value problem therefore satisfies the relation

$$\begin{aligned} \mathscr{E}_U + \mathscr{E}_T &= \int T_{ij} \partial_i u_j\, dV = \int \nu_i T_{ij} u_j\, dS - \int \partial_i T_{ij} u_j\, dV \\ &= \int \nu_i T_{ij} u_j\, dS + \int \rho K_j u_j\, dV, \end{aligned} \tag{6.13}$$

in which the equation of equilibrium (II, 2.7) has been used in the transition to the last expression. Now, $\mathscr{E}_U$ as well as $\mathscr{E}_T$ represents the elastic energy stored in the deformed body, i.e., we have $\mathscr{E}_U = \mathscr{E}_T$ and hence by (6.13)

$$\mathscr{E}_U = \mathscr{E}_T = \tfrac{1}{2} \left\{ \int \nu_i T_{ij} u_j\, dS + \int \rho K_j u_j\, dV \right\}. \tag{6.14}$$

Moreover, since

$$\int \nu_i T_{ij} u_j\, dS = \int [T_j^{(\nu)} u_j]'\, dS + \int [T_j^{(\nu)} u_j]''\, dS, \tag{6.15}$$

the right side of (6.10) as well as the left side of (6.11) have the value

$$\tfrac{1}{2} \left\{ \int [\nu_i T_{ij} u_j]''\, dS - \int [T_j^{(\nu)} u_j]'\, dS - \int \rho K_j u_j\, dV \right\}. \tag{6.16}$$

According to (6.10), (6.11) and (6.16), we have, therefore,

$$\begin{aligned} \mathscr{E}_U^* - \int \rho K_j u_j^*\, dV &- \int [T_j^{(\nu)} u_j^*]'\, dS \\ &> \tfrac{1}{2} \left\{ \int [\nu_i T_{ij} u_j]''\, dS - \int [T_j^{(\nu)} u_j]'\, dS - \int \rho K_j u_j\, dV \right\} \\ &> \int [\nu_i T_{ij}^{**} u_j]''\, dS - \mathscr{E}_T^{**}. \end{aligned} \tag{6.17}$$

To present a typical application of this continued inequality, we return to the torsion problem discussed in Section 5. On account of the linearity of the fundamental equations of elastostatics, the torque, the stresses, and the warping are proportional to the specific angle of twist θ. Furthermore, the torque and the stresses are proportional to the shear modulus. To avoid carrying along unessential constants, we shall base our calculations on the assumption that the specific angle of twist θ, the shear modulus μ, and the length l of the bar, all have the value 1.

Since the body force K_j and the prescribed components of the surface traction $T_j^{(\nu)}$ vanish, the terms containing these symbols can be deleted in (6.17). The prescribed components of the surface displacement vanish on $x_3 = 0$ and correspond to a rotation by the unit angle on $x_3 = 1$. The work $\int [\nu_j T_{ij} u_j]'' \, dS$ of the surface tractions $\nu_i T_{ij}$ on the prescribed displacements therefore equals the torque M_3 for the unit specific angle of twist, i.e. the torsional rigidity D. In a similar way, the expression $\int [\nu_i T_{ij}^{**} u_j]'' \, dS$ represents the moment M_3^{**} of the surface tractions $\nu_i T_{ij}^{**}$ in the terminal section $x_3 = 1$ with respect to the x_3-axis.

A displacement field u_i^* that satisfies the kinematical boundary conditions is given by

$$u_1^* = -x_2 x_3, \quad u_2^* = x_1 x_3, \quad u_3^* = \varphi^*(x_1, x_2). \tag{6.18}$$

Except for

$$U_{13}^* = U_{31}^* = \tfrac{1}{2}(\partial_1 \varphi^* - x_2), \quad U_{23}^* = U_{32}^* = \tfrac{1}{2}(\partial_2 \varphi^* + x_1), \tag{6.19}$$

all components of the deformation vanish, and (6.2) furnishes

$$2\mathscr{E}_U^* = \int [(\partial_1 \varphi^* - x_2)^2 + (\partial_2 \varphi^* + x_1)^2] \, dA, \tag{6.20}$$

where dA denotes the surface element of the cross section.

A stress field T_{ij}^{**} that satisfies the statical boundary conditions can be derived from a stress function $\psi^{**}(x_1, x_2)$ that vanishes on the boundary of the cross section (see 5.7, 5.10). Except for

$$T_{13}^{**} = T_{31}^{**} = \partial_2 \psi^{**}, \quad T_{23}^{**} = T_{32}^{**} = -\partial_1 \psi^{**}, \tag{6.21}$$

all stress components vanish, and (6.3) yields

$$2\mathscr{E}_T^{**} = \int [(\partial_1 \psi^{**})^2 + (\partial_2 \psi^{**})^2] \, dA. \tag{6.22}$$

In analogy to (6.15), we have

$$M_3^{**} = 2\int \psi^{**} \, dA. \tag{6.23}$$

For the torsion problem, (6.17) therefore reduces to

$$\int [(\partial_1\varphi^* - x_2)^2 + (\partial_2\varphi^* + x_1)^2]\, dA > D$$
$$> 4\int \psi^{**}\, dA - \int [(\partial_1\psi^{**})^2 + (\partial_2\psi^{**})^2]\, dA. \qquad (6.24)$$

Since this continued inequality remains valid if we replace φ^* by $\alpha\varphi^*$ and ψ^{**} by $\beta\psi^{**}$, we shall choose the constants α and β in such a way that the gap between the bounds for the torsional rigidity D in (6.24) becomes as small as possible. To this end, we introduce the abbreviations

$$\left.\begin{aligned} \Phi^2 &= \int [(\partial_1\varphi^*)^2 + (\partial_2\varphi^*)^2]\, dA, \\ \Psi &= \int [x_2\partial_1\varphi^* - x_1\partial_2\varphi^*]\, dA, \\ I_P &= \int (x_1^2 + x_2^2)\, dA; \end{aligned}\right\} \qquad (6.25)$$

here, I_P is the polar moment of inertia of the cross section $x_3 = 0$ with respect to the origin. If φ^* in (6.24) is replaced by $\alpha\varphi^*$, the upper bound for D becomes

$$\alpha^2\Phi^2 - 2\alpha\Psi + I_P = \left(\alpha\Phi - \frac{\Psi}{\Phi}\right)^2 + I_P - \frac{\Psi^2}{\Phi^2}. \qquad (6.26)$$

The square of the parenthesis in (6.26) cannot be negative. For a chosen warping function φ^*, the least upper bound in (6.24) is therefore given by $I_P - (\Psi^2/\Phi^2)$. Determining the highest lower bound in a similar manner, we find

$$I_P - \frac{\left\{\int [x_2\partial_1\varphi^* - x_1\partial_2\varphi^*]\, dA\right\}^2}{\int [(\partial_1\varphi^*)^2 + (\partial_2\varphi^*)^2]\, dA} > D > \frac{4\left\{\int \psi^{**}\, dA\right\}^2}{\int [(\partial_1\psi^{**})^2 + (\partial_2\psi^{**})^2]\, dA}. \qquad (6.27)$$

We apply the continued inequality (6.27) to the square cross section bounded by the lines $x_1 = \pm 1$, $x_2 = \pm 1$. This cross section is symmetric with respect to the lines $x_1 = 0$, $x_2 = 0$, $x_1 - x_2 = 0$, and $x_1 + x_2 = 0$. As is readily seen, the stress function must be symmetric with respect to these lines and the warping function antisymmetric. The warping function

$$\varphi^* = x_1x_2(x_1^2 - x_2^2) \qquad (6.28)$$

satisfies this condition of antisymmetry; by (6.27), it furnishes the upper bound 2.2519 for the torsional rigidity. The stress function

$$\psi^{**} = (1 - x_1^2)(1 - x_2^2) \tag{6.29}$$

vanishes on the boundary of the square and has the necessary symmetry properties; it yields the lower bound 2.2222 for the torsional rigidity. As is indicated by (5.23), the torsional rigidity increases by the factor a^4 if the linear dimensions of the cross section increase by the factor a. The torsional rigidity D of a square cross section of the side $2a$ is therefore bounded by

$$2.2519\mu a^4 > D > 2.2222\mu a^4. \tag{6.30}$$

Closer bounds for the torsional rigidity may be obtained by incorporating suitable parameters in the tentative expressions for the warping function and the stress function, and determining these parameters to bring the bounds as close to each other as is possible.

7. Elastic waves. The fundamental equations of *elastokinetics* are readily obtained from (4.13) by letting the infinitesimal displacement u_i depend not only on the position but also on the time and replacing the specific body force K_i by $-\partial_{00}u_i$; thus

$$\rho\partial_{00}u_i = \mu\partial_{jj}u_i + (\lambda + \mu)\partial_{ij}u_j. \tag{7.1}$$

To investigate the propagation of a plane wave in an elastic continuum, we choose the x_3-axis perpendicular to the direction of propagation of the wave and denote the unit vector in the direction of propagation by l_i. One speaks of *longitudinal* or *transverse* waves according to whether the oscillations of the particles are along the direction of propagation or perpendicular to it.

If the typical particle performs a harmonic oscillation, a longitudinal wave with the direction of propagation l_i, the amplitude A, the wave length Λ, and the velocity of propagation c is therefore given by

$$u_i = Al_i \sin\frac{2\pi(l_px_p - ct)}{\Lambda}, \tag{7.2}$$

and a transverse wave by

$$u_i = A\epsilon_{iq3}l_q \sin\frac{2\pi(l_px_p - ct)}{\Lambda}. \tag{7.3}$$

Equation (7.2) as well as (7.3) yield

$$\partial_{00}u_i = -c^2\left(\frac{2\pi}{\Lambda}\right)^2 u_i, \quad \partial_{ij}u_k = -\left(\frac{2\pi}{\Lambda}\right)^2 l_il_ju_k. \tag{7.4}$$

The expressions (7.2) and (7.3) thus will satisfy (7.1) if the velocity of propagation has the value

$$c_L = [(\lambda + 2\mu)/\rho]^{1/2} \tag{7.5}$$

for the longitudinal wave and the value

$$c_T = (\mu/\rho)^{1/2} \tag{7.6}$$

for the transverse wave.

Note that, for the harmonic waves of infinitesimal amplitude considered here, the velocities of propagation (7.5) and (7.6) are independent of the amplitude A. This statement remains valid for the more comprehensive class of waves that may be obtained by the superposition of harmonic waves as in a Fourier series or a Fourier integral.

The ratio of the velocities c_L and c_T, which can be written as

$$\frac{c_L}{c_T} = \left[\frac{2(1-\sigma)}{1-2\sigma}\right]^{1/2}, \tag{7.7}$$

depends only on Poisson's ratio σ, and is independent of Young's modulus E or the density ρ.

In an unbounded elastic continuum, each of the two kinds of waves may appear alone. In a bounded continuum, however, the boundary conditions require, as a rule, the simultaneous appearance of both kinds of waves. To illustrate this, we consider the elastic half-space $x_1 \leq 0$, the surface of which is to be free from surface tractions. On the plane $x_1 = 0$, the stress components T_{11}, T_{12}, and T_{13} therefore vanish everywhere and at all times.

Consider the longitudinal wave

$$u_i = A_L l_i \sin \frac{2\pi(l_p x_p - c_L t)}{\Lambda_L}; \tag{7.8}$$

this has the amplitude A_L and the wave length Λ_L and propagates in the direction of the unit vector l_i, which is supposed to be perpendicular to the x_3-direction. It is readily seen that this wave does not fulfill the boundary conditions at the stress-free surface $x_1 = 0$. Indeed, the deformation corresponding to (7.8) is

$$U_{ij} = l_i l_j \frac{2\pi A_L}{\Lambda_L} \cos \frac{2\pi(l_p x_p - c_L t)}{\Lambda_L}. \tag{7.9}$$

Since $l_i l_i = 1$, Hooke's law (3.6) furnishes the stress

$$T_{ij} = (\lambda\delta_{ij} + 2\mu l_i l_j) \frac{2\pi A_L}{\Lambda_L} \cos \frac{2\pi(l_p x_p - c_L t)}{\Lambda_L}. \tag{7.10}$$

For $x_1 = 0$, we therefore have

$$\left.\begin{aligned} T_{11} &= (\lambda + 2\mu l_1^2) \frac{2\pi A_L}{\Lambda_L} \cos \frac{2\pi(l_2 x_2 - c_L t)}{\Lambda_L}, \\ T_{12} &= 2\mu l_1 l_2 \frac{2\pi A_L}{\Lambda_L} \cos \frac{2\pi(l_2 x_2 - c_L t)}{\Lambda_L}, \\ T_{13} &= 0. \end{aligned}\right\} \tag{7.11}$$

For these stress components to vanish identically in x_2 and t, the amplitude A_L would have to be zero. If, therefore, the *incident* wave (7.8) is to appear with nonvanishing amplitude in the half-space $x_1 \leq 0$, *reflected* waves must appear simultaneously so that the boundary conditions on $x_1 = 0$ may be fulfilled.

We tentatively set

$$u_i = A_L l_i \sin \frac{2\pi(l_p x_p - c_L t)}{\Lambda_L} + A'_L l'_i \sin \frac{2\pi(l'_p x_p - c_L t)}{\Lambda'_L} + A_T \epsilon_{iq3} m_q \sin \frac{2\pi(m_p x_p - c_T t)}{\Lambda_T}, \tag{7.12}$$

that is, we superimpose on the wave (7.8) a longitudinal wave with the direction of propagation l'_i, the amplitude A'_L and the wave length Λ'_L, and a transverse wave with the direction of propagation m_i, the amplitude A_T, and the wave length Λ_T. From (7.12), we determine the surface tractions T_{1i} at $x_1 = 0$ in the same way as above; we find

$$T_{11} = (\lambda + 2\mu l_1^2) \frac{2\pi A_L}{\Lambda_L} \cos \frac{2\pi(l_2 x_2 - c_L t)}{\Lambda_L} + (\lambda + 2\mu l_1'^2) \frac{2\pi A'_L}{\Lambda'_L} \cos \frac{2\pi(l'_2 x_2 - c_L t)}{\Lambda'_L} + 2\mu m_1 m_2 \frac{2\pi A_T}{\Lambda_T} \cos \frac{2\pi(m_2 x_2 - c_T t)}{\Lambda_T}, \tag{7.13}$$

$$T_{12} = 2\mu l_1 l_2 \frac{2\pi A_L}{\Lambda_L} \cos \frac{2\pi(l_2 x_2 - c_L t)}{\Lambda_L} + 2\mu l'_1 l'_2 \frac{2\pi A'_L}{\Lambda'_L} \cos \frac{2\pi(l'_2 x_2 - c_L t)}{\Lambda'_L} + \mu(m_2^2 - m_1^2) \frac{2\pi A_T}{\Lambda_T} \cos \frac{2\pi(m_2 x_2 - c_T t)}{\Lambda_T}, \tag{7.14}$$

$$T_{13} = 0. \tag{7.15}$$

The stress components (7.13) and (7.14) can only be made to vanish identically in x_2 and t, if the arguments of the three cosines coincide. We thus have

$$\frac{l_2}{\Lambda_L} = \frac{l'_2}{\Lambda'_L}, \quad \frac{c_L}{\Lambda_L} = \frac{c_L}{\Lambda'_L} \tag{7.16}$$

and

$$\frac{l_2}{\Lambda_L} = \frac{m_2}{\Lambda_T}, \quad \frac{c_L}{\Lambda_L} = \frac{c_T}{\Lambda_T}. \tag{7.17}$$

It follows from (7.16) that

$$l_2 = l_2', \quad \Lambda_L = \Lambda_L'. \tag{7.18}$$

Since l_i and l_i' are unit vectors with vanishing third components, the first equation (7.18) yields

$$l_1 = \pm l_1'. \tag{7.19}$$

If we chose $l_1 = l_1'$, the two longitudinal waves could be combined and the boundary conditions would furnish $A_L = -A_L'$, $A_T = 0$, i.e., $u_i \equiv 0$. We therefore choose

$$l_1 = -l_1'. \tag{7.20}$$

It then follows from (7.17) that

$$\frac{l_2}{m_2} = \frac{\Lambda_L}{\Lambda_T} = \frac{c_L}{c_T}. \tag{7.21}$$

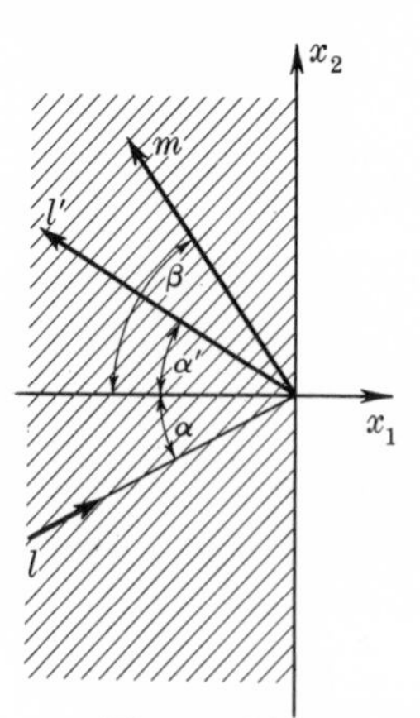

Figure 26

With reference to Figure 26, we introduce the angles α, α', and β between the x_1-axis and the directions of propagation of the waves. The first equation (7.18), together with (7.20) and (7.21) can then be combined as follows:

$$\alpha = \alpha', \quad \frac{\sin \alpha}{\sin \beta} = \frac{\Lambda_L}{\Lambda_T} = \frac{c_L}{c_T}. \tag{7.22}$$

In view of (7.18) and (7.22), the condition that the shearing stress (7.14) should vanish yields

$$2(A_L - A_L') \cos \alpha \sin \beta - A_T \cos 2\beta = 0. \tag{7.23}$$

In a similar way, the vanishing of the normal stress (7.13) leads to the condition

$$(A_L + A_L')(\lambda + 2\mu \cos^2 \alpha) \sin \beta - A_T \mu \sin 2\beta \sin \alpha = 0. \tag{7.24}$$

We transform this equation by writing the contents of the second parenthesis as $\lambda + 2\mu - 2\mu \sin^2 \alpha$ and using (7.5), (7.6) and the second equation (7.22) to replace $\lambda + 2\mu$ by $\mu \sin^2 \alpha/\sin^2 \beta$. We obtain

$$(A_L + A_L') \sin \alpha \cos 2\beta - A_T \sin \beta \sin 2\beta = 0. \tag{7.25}$$

From the specifications of the incident wave those of the reflected waves are found as follows: the angles α' and β are given by (7.22), and the wave lengths, by the second equations (7.18) and (7.22); (7.23) and (7.25) then form an inhomogeneous linear system for the amplitudes A_L' and A_T.

In a *bounded* elastic continuum *surface waves* can occur in addition to the longitudinal and transverse waves discussed so far. To show this, we again consider the half-space $x_1 \leq 0$ with traction-free surface and set

$$u_r = A_r \exp [\alpha x_1 + i\beta(x_2 - ct)], \tag{7.26}$$

where i is the imaginary unit and A_r denotes an amplitude vector with vanishing third component. The coefficient α in (7.26) is supposed to be real and positive, so that the displacements tend to zero for $x_1 = -\infty$.

According to (7.26),

$$\begin{aligned} \partial_{00}u_r &= -c^2\beta^2 u_r, \\ \partial_{pq}u_r &= (\alpha\delta_{1p} + i\beta\delta_{2p})(\alpha\delta_{1q} + i\beta\delta_{2q})u_r. \end{aligned} \tag{7.27}$$

Because of (7.5) and (7.6) the equation of motion (7.1) can therefore be written as follows:

$$-c^2\beta^2 u_r = c_T^2(\alpha^2 - \beta^2)u_r + (c_L^2 - c_T^2)(\alpha\delta_{1r} + i\beta\delta_{2r})(\alpha u_1 + i\beta u_2). \tag{7.28}$$

When u_r is substituted from (7.26) and the common exponential factor is suppressed, the vector equation (7.28), which has identically vanishing third component, furnishes the following homogeneous linear equations for the amplitudes A_1 and A_2:

$$\begin{aligned} [c_L^2\alpha^2 + (c^2 - c_T^2)\beta^2]A_1 + i(c_L^2 - c_T^2)\alpha\beta A_2 &= 0, \\ i(c_L^2 - c_T^2)\alpha\beta A_1 + [c_T^2\alpha^2 + (c^2 - c_L^2)\beta^2]A_2 &= 0. \end{aligned} \tag{7.29}$$

For these equations to have a nontrivial solution, the determinant of the coefficients must vanish. This condition can be written in the form

$$\left[\alpha^2 - \left(1 - \frac{c^2}{c_L^2}\right)\beta^2\right]\left[\alpha^2 - \left(1 - \frac{c^2}{c_T^2}\right)\beta^2\right] = 0 \tag{7.30}$$

and furnishes the following values for α:

$$\alpha' = \beta\left(1 - \frac{c^2}{c_L^2}\right)^{1/2}, \quad \alpha'' = \beta\left(1 - \frac{c^2}{c_T^2}\right)^{1/2}. \tag{7.31}$$

For α to be real, it is sufficient that $c < c_T$, because $c_L > c_T$ by (7.5) and (7.6).

Substitution of α' into the first equation (7.29) furnishes the amplitudes

$$A_1' = -i\alpha' C', \quad A_2' = \beta C', \tag{7.32}$$

which are only determined to within a common factor C'. To the value α'', on the other hand, correspond the amplitudes

$$A_1'' = i\beta C'', \quad A_2'' = -\alpha'' C''. \tag{7.33}$$

We now have to take account of the condition that at the surface $x_1 = 0$ the stress components T_{11}, T_{12}, and T_{13} must vanish identically in x_2 and t. According to (7.26), we have

$$U_{pq} = \tfrac{1}{2}(\alpha\delta_{1p} + i\beta\delta_{2p})u_q + \tfrac{1}{2}(\alpha\delta_{1q} + i\beta\delta_{2q})u_p, \tag{7.34}$$

and (3.6), (7.5), and (7.6) yield

$$\left.\begin{aligned} T_{11}/\rho &= c_L^2 \alpha u_1 + (c_L^2 - 2c_T^2) i\beta u_2, \\ T_{12}/\rho &= c_T^2 (i\beta u_1 + \alpha u_2), \\ T_{13}/\rho &= 0. \end{aligned}\right\} \tag{7.35}$$

With

$$u_r = A_r' \exp\,[\alpha' x_1 + i\beta(x_2 - ct)] + A_r'' \exp\,[\alpha'' x_1 + i\beta(x_2 - ct)], \tag{7.36}$$

the condition of vanishing surface tractions and (7.32) and (7.33) therefore give the following homogeneous linear equations for C' and C'':

$$\begin{aligned} \left(2 - \frac{c^2}{c_T^2}\right)\beta C' - 2\alpha'' C'' &= 0, \\ 2\alpha' C' - \left(2 - \frac{c^2}{c_T^2}\right)\beta C'' &= 0. \end{aligned} \tag{7.37}$$

On account of (7.31) the determinant of the coefficients of these equations vanishes if

$$\left(2 - \frac{c^2}{c_T^2}\right)^4 = 16\left(1 - \frac{c_T^2}{c_L^2}\frac{c^2}{c_T^2}\right)\left(1 - \frac{c^2}{c_T^2}\right). \tag{7.38}$$

With the abbreviations

$$\frac{c_T^2}{c_L^2} = a, \quad \frac{c^2}{c_T^2} = b, \tag{7.39}$$

this equation assumes the form

$$b^3 - 8b^2 + 8(3 - 2a)b - 16(1 - a) = 0. \tag{7.40}$$

If, for example, Poisson's ratio has the value 1/4, (7.7) gives

$$a = \frac{c_T^2}{c_L^2} = \frac{1}{3} \tag{7.41}$$

and (7.40) reduces to

$$(3b^2 - 12b + 8)(b - 4) = 0. \tag{7.42}$$

The only root of this cubic equation which yields real values of α is

$$b = 2(1 - \tfrac{1}{3}\sqrt{3}), \tag{7.43}$$

furnishing

$$c = 0.9194c_T \tag{7.44}$$

and

$$\alpha' = 0.8475\beta, \quad \alpha'' = 0.3933\beta, \quad C'' = 1.4679C'. \tag{7.45}$$

Setting $C = -i\beta C'$ and considering only the real part of u_r, we obtain the solution

$$\begin{aligned} u_1 &= C(0.8475e^{\alpha' x_1} - 1.4679e^{\alpha'' x_1}) \cos \beta(x_2 - ct), \\ u_2 &= -C(e^{\alpha' x_1} - 0.5773e^{\alpha'' x_1}) \sin \beta(x_2 - ct), \end{aligned} \tag{7.46}$$

in which α' and α'' are to be found from an assumed β by means of (7.45), whereas c is to have the value (7.44).

These surface waves are called *Rayleigh* † *waves* after their discoverer. According to (7.44), their velocity of propagation is but slightly smaller than that of the transverse waves. Since α' and α'' are proportional to β and hence inversely proportional to the wave length, short waves die out more rapidly with increasing distance from the free surface than long waves.

PROBLEMS

1.1. Let $\mu_i^{(\alpha)}$, $(\alpha = 1, 2, 3)$, be the unit vectors of three material directions at the typical particle P that instantaneously coincide with the principal directions of the rate of deformation. Write the stress tensor in the form $T_{ij} = \sum_{\alpha,\beta} C_{\alpha\beta}\mu_i^{(\alpha)}\mu_j^{(\beta)}$, and define the stress rate so that it vanishes when $\dot{C}_{\alpha\beta} = 0$. Show that this procedure yields Jaumann's definition of the stress rate.

1.2. Show that Green's definition of the stress rate can be obtained in the following manner. The stress tensor is written in the form $T_{ij} = \sum_{\alpha,\beta} K_{\alpha\beta} l_i^{(\alpha)} l_j^{(\beta)}$, where the vectors $l_i^{(\alpha)}$, $(\alpha = 1, 2, 3)$, are proportional to three material line elements $dx_i^{(\alpha)}$ that emanate from P and are not coplanar. The rate of stress is defined in such a way that it vanishes when $\dot{K}_{\alpha\beta} = 0$.

† Lord Rayleigh (J. W. Strutt), Proc. London Math. Soc. *17* (1885) 4.

1.3. Defining the vectors $l_i^{(\alpha)}$ as in Problem 1.2, let $dP_i = \sum_\alpha dP_\alpha l_i^{(\alpha)}$ be the infinitesimal force transmitted in the typical material surface element (see Problem 1.7 of Chapter III). Show that Truesdell's definition of the stress rate is obtained by requiring that the stress rate should vanish when $dP_\alpha^{\cdot} = 0$.

1.4. Starting from Green's definition of the stress rate, form a symmetric tensor of the second order that can be interpreted as the second rate of stress.

1.5. Prove that, considered as functions of time, the basic invariants of the stress tensor at a particle are stationary, whenever Jaumann's stress rate vanishes at this particle.

1.6. Show that, contrary to the result obtained in Problem 1.5, the vanishing of Green's or Truesdell's stress rate does not imply stationary behavior of the basic invariants of the stress tensor at a particle.

2.1. Investigate simple shear of linear hypoelastic materials for which the contents of the bracket in (2.10) is positive or negative, and express the stress components in terms of the angle θ defined by (2.12).

2.2. Investigate the mechanical behavior of typical linear hypoelastic materials under the combined extension and shear specified by the velocity field

$$v_1 = 2ax_1 + 2bx_2, \quad v_2 = -ax_2, \quad v_3 = -ax_3,$$

where a and b are constants.

3.1. To reflect the combined influence of the stress T_{ij} and the temperature rise Θ, (3.7) must be modified by the addition of the term $\alpha\Theta\delta_{ij}$ on the right side, α being the coefficient of linear thermal expansion. Solve the resulting equation with respect to T_{ij}.

3.2. A material with the constitutive equation (2.5) is initially under the uniform hydrostatic stress $-p\delta_{ij}$. When it is subjected to the infinitesimal displacements $u_i = a_{ij}x_j$, where the coefficients a_{ij} are constants, the material assumes the state of stress T_{ij}. Express T_{ij} in terms of a_{ij} and p.

3.3. Treat the modification of Problem 3.2 obtained by replacing the initial hydrostatic state of stress by the uniaxial state of stress for which $T_{11} = -p$ is the only nonvanishing stress component.

4.1. A body with the constitutive equation (3.6) occupies the simply connected region V with the regular surface S. In the absence of body forces, it is subjected to an equilibrium system of surface tractions $T_i^{(\nu)}$, which produce the infinitesimal displacements u_i. Denoting a second equilibrium system of surface tractions by $T_i^{(\nu)*}$ and the corresponding infinitesimal displacements by $\overset{*}{u}_i$, prove the *reciprocity theorem*

$$\int T_i^{(\nu)*} u_i \, dS = \int T_i^{(\nu)} u_i^* \, dS.$$

4.2. The reciprocity theorem of Problem 4.1 can be written in the alternative form

$$\int T^*_{ij} U_{ij}\, dV = \int T^{(\nu)}_i u^*_i\, dS,$$

in which T^*_{ij} is the stress field corresponding to the surface tractions $T^{(\nu)*}_i$ and U_{ij} is the deformation associated with the displacements u_i. With the use of suitable homogeneous stress fields T^*_{ij}, this equation furnishes average values of typical components of the deformation U_{ij}. Use this technique to prove the following statement: a truncated right circular cone of the height h experiences the volume decrease $Ph/(3\lambda + 2\mu)$ when it is axially compressed between smooth rigid plates, P being the axial force exerted by one plate on the cone.

4.3. Specialize (4.18) for a state of *plane deformation*, in which the displacement components u_1 and u_2 are independent of x_3, while the displacement component u_3 and the body force K_i vanish identically.

4.4. For the plane deformation considered in Problem 4.3, the stress components T_{ij} can be derived from a stress function $\chi(x_1, x_2)$ as in Problem (2.5) of Chapter II. Establish the differential equation for this stress function. Along a closed curve L in the x_1, x_2-plane, let an equilibrium system of tractions $T^{(\nu)}_j = T_{ij}\nu_i$ be given, ν_i being the unit vector of the exterior normal of L. Derive the corresponding boundary conditions for the stress function χ.

4.5. Considering the stress field of Problem 4.4, join the typical point P of the x_1, x_2-plane to the origin O by means of a regular arc a. Let OP specify the positive direction on this arc and define the unit normal vector ν_i so that its direction is obtained from that of the arc by a counterclockwise rotation of 90°. The resultant of the tractions transmitted across OP then equals $R_j = \int T_{ij}\nu_i\, ds$, where ds denotes the arc element and the integration is extended over the entire arc OP. Prove that R_j depends only on the position of the endpoints O and P but not on the shape of the arc, and that the plane vector field R_j has vanishing divergence and harmonic curl.

4.6. Specialize (4.13) for the plane deformation considered in Problem 4.3. Show that the resulting relation can be satisfied by setting $u_i = \partial_i \varphi + (\lambda + 2\mu)\epsilon_{3ij}\partial_j \psi$, where the functions $\varphi(x_1, x_2)$ and $\psi(x_1, x_2)$ are derived from a biharmonic scalar field $\Psi(x_1, x_2)$ by means of $\varphi = \partial_2 \Psi$, $\psi = -\partial_1 \Psi$.

4.7. A body with the constitutive equation obtained in Problem (3.1) is initially stress-free and at uniform temperature; in the absence of body and surface forces, it experiences the non-uniform temperature increase $\Theta(x)$. Establish the differential equation and the boundary condition for the resulting field of thermal stresses, and show that the solution of this boundary value problem is unique.

5.1. The expression (5.19) for the stress function ψ of a twisted elliptic cylinder is suggested by the condition that ψ must vanish on the boundary of the cross section. Try to treat the torsion of a regular triangular prism in a similar manner.

5.2. To discuss the torsion of a circular shaft of variable diameter, introduce cylindrical coordinates ρ, θ, ζ, the ζ-axis of which coincides with the axis of the shaft, and write the infinitesimal displacements in the form $u_\rho = 0$, $u_\theta = \rho\varphi(\rho, \zeta)$, $u_\zeta = 0$. Establish the differential equation for φ and the boundary condition at the shaft surface $\rho = f(\zeta)$.

5.3. An alternative way of treating the torsion of a circular shaft of variable diameter starts from the assumption that $T_{\rho\theta}$ and $T_{\theta\zeta}$ are the only nonvanishing stress components. Show that the equation of equilibrium can be satisfied by setting $T_{\rho\theta} = \rho^{-2}\partial\psi/\partial\zeta$, $T_{\theta\rho} = -\rho^{-2}\partial\psi/\partial\rho$, where $\psi(\rho, \zeta)$ must be twice continuously differentiable. Establish the differential equation and the boundary condition for ψ.

6.1. Prove the inequality (6.11).

6.2. Improve the bounds for the torsional rigidity of a square prism as much as is possible by adding the terms $\alpha x_1 x_2$ and $\beta(1 - x_1^4)(1 - x_2^4)$ in (6.28) and (6.29), respectively.

6.3. Prove that the torsional rigidity of a cylinder with simply connected cross section cannot exceed the product of the shear modulus by the polar moment of inertia of the cross section with respect to its centroid.

6.4. Show that the torsional rigidity of a cylinder with simply connected cross section attains the upper bound obtained in Problem 6.3 only if the cross section is circular.

7.1. Generalize the elastostatic reciprocity theorem of Problem 4.1 to elastokinetic situations.

7.2. An elastic body performs the infinitesimal oscillations $u_i(x, t)$ in the absence of body and surface forces. At the instant $t = 0$ the displacement u_i and the velocity $\partial_0 u_i$ are given as functions of position. Assuming that a motion satisfying these initial conditions exists, show that it is unique.

CHAPTER IX

Finite Strain †

1. Almansi's strain tensor. In most of the constitutive equations considered so far, the kinematical aspects of the mechanical behavior are represented by the rate of deformation; the only exceptions are the constitutive equation of the perfect fluid (IV, 5.17), which does not contain any kinematical variables, and Hooke's law (VIII, 3.6), which is however restricted to infinitesimal deformations from the stress-free state. As was stated in Section 3 of Chapter VIII, the elastic deformations of numerous engineering materials, for instance those of the structural metals, may for many practical purposes be treated as infinitesimal. For materials such as rubber, however, this simplified treatment of elastic deformations will not, as a rule, be adequate. Finite deformations will therefore be studied in this chapter.

While the rate of deformation is defined with respect to the instantaneous state of motion, any acceptable definition of deformation is based on the comparison of the instantaneous shape of an element of the continuum with its shape in some reference state, which will be called the *initial state* of the continuum. To define the rate of deformation, we best describe the motion of the continuum by the time-dependent velocity field

$$v_i = v_i(x, t); \tag{1.1}$$

in this relation, x stands for the coordinates x_1, x_2, x_3 with respect to *fixed* rectangular axes, t denotes the time, and v_i is the velocity vector of the particle that has the position x at the time t. To define the deformation, however, it seems preferable to describe the motion of the continuum by giving the instantaneous coordinates x_i of the typical particle as functions of the time t and its coordinates a_i in the initial state:

$$x_i = x_i(a, t). \tag{1.2}$$

Here, a stands for the *initial coordinates* a_1, a_2, a_3, which are taken with respect to the same axes as the *instantaneous* coordinates x_1, x_2, x_3. The symbol a may be treated as the *label* that characterizes the considered particle.

† While the exposition of this chapter largely follows an unpublished manuscript of the author that dates from 1944, the nomenclature has been strongly influenced by C. Truesdell, Journal Rat. Mech. Analysis *1* (1952) 125.

Equations (1.1) and (1.2) use distinct sets of independent variables, which are usually named after Euler and Lagrange, respectively. This well-established nomenclature will be retained in the following, even though it cannot be justified on historical grounds.†

The one-dimensional example of the flow of vehicles on a one-way street, on which passing is forbidden, may serve to illustrate the difference between these two ways of describing the same motion. The Eulerian description corresponds to the observations of traffic policemen, who report on the velocities with which vehicles pass their fixed observation stations. The Lagrangian description, however, corresponds to the observations of drivers, who report on their progress along the street.

If passing were allowed, two vehicles could have the same coordinate x at the same time t in this one-dimensional treatment of traffic. The function $x(a, t)$ would then cease to define a one-to-one mapping of the initial arrangement of the vehicles onto the instantaneous arrangement. In a continuum, however, this situation cannot arise, because distinct particles cannot assume the same position at the same instant. The three equations represented by (1.2) thus can always be solved in a unique manner with respect to the initial coordinates to yield the inverse description

$$a_i = a_i(x, t) \tag{1.3}$$

of the considered motion. In this description, the same independent variables are used as in the preceding chapters. The formulas based on this description of the motion thus follow the pattern of the preceding investigations and will therefore be discussed first.

Assuming the motion of the continuum to be given in the form (1.3), consider the typical particle P and two material line elements PP' and PP'' emanating from it. If dx_i and δx_i are the components of the vectors PP' and PP'' at the time t, their components in the initial state are

$$da_i = \partial j a_i \, dx_j, \quad \delta a_i = \partial_k a_i \, \delta x_k. \tag{1.4}$$

If the initial and instantaneous positions of the neighborhood of the particle P correspond to two positions of a rigid body, we shall say that this neighborhood can be brought *without strain* from its initial to its instantaneous position. Note that in this connection only the initial and instantaneous configurations are considered, but not the way in which the transition from one to the other is achieved during the motion described by (1.3). If the rate of deformation vanishes throughout this transition, we shall say that this transition does not involve any deformation. In the following, the term *deformation* will be used to indicate the investigation of a continuous sequence of configurations, and the term *strain*, to indicate the comparison of the initial and instantaneous configurations without reference to the deformation leading from one to the other.

† See, for instance, C. Truesdell, Journal Rat. Mech. Analysis *1* (1952) 125, Footnote 5 on p. 139.

If the neighborhood of P has not experienced any strain, the material triangle $PP'P''$ has the same shape in the instantaneous state as it had in the initial state. Accordingly, the difference

$$dx_i\,\delta x_i - da_i\,\delta a_i = (\delta_{jk} - \partial_j a_i \partial_k a_i)\,dx_j\,\delta x_k \tag{1.5}$$

vanishes for any choice of the particles P' and P'' in the neighborhood of P, that is, in the absence of strain the symmetric tensor

$$U_{jk} = \tfrac{1}{2}(\delta_{jk} - \partial_j a_i \partial_k a_i) \tag{1.6}$$

vanishes. Conversely, the vanishing of this tensor, which will be called *Almansi's* † *strain tensor*, indicates the absence of strain. At first glance, the inclusion of the factor $\frac{1}{2}$ in the definition of this strain tensor might appear arbitrary; it will be justified later.

To investigate the mechanical meaning of the components of Almansi's strain tensor, denote the instantaneous lengths of the material line elements PP' and PP'' by ds and δs, respectively, and their instantaneous angle by θ, and the corresponding quantities in the initial state by $d\bar{s}$, $\delta\bar{s}$, and $\bar{\theta}$. Finally, let μ_i and ν_i be the unit vectors of the instantaneous directions of PP' and PP''. Because of (1.6), equation (1.5) can then be written as follows:

$$\cos\theta - \frac{d\bar{s}\;\delta\bar{s}}{ds\;\delta s}\cos\bar{\theta} = 2U_{ij}\mu_i\nu_j. \tag{1.7}$$

If, in particular, P'' coincides with P', (1.7) reduces to

$$1 - \left(\frac{d\bar{s}}{ds}\right)^2 = 2U_{ij}\mu_i\mu_j. \tag{1.8}$$

The quotient of the instantaneous length ds and the initial length $d\bar{s}$ of the considered line element will be called its *length ratio* and be denoted by $\lambda^{(\mu)}$. According to (1.8), we have

$$\lambda^{(\mu)} = (1 - 2U_{ij}\mu_i\mu_j)^{-1/2}. \tag{1.9}$$

Material line elements that are instantaneously parallel to the coordinate axes, thus have the length ratios

$$\lambda^{(1)} = (1 - 2U_{11})^{-1/2},\quad \lambda^{(2)} = (1 - 2U_{22})^{-1/2},\quad \lambda^{(3)} = (1 - 2U_{33})^{-1/2}. \tag{1.10}$$

Next, consider material line elements PP' and PP'' that are instantaneously orthogonal. Equation (1.7) then furnishes

$$-\frac{d\bar{s}\;\delta\bar{s}}{ds\;\delta s}\cos\bar{\theta} = 2U_{ij}\mu_i\nu_i. \tag{1.11}$$

† E. Almansi, Rend. Lincei (5A) *20* (1) (1911) 705.

in which $d\bar{s}/ds$ and $\delta\bar{s}/\delta s$ may be replaced by $1/\lambda^{(\mu)}$ and $1/\lambda^{(\nu)}$. The angle formed by the considered line elements equals $\bar{\theta}$ in the initial state and $\pi/2$ in the instantaneous state. The factor $-\cos\bar{\theta}$ in (1.11) may therefore be written as the sine of the angle decrease $-\left(\frac{\pi}{2} - \bar{\theta}\right)$, which will be denoted by $\omega^{(\mu\nu)}$. Equation (1.11) thus is equivalent to

$$\omega^{(\mu\nu)} = \arcsin\,(2\lambda^{(\mu)}\lambda^{(\nu)}U_{ij}\mu_i\nu_j). \tag{1.12}$$

For material line elements that instantaneously have the x_1- and x_2-directions, the angle decrease is therefore given by

$$\omega^{(12)} = \arcsin\,(2\lambda^{(1)}\lambda^{(2)}U_{12}). \tag{1.13}$$

If the components of Almansi's strain tensor are small in comparison to 1, the first equation (1.10) may be approximated by $\lambda^{(1)} = 1 + U_{11}$, and (1.13) by $\omega^{(12)} = 2U_{12}$. *For infinitesimal deformation* from the initial state, U_{11} is therefore the extension in the x_1-direction, and U_{12} one half of the angle decrease for the x_1- and x_2-directions, that is, Almansi's strain tensor is identical with the deformation tensor used in Section 3 of Chapter VIII. This fact justifies the introduction of the factor $\frac{1}{2}$ in (1.6).

We now consider three material line elements that emanate from the particle P and are not coplanar. In the instantaneous state, let these line elements be given by the infinitesimal vectors dx_i, δx_i, and Δx_i. According to (I, 6.4), the instantaneous volume of the parallelepiped specified by these three vectors equals

$$dV = \epsilon_{ijk}\, dx_i\, \delta x_j\, \Delta x_k, \tag{1.14}$$

and by (1.3) the corresponding volume in the initial state is

$$d\bar{V} = \epsilon_{ijk}\partial_p a_i \partial_q a_j \partial_r a_k\, dx_p\, \delta x_q\, \Delta x_r. \tag{1.15}$$

The *Jacobian* ∂a of the transformation (1.3) is defined as

$$\partial a = \begin{bmatrix} \partial_1 a_1 & \partial_1 a_2 & \partial_1 a_3 \\ \partial_2 a_1 & \partial_2 a_2 & \partial_2 a_3 \\ \partial_3 a_1 & \partial_3 a_2 & \partial_3 a_3 \end{bmatrix}. \tag{1.16}$$

As is readily verified,

$$\epsilon_{ijk}\partial_p a_i \partial_q a_j \partial_r a_k = \partial a\; \epsilon_{pqr}. \tag{1.17}$$

With the use of (1.14), equation (1.15) can therefore be written as

$$d\bar{V} = \partial a\, dV. \tag{1.18}$$

The *volume ratio* $dV/d\bar{V}$ thus equals the reciprocal of the Jacobian ∂a. Conservation of matter requires that to a nonvanishing instantaneous volume there corresponds a nonvanishing initial volume. Consequently, the Jacobian ∂a cannot vanish.

According to Section 7 of Chapter I, the symmetric tensor U_{ij} possess at least one system of principal axes. If these principal axes are taken as coordinate axes, the matrix of the strain tensor assumes diagonal form. Because of (1.13) this means that material line elements that emanate from the considered particle P in the principal directions of U_{ij} were also orthogonal in the initial state. There exists therefore a triple of material directions at P that are orthogonal both in the initial and the instantaneous state. If these directions are marked in the initial state, the neighborhood of P may be brought from its initial to its instantaneous position by the following sequence of steps: 1) the translation that brings the particle P into its new position; 2) the rotation that lets the marked directions coincide with the corresponding principal directions of Almansi's strain tensor; and 3) the simultaneous extension in these principal directions, whereby, for example, the length ratio λ_{I} for the principal direction μ^{I} is related to the associated principal value U_{I} of the strain tensor by

$$\lambda_{\mathrm{I}} = (1 - 2U_{\mathrm{I}})^{-1/2}. \tag{1.19}$$

It follows from the stationary character of the principal values of a symmetric tensor that the length ratio remains stationary in the transition from a principal direction to a neighboring direction.

Equation (1.19) and the corresponding equations for the other principal length ratios λ_{II} and λ_{III}, as well as the relation $dV/d\overline{V} = \lambda_{\mathrm{I}}\lambda_{\mathrm{II}}\lambda_{\mathrm{III}}$ show that

$$\left(\frac{d\overline{V}}{dV}\right)^2 = (1 - 2U_{\mathrm{I}})(1 - 2U_{\mathrm{II}})(1 - 2U_{\mathrm{III}})$$

$$= 1 - 2\mathcal{U}_{(1)} - 4\mathcal{U}_{(2)} - 8\mathcal{U}_{(3)}; \tag{1.20}$$

here, $\mathcal{U}_{(1)}$, $\mathcal{U}_{(2)}$ and $\mathcal{U}_{(3)}$ are the basic invariants of Almansi's strain tensor.

If the motion of a continuum is specified in the form (1.3), the alternative specification (1.1) of this motion can be obtained as follows. While the position x_i of a moving particle varies, its label a_i remains the same, that is the material rate of change of a_i vanishes. According to (III, 4.8), we therefore have

$$v_p\partial_p a_i + \partial_0 a_i = 0. \tag{1.21}$$

The three components of this vector equation form a system of three inhomogeneous linear equations for the velocity components $v_p(x, t)$. The determinant of the coefficients in these equations is the Jacobian ∂a of the transformation (1.3). As has been shown above, this determinant cannot vanish, so that the three equations represented by (1.21) always furnish unique expressions for the velocity components as functions of the initial coordinates and the time.

It follows from (1.21) that

$$(\partial_p a_i)^{\cdot} = (\partial_0 + v_k \partial_k)\partial_p a_i$$
$$= \partial_k(\partial_0 + v_k \partial_k)a_i - \partial_p v_k \partial_k a_i = -\partial_p v_k \partial_k a_i. \qquad (1.22)$$

On account of (1.6) and (III, 4.8) the material rate of change of Almansi's strain tensor is therefore given by

$$U^{\cdot}_{pq} = -\tfrac{1}{2}[(\partial_p a_i)^{\cdot}\partial_q a_i + \partial_p a_i(\partial_q a_i)^{\cdot}]$$
$$= \partial_p v_k(\tfrac{1}{2}\delta_{kq} - U_{kq}) + \partial_q v_k(\tfrac{1}{2}\delta_{kp} - U_{kp})$$
$$= V_{pq} - U_{pk}\partial_q v_k - U_{qk}\partial_p v_k. \qquad (1.23)$$

Writing the vector gradient of the velocity field in (1.23) as the sum of its symmetric and antisymmetric parts, and using the symmetry or antisymmetry properties of the tensors in the resulting equation, we obtain

$$U^{\cdot}_{pq} - U_{pk}\partial[_k v_q] - U_{qk}\partial[_k v_p] = V_{pq} - U_{pk}V_{kq} - U_{qk}V_{kp}. \qquad (1.24)$$

The left side of this equation has a structure analogous to that of the stress rate (VIII, 1.7); it will therefore be called *Almansi's strain rate* and be denoted by U^{∇}_{jk}. As is seen from the relation

$$U^{\nabla}_{jk} = V_{jk} - U_{jp}V_{pk} - U_{kp}V_{pj}, \qquad (1.25)$$

which is equivalent to (1.24), in the initial state ($U_{jk} = 0$) Almansi's strain rate U^{∇}_{jk} is identical with the rate of deformation V_{jk}.

2. Green's strain tensor. The ease with which we can use formulas of the preceding chapters renders Eulerian variables attractive from the mathematical point of view. From the standpoint of physics, however, Lagrangian variables seem particularly suited to the description of the motion of a continuum for which the initial state is not an arbitrarily chosen reference state, but a *natural* state of the continuum such as the homogeneous stress-free state of an elastic body. The use of Lagrangian variables then enables us to treat all kinematical questions in a particularly simple manner. In exchange, however, for this advantage on the kinematic side, we must accept a certain complication on the static side, as will be seen in Section 4.

Since the initial coordinates a_i and the time are now used as independent variables, new symbols must be introduced to indicate partial differentiation with respect to these variables. The partial differentiation with respect to a_i will be denoted by the operator D_i, and that with respect to the time by D_0. These operators are only to act on the immediately following symbol, unless the contrary is indicated by the use of parentheses or brackets.

As before, consider the material line elements PP' and PP'', which are given by the vectors da_i and δa_i in the initial state, and by the vectors dx_i

and δx_i in the instantaneous state. In analogy to (1.4), we have

$$dx_i = D_j x_i \, da_j, \quad \delta x_i = D_k x_i \, \delta a_k. \tag{2.1}$$

The substitution of the first equation (2.1) in the first equation (1.4) and the inverse substitution furnish the relations

$$\partial_p a_i D_j x_p = \delta_{ij}, \quad D_p x_i \partial_j a_p = \delta_{ij}. \tag{2.2}$$

For fixed j, the first of these relations represents a nonhomogeneous system of linear equations for $D_j x_1$, $D_j x_2$, and $D_j x_3$. Since the determinant of the coefficients in these equations is the nonvanishing Jacobian ∂a, the quantities $D_j x_p$ can be uniquely expressed in terms of the quantities $\partial_p a_i$.

Differentiation of the first equation (2.2) with respect to $\partial_r a_s$ furnishes

$$\delta_{pr}\delta_{is}D_j x_p + \partial_p a_i \frac{\partial(D_j x_p)}{\partial(\partial_r a_s)} = 0. \tag{2.3}$$

Multiplication of this relation by $D_i x_k$ and use of (2.2) yields

$$\frac{\partial(D_j x_k)}{\partial(\partial_r a_s)} = -D_j x_r D_s x_k. \tag{2.4}$$

In a similar way, one finds

$$\frac{\partial(\partial_j a_k)}{\partial(D_r x_s)} = -\partial_j a_r \partial_s a_k. \tag{2.5}$$

It follows from (2.1) that

$$dx_i \, \delta x_i - da_i \, \delta a_i = (D_j x_i D_k x_i - \delta_{jk}) \, da_j \, \delta a_k, \tag{2.6}$$

and this relation suggests the introduction of *Green's* † *strain tensor*

$$\overline{U}_{jk} = \tfrac{1}{2}(D_j x_i D_k x_i - \delta_{jk}). \tag{2.7}$$

To find the mechanical meaning of the components of this tensor, we proceed as in Section 1. Instead of (1.7), we now have the equation

$$\frac{ds}{d\bar{s}} \frac{\delta s}{\delta \bar{s}} \cos\theta - \cos\bar{\theta} = 2\overline{U}_{ij}\alpha_i\beta_j, \tag{2.8}$$

on the left side of which the symbols have the same meaning as in (1.7), while α_i and β_i are unit vectors with the directions of da_i and δa_i, respectively. A material line element that *initially* had the a_1-direction, thus has the length ratio

$$\bar{\lambda}^{(1)} = (1 + 2\overline{U}_{11})^{1/2}, \tag{2.9}$$

and the initially right angle between material line elements that initially

† G. Green, Trans. Cambridge Philos. Soc. 7 (1839–42) 121.

had the a_1- and a_2-directions decreases by

$$\bar{\omega}^{(12)} = \text{arc sin} \frac{2\bar{U}_{12}}{\bar{\lambda}^{(1)}\bar{\lambda}^{(2)}}. \tag{2.10}$$

Equations (2.9) and (2.10) show that, *for infinitesimal deformation from the initial state*, $\bar{U}_{11}$ represents the extension in the a_1-direction and $\bar{U}_{12}$ half the angle decrease for the a_1- and a_2-directions, that is, Green's strain tensor is identical with the deformation tensor introduced in Section 3 of Chapter VIII.

It can be shown in a similar way as in Section 1 that the volume ratio $dV/d\bar{V}$ is given by the Jacobian Dx with the typical element $D_i x_j$. This also follows from the fact that the product of the Jacobians of the transformation (1.2) and its inverse (1.3) must have the value 1. As the Jacobian ∂a, the Jacobian Dx cannot vanish, because this would violate the principle of conservation of mass.

The principal axes and values of the symmetric tensor $\bar{U}_{ij}$ can be interpreted mechanically in a way similar to those of the tensor U_{ij}. As has been shown in Section 1, there exists at least one triple of instantaneously orthogonal material directions at the typical particle that were also initially orthogonal. Whereas the *instantaneous* directions indicate a system of principal axes of the tensor U_{ij}, the corresponding *initial* directions indicate a system of principal axes of the tensor $\bar{U}_{ij}$. The length ratio λ_{I} for the first principal direction can therefore be written either in the form (1.19) or in the form $\lambda_{\text{I}} = (1 + 2\bar{U}_{\text{I}})^{1/2}$, which follows from (2.9). Corresponding principal values of the two strain tensors thus are related by equations of the form

$$U_{\text{I}} = \frac{\bar{U}_{\text{I}}}{1 + 2\bar{U}_{\text{I}}}, \quad \bar{U}_{\text{I}} = \frac{U_{\text{I}}}{1 - 2U_{\text{I}}}. \tag{2.11}$$

From (2.11), relations between the basic invariants of the two tensors are readily derived. One finds, for example,

$$\begin{aligned} \bar{\mathscr{U}}_{(1)} &= \bar{U}_{\text{I}} + \bar{U}_{\text{II}} + \bar{U}_{\text{III}} \\ &= \frac{\mathscr{U}_{(1)} + 4\mathscr{U}_{(2)} + 12\mathscr{U}_{(3)}}{1 - 2\mathscr{U}_{(1)} - 4\mathscr{U}_{(2)} - 8\mathscr{U}_{(3)}}. \end{aligned} \tag{2.12}$$

If the motion of the continuum is specified in the form (1.2), the alternative specification (1.1) can be obtained as follows. Partial differentiation of (1.2) with respect to t furnishes

$$\bar{v}_i = \bar{v}_i(a, t) = D_0 x_i. \tag{2.13}$$

Both sides of (2.13) are of course functions of the Lagrangian variables a, t, but since (1.2) represents a one-to-one mapping of the initial on to the instantaneous configuration, the specification (1.2) in principle yields the equivalent specification (1.3). With the aid of the latter, (2.13) can then be written in the form (1.1).

Equation (2.13) exhibits an advantage of the Lagrangian variables: the material rate of change is obtained by the application of the operator D_0. For example, the acceleration of the particle with the initial position a_i is $D_{00}a_i$.

To derive an important expression for the material rate of change $D_0\overline{U}_{ij}$ of Green's strain tensor, use (2.7) to rewrite (2.6) in the form

$$dx_i\,\delta x_i - da_i\,\delta a_i = 2\overline{U}_{ij}\,da_i\,\delta a_j. \tag{2.14}$$

On the left of this equation, the material rate of change of the first term is given by (III, 1.10), while that of the second term vanishes. Because of (III, 1.11), we have, therefore,

$$V_{ij}\,dx_i\,\delta x_j = D_0\overline{U}_{ij}\,da_i\,\delta a_j. \tag{2.15}$$

We now use (2.1) to express dx_i, δx_i in (2.15) in terms of da_i, δa_i and take account of the fact that the resulting equation must hold for an arbitrary choice of da_i and δa_i. We thus obtain

$$D_0\overline{U}_{ij} = V_{pq}D_ix_pD_jx_q. \tag{2.16}$$

The comparison of (2.16) with the corresponding equation (1.23) is instructive. As is shown by the latter, the material rate of change $\dot{U}_{ij}$ of Almansi's strain tensor need not vanish when the neighborhood of the considered particle moves as a rigid body, that is, when V_{ij} vanishes at this particle. Accordingly, $\dot{U}_{ij}$ cannot be used in constitutive equations as a measure of the rate of change of the strain U_{ij}, and Almansi's strain rate, which can be so used, must be defined separately (see 1.25). As follows from (2.16), the material rate of change $D_0\overline{U}_{ij}$ of Green's strain tensor vanishes when the neighborhood of the considered particle moves as a rigid body. The material rate of change $D_0\overline{U}_{ij}$, which will be called *Green's strain rate*, can therefore be directly used in constitutive equations. This is a further advantage of Lagrangian variables.

3. Other strain tensors. If the neighborhood of the typical particle P does not experience any strain, the strain tensors introduced in Sections 1 and 2 vanish. If one is ready to accept strain tensors that indicate the absence of strain in some other manner, one may introduce the strain tensors

$$C_{ij} = \partial_ia_k\partial_ja_k \tag{3.1}$$

and

$$\overline{C}_{ij} = D_ix_kD_jx_k, \tag{3.2}$$

which will be named after Cauchy.† The comparison of (3.1) and (3.2)

† A. Cauchy, *Exercises de Mathématiques*, Vol. 2, Paris, 1827, pp. 1, 42, 60, 108; Vol. 3, Paris, 1828, pp. 160, 188, 213, 237.

with (2.4) and (2.5) shows that

$$C_{ij} = -\frac{\partial(\partial_i a_k)}{\partial(D_k x_j)} \tag{3.3}$$

and

$$\bar{C}_{ij} = -\frac{\partial(D_i x_k)}{\partial(\partial_k a_j)}. \tag{3.4}$$

According to (1.6) and (3.1),

$$C_{ij} = \delta_{ij} - 2U_{ij}. \tag{3.5}$$

In the absence of strain, we therefore have $C_{ij} = \delta_{ij}$. Equation (3.5) shows that any system of principal axes of the tensor U_{ij} is also a system of principal axes of the tensor C_{ij}. As has been discussed in Section 1, such a system indicates three instantaneously orthogonal material directions that were also initially orthogonal. Corresponding principal values of the tensors C_{ij} and U_{ij} are related by means of equations of the form

$$C_{\mathrm{I}} = 1 - 2U_{\mathrm{I}}. \tag{3.6}$$

According to (1.19) the length ratio for the principal direction μ^{I} of C_{ij} is given by

$$\lambda_{\mathrm{I}} = C_{\mathrm{I}}^{-1/2}. \tag{3.7}$$

By its definition, the length ratio is a finite positive number. The tensor C_{ij} thus has a unique inverse B_{ij} such that

$$C_{ip}B_{pj} = B_{ip}C_{pj} = \delta_{ij}. \tag{3.8}$$

As is readily verified, (3.8) is fulfilled by

$$B_{ij} = D_k x_i D_k x_j. \tag{3.9}$$

The tensor B_{ij} has the same principal axes as C_{ij} and its principal values are reciprocal to those of C_{ij}. On account of (3.7) the principal values of B_{ij} are, therefore, the squares of the length ratios for the principal directions; thus,

$$\lambda_{\mathrm{I}}^2 = \frac{1}{1 - 2U_{\mathrm{I}}} = \frac{1}{C_{\mathrm{I}}} = B_{\mathrm{I}}. \tag{3.10}$$

The relations between corresponding principal values of the tensors **U**, **C**, and **B** that are indicated by (3.10) can be used to express the basic invariants of one of these tensors by those of another one. We find, for instance,

$$\begin{aligned} \mathscr{C}_{(2)} &= -(C_{\mathrm{I}}C_{\mathrm{II}} + C_{\mathrm{II}}C_{\mathrm{III}} + C_{\mathrm{III}}C_{\mathrm{I}}) \\ &= -\frac{B_{\mathrm{I}} + B_{\mathrm{II}} + B_{\mathrm{III}}}{B_{\mathrm{I}}B_{\mathrm{II}}B_{\mathrm{III}}} = -\frac{\mathscr{B}_{(1)}}{\mathscr{B}_{(3)}}. \end{aligned} \tag{3.11}$$

We leave the corresponding discussion of the tensor $\overline{C}_{ij}$ to the reader. The tensor

$$\overline{B}_{ij} = \partial_k a_i \partial_k a_j \tag{3.12}$$

is reciprocal to $\overline{C}_{ij}$.

The tensors B_{ij} and $\overline{B}_{ij}$ will be called *Finger's* † *strain tensors*. The comparison of (3.9) and (3.12) with (2.4) and (2.5) shows that

$$B_{ij} = -\frac{\partial(D_k x_j)}{\partial(\partial_i a_k)}, \tag{3.13}$$

$$\overline{B}_{ij} = -\frac{\partial(\partial_k a_j)}{\partial(D_i x_k)}. \tag{3.14}$$

According to (I, 7.9), (1.17) and the first equation (I, 6.5) the determinant $\overline{\mathscr{B}}_{(3)}$ of the tensor $\overline{B}_{ij}$ is given by

$$\begin{aligned}\overline{\mathscr{B}}_{(3)} &= \tfrac{1}{6}\epsilon_{ijk}\epsilon_{pqr}\overline{B}_{ip}\overline{B}_{jq}\overline{B}_{kr}\\ &= \tfrac{1}{6}\epsilon_{ijk}\epsilon_{pqr}\partial_l a_i \partial_l a_p \partial_m a_j \partial_m a_q \partial_n a_k \partial_n a_r\\ &= \tfrac{1}{6}(\epsilon_{ijk}\partial_l a_i \partial_m a_j \partial_n a_k)(\epsilon_{pqr}\partial_l a_p \partial_m a_q \partial_n a_r)\\ &= \tfrac{1}{6}(\epsilon_{lmn}\partial a)(\epsilon_{lmn}\partial a) = (\partial a)^2.\end{aligned} \tag{3.15}$$

Similarly,

$$\mathscr{B}_{(3)} = (Dx)^2. \tag{3.16}$$

The Jacobians in (3.15) and (3.16) may also be expressed in terms of the ratio $\rho/\overline{\rho}$ of the instantaneous and initial densities at the considered particle. Indeed, it follows from (1.18) and the principle of conservation of mass that

$$\partial a = \rho/\overline{\rho}. \tag{3.17}$$

Conversely,

$$Dx = \overline{\rho}/\rho. \tag{3.18}$$

To discuss the geometrical meaning of *Finger's strain tensors*, consider again the material line elements PP' and PP'' that emanate from the typical particle P and are represented by the vectors da_i and δa_i in the initial state and by the vectors dx_i and δx_i in the instantaneous state. The magnitude of the vector product

$$dF_i = \epsilon_{ijk}\, dx_j\, \delta x_k \tag{3.19}$$

then represents the area dF of the parallelogram specified by the instantaneous positions of P, P' and P'', and the direction of this vector product is normal to the plane of this parallelogram. The vector product

$$d\overline{F}_i = \epsilon_{ijk}\, da_j\, \delta a_k \tag{3.20}$$

can be interpreted in a similar manner.

† J. Finger, Sitz. ber. Akad. Wiss. Wien (IIa) *103* (1894) 1073.

Substitution of (1.4) into (3.20) yields

$$d\bar{F}_i = \epsilon_{ijk}\partial_q a_j \partial_r a_k \, dx_q \, \delta x_r, \tag{3.21}$$

and multiplication of this relation by $\partial_p a_i$ and use of (1.17) and (3.17) furnishes

$$\partial_p a_i \, d\bar{F}_i = \partial a \, dF_p = \frac{\rho}{\bar{\rho}} dF_p. \tag{3.22}$$

According to (3.22) and (3.15), the square of the instantaneous area is given by

$$dF^2 = dF_p \, dF_p = \frac{1}{(\partial a)^2} \partial_p a_i \partial_p a_j \, d\bar{F}_i \, d\bar{F}_j$$

$$= \frac{\bar{B}_{ij}}{\overline{\mathscr{B}}_{(3)}} d\bar{F}_i \, d\bar{F}_j \tag{3.23}$$

The structure of this formula closely resembles that of the formula

$$ds^2 = dx_p \, dx_p = D_i x_p D_j x_p \, da_i \, da_j = \bar{C}_{ij} \, da_i \, da_j, \tag{3.24}$$

which follows from (2.1). The tensor $\bar{B}_{ij}/\overline{\mathscr{B}}_{(3)}$ thus represents the change in area in exactly the same way in which the tensor $\bar{C}_{ij}$ represents the change in length, and a similar statement applies to the tensors $B_{ij}/\mathscr{B}_{(3)}$ and C_{ij}. These results are due to Truesdell. †

As follows from (3.24), the length ratio for a principal direction of $\bar{C}_{ij}$ is related to the corresponding principal value of this tensor by an equation of the form

$$\lambda_{\mathrm{I}}^2 = \bar{C}_{\mathrm{I}}. \tag{3.25}$$

Since the tensor $\bar{B}_{ij}$ is reciprocal to $\bar{C}_{ij}$, we have

$$\lambda_{\mathrm{I}}^2 = \bar{C}_{\mathrm{I}} = \frac{1}{\bar{B}_{\mathrm{I}}}. \tag{3.26}$$

The comparison of (3.10) and (3.26) shows that C_{ij} and $\bar{B}_{ij}$ have the same principal values. All the same, these tensors are not identical, because their principal axes do not coincide. In fact, when the principal directions of $\bar{B}_{ij}$ are regarded as material directions, they are transformed by the considered strain into the principal directions of C_{ij}. From the equality of the principal values of $\bar{B}_{ij}$ and C_{ij} it follows that corresponding basic invariants of these tensors are equal to each other, and the same is true for corresponding basic invariants of the tensors B_{ij} and $\bar{C}_{ij}$.

4. Lagrange's and Kirchhoff's stress tensors. Several advantages of the Lagrangian variables were pointed out in Section 2. As is to be expected,

† C. Truesdell, Quarterly Appl. Math. *15* (1958) 434.

however, the use of these variables also entails some disadvantages. These stem from the fact that the stresses transmitted in the instantaneous state must now be referred to the initial state in a way that is physically artificial though mathematically consistent.

If T_{ij} is the stress tensor referred to the instantaneous state, the infinitesimal force dP_j transmitted in the surface element dF_i (see 3.19) is given by

$$dP_j = T_{ij}\, dF_i. \tag{4.1}$$

Equation (4.1) suggests the following way of defining a stress tensor $\overline{T}_i^j$ that is referred to the initial state:

$$dP_j = \overline{T}_{ij}\, d\overline{F}_i. \tag{4.2}$$

The initial surface element $d\overline{F}_i$ in (4.2) is defined by (3.20). For convenient reference, the tensors T_{ij} and $\overline{T}_{ij}$ will be called the *Eulerian* and the *Lagrangian stress tensor*, respectively.

Substitution of dF_i from (3.22) into (4.1) and comparison with (4.2) yields

$$\overline{T}_{ij} = \frac{\bar{\rho}}{\rho}\, \partial_p a_i T_{pj}. \tag{4.3}$$

As this relation shows, the Lagrangian stress tensor is not symmetric as a rule. This tensor is therefore difficult to use in constitutive equations that are to represent the stress components in terms of the components of the symmetric strain tensor. This difficulty can be avoided as follows. Before the infinitesimal force dP_j transmitted in the instantaneous state is referred to the surface element in the initial state, let it be subjected to the same transformation that changes the instantaneous side dx_i of the surface element into the corresponding initial side da_i. In analogy with (1.4), this transformed force is given by

$$d\overline{P}_j = \partial_q a_j\, dP_q. \tag{4.4}$$

A modified stress tensor $\overline{S}_{ij}$ is now defined by setting

$$d\overline{P}_j = \overline{S}_{ij}\, d\overline{F}_i. \tag{4.5}$$

Substitution of dP_q from (4.1) into (4.4) and comparison with (4.5) furnishes

$$\overline{S}_{ij} = \frac{\bar{\rho}}{\rho}\, \partial_p a_i \partial_q a_j T_{pq}. \tag{4.6}$$

This relation clearly exhibits the symmetry of the tensor $\overline{S}_{ij}$, which will be called *Kirchhoff's* † *stress tensor*. On account of its symmetry this stress

† G. Kirchhoff, Sitz. ber. Akad. Wiss. Wien *9* (1852) 762. Independently of Kirchhoff, E. Trefftz (Zeitschrift angew. Math. Mech. *13* (1933) 160) and R. Kappus (*ibid. 19* (1939) 271, 344) have emphasized the advantages of this stress tensor.

tensor is better suited to the formulation of constitutive equations than the unsymmetric stress tensor $\overline{T}_{ij}$.

Substitution of (4.3) into (4.6) yields

$$\overline{S}_{ij} = \overline{T}_{iq}\partial_q a_j = \overline{T}_{jp}\partial_p a_i. \tag{4.7}$$

Equations (2.2) enable us to solve (4.3), (4.6), and (4.7) with respect to the stress tensors appearing on the right sides. Thus,

$$T_{ij} = \frac{\rho}{\bar{\rho}} D_p x_i \overline{T}_{pj} = \frac{\rho}{\bar{\rho}} D_p x_i D_q x_j \overline{S}_{pq}, \tag{4.8}$$

$$\overline{T}_{ij} = \overline{S}_{ip} D_p x_j. \tag{4.9}$$

The complete analogy between equation (4.6) and its inverse contained in (4.8) clearly indicates that Kirchhoff's stress tensor plays the same role for Lagrangian variables as does the Eulerian stress tensor for Eulerian variables. As the following discussion will show, Green's strain rate $D_0\overline{U}_{ij}$ and the rate of deformation V_{ij} correspond to each other in the same way.

As was noted in connection with (IV, 4.8), the power of the stresses per unit of volume is $T_{ij}V_{ij}$; the power per unit of mass thus equals $T_{ij}V_{ij}/\rho$. With the aid of (4.8) and (2.16), this expression can be transformed as follows:

$$\frac{1}{\rho} T_{ij}V_{ij} = \frac{1}{\bar{\rho}} D_p x_i D_q x_j \overline{S}_{pq} V_{ij} = \frac{1}{\bar{\rho}} \overline{S}_{pq} D_0 \overline{U}_{pq}. \tag{4.10}$$

Assuming the initial density $\bar{\rho}$ to be independent of position, we deduce from the equation of continuity (IV, 1.3) that

$$(\partial_0 + v_k\partial_k)\frac{\bar{\rho}}{\rho} = \left(\frac{\bar{\rho}}{\rho}\right)^{\cdot} = -\frac{\bar{\rho}}{\rho^2}\rho^{\cdot} = \frac{\bar{\rho}}{\rho}\partial_k v_k. \tag{4.11}$$

To compute $D_0\overline{S}_{ij}$, we apply the operator D_0 to the left side of (4.6), and the corresponding operator $\partial_0 + v_k\partial_k$ to the right side of this equation. With the aid of (1.22), we thus obtain

$$D_0\overline{S}_{ij} = \frac{\bar{\rho}}{\rho}[\partial_k v_k \partial_p a_i \partial_q a_j T_{pq} - \partial_p v_k \partial_k a_i \partial_q a_j T_{pq} - \partial_p a_i \partial_k a_j \partial_q v_k T_{pq} + \partial_p a_i \partial_q a_j T^{\cdot}_{pq}]. \tag{4.12}$$

Choosing appropriate dummy subscripts and using the symmetry of T_{pq}, we finally write (4.12) in the form

$$D_0\overline{S}_{ij} = \frac{\bar{\rho}}{\rho}\partial_p a_i \partial_q a_j [T^{\cdot}_{pq} + \partial_k v_k T_{pq} - T_{pk}\partial_k v_q - T_{qk}\partial_k v_p]. \tag{4.13}$$

Note that the bracket in this equation contains the p, q-component of Truesdell's stress rate (VIII, 1.8). As has been shown in Section 1 of

Chapter VIII, this stress rate vanishes if the neighborhood of the considered particle instantaneously moves as a rigid body and the state of stress remains constant when seen from the standpoint of the material. According to (4.13) the tensor $D_0\bar{S}_{ij}$, which will be called *Kirchhoff's stress rate*, also vanishes under these conditions. Equations (4.13) and (4.6) show that the stress rates of Kirchhoff and Truesdell have the same relation to each other as the stress tensors of Kirchhoff and Euler.

For the Lagrangian stress tensor (4.3) one readily obtains the relation

$$D_0\bar{T}_{ij} = \frac{\bar{\rho}}{\rho}\,\partial_p a_i[T^{\bullet}_{pj} + \partial_k v_k T_{pq} - T_{jk}\partial_k v_p], \tag{4.14}$$

which has essentially been given by Hill.† As follows from the definition (4.2) of the Lagrangian stress tensor, the vanishing of $D_0\bar{T}_{ij}$ indicates that, despite the instantaneous rotation and deformation of the typical surface element, the force transmitted across it remains constant.

To conclude this section, let us derive the equations of motion that replace (II, 2.6) when the Lagrangian stress tensor or Kirchhoff's stress tensor, and Lagrangian variables are used. Consider the particles that instantaneously fill the region V with the surface S, and denote the region that these particles filled in the initial state by $\bar{V}$ and its surface by $\bar{S}$. Furthermore, let dF and $d\bar{F}$ be corresponding typical elements of F and $\bar{F}$, and denote the unit vectors along the exterior normals of these surface elements by ν_i and $\bar{\nu}_i$, respectively.

According to (4.2) the resultant R_k of the surface forces that are instantaneously transmitted onto the continuum in V is given by the relation

$$R_k = \int \bar{T}_{ik}\bar{\nu}_i\,d\bar{F} = \int D_i\bar{T}_{ik}\,d\bar{V}, \tag{4.15}$$

in which Gauss's theorem has been used in the transition to the last term. In accordance with the Lagrangian point of view, let the specific body force at the typical particle be given as a function $\bar{K}_k(a, t)$ of the initial position of this particle and the time. The resultant of the body forces that instantaneously act on the continuum in V can then be written as $\int \bar{\rho}\bar{K}_k\,d\bar{V}$. Application of the momentum theorem to the continuum in V therefore yields

$$\int [\bar{\rho}D_{00}x_k - \bar{\rho}\bar{K}_k - D_i\bar{T}_{ik}]\,d\bar{V} = 0. \tag{4.16}$$

Since (4.16) holds for an arbitrary simply connected region filled by the continuum, the integrand must vanish. The equation of motion with the

† R. Hill, Journal Mech. Phys. Solids *5* (1957) 229, equation (19).

Lagrangian stress tensor thus has the form

$$\bar{\rho} D_{00} x_k = \bar{\rho} \overline{K}_k + D_i \overline{T}_{ik}. \tag{4.17}$$

Substitution of $\overline{T}_{ik}$ from (4.9) into (4.17) then yields the following equation of motion with Kirchhoff's stress tensor:

$$\bar{\rho} D_{00} x_k = \bar{\rho} \overline{K}_k + D_i (\overline{S}_{ij} D_j x_k). \tag{4.18}$$

CHAPTER X

Elastic and Hyperelastic Materials

1. Elastic materials. The hypoelastic behavior discussed in Chapter VIII corresponds to a minimal requirement that a material must fulfill, if it is in any sense to qualify as elastic. In this section, we shall discuss another definition of elastic behavior and show that, for isotropic materials, it represents a special case of hypoelastic behavior.

A material will be called *elastic*, if it possesses a homogeneous stress-free *natural state*, and if in an appropriately defined finite neighborhood of this state there exists a one-to-one correspondence between the Eulerian stress tensor T and Almansi's strain tensor U. A body that consists of this material thus returns to its original shape whenever all stresses are reduced to zero.

The following discussion will be restricted to *isotropic* elastic materials, and it will be assumed that the Eulerian stress tensor T can be written as a polynomial of Almansi's strain tensor U. To investigate the mathematical structure of the material derivative $T^{\bullet}_{ij}$, consider a typical term of this polynomial, say the quadratic term $Q_{ij} = U_{ip}U_{pj}$, the coefficient of which is independent of the state of strain and can therefore be disregarded in the following discussion. By the symmetry of U, we have

$$Q^{\bullet}_{ij} = U^{\bullet}_{ip}U_{pj} + U^{\bullet}_{jp}U_{pi}. \tag{1.1}$$

We now solve (IX, 1.24) with respect to $U^{\bullet}_{pq}$ and substitute the result into (1.1). Most terms of the equation obtained in this manner are linear in the components of the rate of deformation V. Note that the coefficient of a component of V in a typical term of this kind depends on the components of the strain U. In the following, we shall indicate these terms by dots, because we are primarily interested in the other terms. With this abbreviation, we find

$$Q^{\bullet}_{ij} = (U_{iq}\partial_{[q}v_{p]} + U_{pq}\partial_{[q}v_{i]})U_{pj} + (U_{jq}\partial_{[q}v_{p]} + U_{pq}\partial_{[q}v_{j]})U_{pi} + \cdots. \tag{1.2}$$

Using the symmetry of U, we write (1.2) in the form

$$Q^{\bullet}_{ij} = (U_{iq}U_{pj} + U_{jq}U_{pi})\partial_{[q}v_{p]} + U_{ip}U_{pq}\partial_{[q}v_{j]} + U_{jp}U_{pq}\partial_{[q}v_{i]} + \cdots. \tag{1.3}$$

Since $\partial_{[q}v_{p]}$ is antisymmetric and its coefficient is symmetric in p and q, the first term on the right vanishes. In the remaining explicitly written terms on the right of (1.3), the tensor $\mathbf{Q}$ can now be introduced. Bringing these terms on to the left side, we finally obtain

$$Q_{ij}^{\cdot} - Q_{iq}\partial_{[q}v_{j]} - Q_{jq}\partial_{[q}v_{i]} = \cdots. \tag{1.4}$$

The comparison of (1.4) with (VIII, 1.7) shows that the left side of (1.4) is the contribution Q_{ij}^{∇} that the term Q_{ij} in the polynomial for T_{ij} makes to the stress rate T_{ij}^{∇}. As is indicated by the dots in (1.4), this contribution is a linear form of the components of the rate of deformation. The coefficients of this form, which are originally functions of the strain components, may be written as functions of the stress components on account of the assumed one-to-one correspondence between the tensors of stress and strain. Accordingly, the quadratic term Q_{ij} in the polynomial for T_{ij} furnishes a contribution to the stress rate T_{ij}^{∇} that has the structure required by the hypoelastic constitutive equation (VIII, 2.1). As is readily verified by induction, a similar remark applies to all terms of the polynomial for T_{ij}. *The definition of elastic materials given above thus characterizes a special case of hypoelastic behavior.* This result is due to Noll.†

2. Hyperelastic materials. A third physically plausible definition of elastic behavior is based on the energy theorem (IV, 4.7) and presupposes *adiabatic motion,* that is a motion in which no part of the continuum receives or loses energy in a nonmechanical manner. The heat flux in this kind of motion has vanishing divergence, and the energy theorem states that the material rate of change of the internal energy equals the power of the stresses per unit mass:

$$e^{\cdot} = \frac{1}{\rho} T_{pq}V_{pq}. \tag{2.1}$$

Passing from the Eulerian variables used in (2.1) to Lagrangian variables and denoting by $\bar{e}(a, t)$ the specific internal energy expressed in the new variables, we use (IX, 4.10) to write (2.1) in the form

$$D_0\bar{e} = \frac{1}{\bar{\rho}}\bar{S}_{ij}D_0\bar{U}_{ij}. \tag{2.2}$$

Equation (2.2) holds for the adiabatic motion of any material. We now introduce the assumption that for the adiabatic motions that are to be considered here the specific internal energy $\bar{e}$ is an analytic function of the components of Green's strain tensor $\bar{\mathbf{U}}$ formed with respect to the homogeneous natural state. The materials characterized by this assumption will be called *hyperelastic.* It will be shown that an *isotropic* hyperelastic material is elastic and hence hypoelastic.

† W. Noll, Journal Rat. Mech. Analysis *4* (1955) 3.

To simplify our formulas, we shall adopt the following convention: any function of the components of a symmetric tensor (for instance $\bar{e}(\bar{U})$), will be written in a form that is symmetric in symmetric components ($\bar{U}_{ij}$ and $\bar{U}_{ji}$), and in forming the derivative of such a function with respect to a typical tensor component ($\bar{U}_{ij}$), symmetric components will be formally treated as independent variables. By this convention, we have

$$\frac{\partial \bar{e}}{\partial \bar{U}_{ij}} = \frac{\partial \bar{e}}{\partial \bar{U}_{ji}} \tag{2.3}$$

and

$$D_0 \bar{e} = \frac{\partial \bar{e}}{\partial \bar{U}_{ij}} D_0 \bar{U}_{ij}. \tag{2.4}$$

It follows from (2.2) and (2.4) that

$$\left(\frac{1}{\bar{\rho}} \bar{S}_{ij} - \frac{\partial \bar{e}}{\partial \bar{U}_{ij}}\right) D_0 \bar{U}_{ij} = 0. \tag{2.5}$$

This equation, both factors of which are symmetric, is not dependent on the choice of the strain rate $D_0 \bar{U}_{ij}$. We thus have the relation

$$\bar{S}_{ij} = \bar{\rho} \frac{\partial \bar{e}}{\partial \bar{U}_{ij}}, \tag{2.6}$$

in which $\bar{\rho}$ denotes the *uniform* density of the natural state. Equation (2.6) suggests the introduction of the *elastic potential*

$$\bar{E} = \bar{\rho} \bar{e}, \tag{2.7}$$

by means of which Kirchhoff's stress tensor can be expressed as follows

$$\bar{S}_{ij} = \frac{\partial \bar{E}}{\partial \bar{U}_{ij}}. \tag{2.8}$$

Since the natural state $\bar{U}_{ij} = 0$ is to be stress free, the derivatives $\partial \bar{E} / \partial \bar{U}_{ij}$ must vanish in this state.

It is occasionally convenient to regard the elastic potential not as a function of the components of the strain tensor $\bar{U}_{ij}$ but as a function of the components of the tensor $D_p x_q$, from which the strain components can be determined by (IX, 2.7). Obviously,

$$\begin{aligned} \frac{\partial \bar{E}}{\partial (D_p x_q)} &= \frac{\partial \bar{E}}{\partial \bar{U}_{ij}} \frac{\partial \bar{U}_{ij}}{\partial (D_p x_q)} \\ &= \frac{1}{2}\left(\frac{\partial \bar{E}}{\partial \bar{U}_{pj}} D_j x_q + \frac{\partial \bar{E}}{\partial \bar{U}_{ip}} D_i x_q\right) = \frac{\partial \bar{E}}{\partial \bar{U}_{pj}} D_j x_q. \end{aligned} \tag{2.9}$$

According to (2.8), (2.9) and (IX, 4.9), we have

$$\bar{T}_{pq} = \frac{\partial \bar{E}}{\partial(D_p x_q)}. \tag{2.10}$$

Substitution of this relation into (IX, 4.8) furnishes

$$T_{ij} = \frac{\rho}{\bar{\rho}} D_p x_i \frac{\partial \bar{E}}{\partial(D_p x_j)}. \tag{2.11}$$

It therefore follows from the symmetry of T_{ij} that

$$D_p x_i \frac{\partial \bar{E}}{\partial(D_p x_j)} = D_p x_j \frac{\partial \bar{E}}{\partial(D_p x_i)}. \tag{2.12}$$

The relations established above hold for an arbitrary hyperelastic material. The following discussion, however, will be restricted to *isotropic* hyperelastic materials. By the theorem mentioned in Section 4 of Chapter VI, the elastic potential then is a function of the basic invariants of Green's strain tensor. As has been remarked in connection with (IX, 2.12) and (IX, 3.11), these basic invariants can be expressed in terms of the basic invariants of one of the other strain tensors.

In particular, we may write the elastic potential as a function E of Almansi's strain components U_{ij} or the components of $\partial_i a_j$. According to (IX, 2.5) and (2.10), we then have

$$\bar{T}_{rs} = \frac{\partial \bar{E}}{\partial(D_r x_s)} = \frac{\partial E}{\partial(\partial_j a_k)} \frac{\partial(\partial_j a_k)}{\partial(D_r x_s)} = -\frac{\partial E}{\partial(\partial_j a_k)} \partial_j a_r \partial_s a_k. \tag{2.13}$$

Substitution of (2.13) into (2.11) and use of (IX, 2.2) furnishes

$$T_{ij} = -\frac{\rho}{\bar{\rho}} \frac{\partial E}{\partial(\partial_i a_p)} \partial_j a_p. \tag{2.14}$$

Since T_{ij} is symmetric, we therefore have

$$\frac{\partial E}{\partial(\partial_i a_p)} \partial_j a_p = \frac{\partial E}{\partial(\partial_j a_p)} \partial_i a_p. \tag{2.15}$$

In the same manner in which (2.9) was derived for Eulerian variables, one now finds the relation

$$\frac{\partial E}{\partial(\partial_i a_p)} = -\frac{\partial E}{\partial U_{ik}} \partial_k a_p \tag{2.16}$$

for Lagrangian variables. Substitution of (2.16) into (2.14) and use of (IX, 1.6) and (IX, 3.5) finally yields

$$T_{ij} = \frac{\rho}{\bar{\rho}} \frac{\partial E}{\partial U_{ik}} (\delta_{kj} - 2U_{kj}) = -2\frac{\rho}{\bar{\rho}} \frac{\partial E}{\partial C_{ik}} C_{kj}. \tag{2.17}$$

As is shown by (IX, 1.20), the ratio $\rho/\bar{\rho} = d\bar{V}/dV$ can be expressed in terms of the basic invariants of U_{ij}. According to (2.17), the Eulerian stress components of an *isotropic* hyperelastic material are therefore functions of Almansi's strain components. By a suitable choice of the elastic potential $\bar{E}(\bar{U})$ or $E(U)$, these relations between the components of $\mathbf{T}$ and $\mathbf{U}$ can be given one-to-one character in some neighborhood of the natural state. *An isotropic hyperelastic material of this kind is a particular elastic and hence hypoelastic material.* This result is also due to Noll.†

To conclude this section, we cast (2.17) into a form that proves useful in the applications. According to (I, 7.6), (I, 7.7) and (I, 7.10) the basic invariants of C_{ij} are given by

$$\left.\begin{aligned} \mathscr{C}_{(1)} &= C_{pp}, \\ \mathscr{C}_{(2)} &= \tfrac{1}{2}(C_{pq}C_{qp} - C_{pp}C_{qq}), \\ \mathscr{C}_{(3)} &= \tfrac{1}{6}(2C_{pq}C_{qr}C_{rp} - 3C_{pq}C_{qp}C_{rr} + C_{pp}C_{qq}C_{rr}). \end{aligned}\right\} \tag{2.18}$$

Accordingly,

$$\left.\begin{aligned} \frac{\partial \mathscr{C}_{(1)}}{\partial C_{ij}} &= \delta_{ij}, \\ \frac{\partial \mathscr{C}_{(2)}}{\partial C_{ij}} &= C_{ij} - C_{kk}\,\delta_{ij}, \\ \frac{\partial \mathscr{C}_{(3)}}{\partial C_{ij}} &= C_{ip}C_{pj} - \mathscr{C}_{(1)}C_{ij} - \mathscr{C}_{(2)}\delta_{ij}. \end{aligned}\right\} \tag{2.19}$$

The right side of the last equation may be transformed as follows. Multiplying the Hamilton-Cayley equation (see I, 7.18) for the tensor $\mathbf{C}$ by the reciprocal tensor $\mathbf{B}$, we find (in Cartesian notation)

$$C_{ip}C_{pj} = \mathscr{C}_{(1)}C_{ij} + \mathscr{C}_{(2)}\delta_{ij} + \mathscr{C}_{(3)}B_{ij}. \tag{2.20}$$

The last equation (2.19) is therefore equivalent to

$$\frac{\partial \mathscr{C}_{(3)}}{\partial C_{ij}} = \mathscr{C}_{(3)}B_{ij}. \tag{2.21}$$

From (2.19) and (2.21), it then follows that

$$\frac{\partial E}{\partial C_{ik}} = \frac{\partial E}{\partial \mathscr{C}_{(1)}}\,\delta_{ik} + \frac{\partial E}{\partial \mathscr{C}_{(2)}}\,(C_{ik} - C_{ll}\,\delta_{ik}) + \frac{\partial E}{\partial \mathscr{C}_{(3)}}\,\mathscr{C}_{(3)}B_{ik}. \tag{2.22}$$

Substitution of (2.22) into (2.17) and use of (2.20) and (IX, 3.8) finally

† W. Noll, Journal Rat. Mech. Analysis *4* (1955) 3.

yields

$$T_{ij} = -2\frac{\rho}{\bar{\rho}}\left[\left(\mathscr{C}_{(2)}\frac{\partial E}{\partial \mathscr{C}_{(2)}} + \mathscr{C}_{(3)}\frac{\partial E}{\partial \mathscr{C}_{(3)}}\right)\delta_{ij} + \frac{\partial E}{\partial \mathscr{C}_{(1)}}C_{ij} + \mathscr{C}_{(3)}\frac{\partial E}{\partial \mathscr{C}_{(3)}}B_{ij}\right]. \tag{2.23}$$

This constitutive law may be further simplified by writing the elastic potential E as a function of the basic invariants of **B**. In analogy to equation (IX, 3.11) one has

$$\mathscr{B}_{(1)} = -\frac{\mathscr{C}_{(2)}}{\mathscr{C}_{(3)}}, \quad \mathscr{B}_{(2)} = -\frac{\mathscr{C}_{(1)}}{\mathscr{C}_{(3)}}, \quad \mathscr{B}_{(3)} = \frac{1}{\mathscr{C}_{(3)}}. \tag{2.24}$$

Accordingly,

$$\left.\begin{aligned} \frac{\partial E}{\partial \mathscr{C}_{(1)}} &= -\frac{1}{\mathscr{C}_{(3)}}\frac{\partial E}{\partial \mathscr{B}_{(2)}}, \quad \frac{\partial E}{\partial \mathscr{C}_{(2)}} = -\frac{1}{\mathscr{C}_{(3)}}\frac{\partial E}{\partial \mathscr{B}_{(1)}}, \\ \frac{\partial E}{\partial \mathscr{C}_{(3)}} &= -\frac{1}{\mathscr{C}_{(3)}}\left[\mathscr{B}_{(1)}\frac{\partial E}{\partial \mathscr{B}_{(1)}} + \mathscr{B}_{(2)}\frac{\partial E}{\partial \mathscr{B}_{(2)}} + \mathscr{B}_{(3)}\frac{\partial E}{\partial \mathscr{B}_{(3)}}\right]. \end{aligned}\right\} \tag{2.25}$$

With the aid of (2.24) and (2.25), equation (2.23) can be written in the following form, which is due to Finger:†

$$T_{ij} = 2\frac{\rho}{\bar{\rho}}\left[\left(\mathscr{B}_{(2)}\frac{\partial E}{\partial \mathscr{B}_{(2)}} + \mathscr{B}_{(3)}\frac{\partial E}{\partial \mathscr{B}_{(3)}}\right)\delta_{ij} + \mathscr{B}_{(3)}\frac{\partial E}{\partial \mathscr{B}_{(2)}}C_{ij} + \frac{\partial E}{\partial \mathscr{B}_{(1)}}B_{ij}\right]. \tag{2.26}$$

In the natural state, we have $x_i = a_i$ and hence by (IX, 3.1) and (IX, 3.9)

$$\left.\begin{aligned} B_{ij} &= C_{ij} = \delta_{ij}, \\ \mathscr{B}_{(1)} &= 3, \quad \mathscr{B}_{(2)} = -3, \quad \mathscr{B}_{(3)} = 1. \end{aligned}\right\} \tag{2.27}$$

Since the natural state is to be stress-free, the derivatives of the elastic potential with respect to the basic invariants of **B** must satisfy the following relation *in the natural state*:

$$\frac{\partial E}{\partial \mathscr{B}_{(1)}} - 2\frac{\partial E}{\partial \mathscr{B}_{(2)}} + \frac{\partial E}{\partial \mathscr{B}_{(3)}} = 0. \tag{2.28}$$

3. Incompressible hyperelastic materials. The mechanical behavior of many practically important materials such as the structural metals can be treated as elastic only as long as the deformations remain very small. Problems concerning the elastic behavior of these materials therefore lie, in general, within the scope of the classical theory of elasticity, which treats the deformations as infinitesimal. On the other hand, this simplified treatment is not, as a rule, adequate for materials such as rubber that are cap-

† J. Finger, Sitz. ber. Akad. Wiss. Wien (IIa) *108* (1894) 1073.

able of large elastic deformations. Many of these materials, however, are practically incompressible. This section will therefore deal with the simplifications of the preceding theory that arise from the incompressibility of a hyperelastic material.

Multiplication of (IX, 2.16) by $\partial_r a_i \partial_s a_j$ and use of (IX, 2.2) lead to

$$V_{rs} = \partial_r a_i \partial_s a_j D_0 \overline{U}_{ij}. \tag{3.1}$$

For an *incompressible* material, we have $V_{rr} = 0$ and hence by (3.1) and (IX, 3.12)

$$\overline{B}_{ij} D_0 \overline{U}_{ij} = 0. \tag{3.2}$$

Since the admissible rates of deformation $D_0 \overline{U}_{ij}$ are now restricted by (3.2), one can no longer conclude that the first factor in (2.5) must vanish, but only that it must be proportional to $\overline{B}_{ij}$. For an incompressible hyperelastic material, equation (2.8) must therefore be replaced by

$$\overline{S}_{ij} = \frac{\partial \overline{E}}{\partial \overline{U}_{ij}} - p\overline{B}_{ij}, \tag{3.3}$$

where p is an arbitrary scalar. Substituting (3.3) into (IX, 4.8) and using (IX, 3.12) and (IX, 2.2), we obtain

$$T_{ij} = -p\delta_{ij} + \frac{\partial \overline{E}}{\partial \overline{U}_{rs}} D_r x_i \, D_s x_j. \tag{3.4}$$

In forming the derivatives $\partial \overline{E}/\partial \overline{U}_{rs}$ in (3.4), we must again treat the nine strain components as independent variables. The last term in (3.4) can therefore be transformed in a similar manner to the right side of (2.8). On account of the incompressibility of the material, we now have $\rho/\bar{\rho} = 1$ and $\mathscr{B}_{(3)} = 1$ (see IX, 3.15 and IX, 3.17), so that E depends only on $\mathscr{B}_{(1)}$ and $\mathscr{B}_{(2)}$. Since the scalar p in (3.4) is arbitrary, we may regard the terms with the factor δ_{ij} in (2.26) as contained in the term $-p\delta_{ij}$ of (3.4). For an *incompressible hyperelastic material*, (2.26) is therefore replaced by the simpler constitutive equation

$$T_{ij} = -p\delta_{ij} + 2\frac{\partial E}{\partial \mathscr{B}_{(1)}} B_{ij} + 2\frac{\partial E}{\partial \mathscr{B}_{(2)}} C_{ij}, \tag{3.5}$$

which is due to Rivlin.†

With the abbreviations

$$\alpha = 2\frac{\partial E}{\partial \mathscr{B}_{(1)}}, \quad \beta = 2\frac{\partial E}{\partial \mathscr{B}_{(2)}}, \tag{3.6}$$

Rivlin's equation may be written in the form

$$T_{ij} = -p\delta_{ij} + \alpha B_{ij} + \beta C_{ij}. \tag{3.7}$$

† R. S. Rivlin, Phil. Trans. Roy. Soc. (A) *241* (1948) 379.

As Mooney † remarked, an equation of the form (3.7), in which α and β are characteristic constants of the material, describes the elastic behavior of rubber with practically sufficient accuracy. The corresponding form of the elastic potential is

$$E = \tfrac{1}{2}\alpha(\mathscr{B}_{(1)} - 3) + \tfrac{1}{2}\beta(\mathscr{B}_{(2)} + 3); \tag{3.8}$$

this vanishes in the natural state on account of (2.27). In the following, we shall however regard the coefficients α and β in (3.7) as defined by (3.6) and only treat them as constants when specific reference is made to Mooney's theory.

Equation (3.7) yields important relations between the principal stresses $T_{\rm I}$, $T_{\rm II}$, $T_{\rm III}$ and the principal length ratios $\lambda_{\rm I}$, $\lambda_{\rm II}$, $\lambda_{\rm III}$. The incompressibility of the material is expressed by the relation

$$\lambda_{\rm I}\lambda_{\rm II}\lambda_{\rm III} = 1. \tag{3.9}$$

By (IX, 3.10), the matrices of the tensors **B** and **C**, referred to principal axes, are therefore given by

$$\mathbf{B} = \begin{bmatrix} \lambda_{\rm I}^2 & 0 & 0 \\ 0 & \lambda_{\rm II}^2 & 0 \\ 0 & 0 & \lambda_{\rm I}^{-2}\lambda_{\rm II}^{-2} \end{bmatrix}, \quad \mathbf{C} = \begin{bmatrix} \lambda_{\rm I}^{-2} & 0 & 0 \\ 0 & \lambda_{\rm II}^{-2} & 0 \\ 0 & 0 & \lambda_{\rm I}^2\lambda_{\rm II}^2 \end{bmatrix}, \tag{3.10}$$

and (3.7) furnishes the principal stresses

$$\left.\begin{aligned} T_{\rm I} &= -p + \alpha\lambda_{\rm I}^2 + \beta\lambda_{\rm I}^{-2}, \\ T_{\rm II} &= -p + \alpha\lambda_{\rm II}^2 + \beta\lambda_{\rm II}^{-2}, \\ T_{\rm III} &= -p + \alpha\lambda_{\rm I}^{-2}\lambda_{\rm II}^{-2} + \beta\lambda_{\rm I}^2\lambda_{\rm II}^2. \end{aligned}\right\} \tag{3.11}$$

For $\lambda_{\rm I} = \lambda_{\rm II}$, the quantity p can be so chosen that $T_{\rm I}$ vanishes as well as $T_{\rm II}$. For the corresponding *uniaxial* state of stress, we have $\lambda_{\rm III} = \lambda_{\rm I}^{-1}\lambda_{\rm II}^{-1} = \lambda_{\rm I}^{-2} = \lambda_{\rm II}^{-2}$ and

$$\begin{aligned} T_{\rm III} &= \alpha(\lambda_{\rm III}^2 - \lambda_{\rm III}^{-1}) + \beta(\lambda_{\rm III}^{-2} - \lambda_{\rm III}) \\ &= \lambda_{\rm III}(\lambda_{\rm III} - \lambda_{\rm III}^{-2})(\alpha - \lambda_{\rm III}^{-1}\beta). \end{aligned} \tag{3.12}$$

On the other hand, p can be so chosen that $T_{\rm III} = 0$. For the corresponding *plane* state of stress, we have

$$\begin{aligned} T_{\rm I} &= \alpha(\lambda_{\rm I}^2 - \lambda_{\rm I}^{-2}\lambda_{\rm II}^{-2}) + \beta(\lambda_{\rm I}^{-2} - \lambda_{\rm I}^2\lambda_{\rm II}^2) \\ &= (\lambda_{\rm I}^2 - \lambda_{\rm I}^{-2}\lambda_{\rm II}^{-2})(\alpha - \lambda_{\rm II}^2\beta) \end{aligned} \tag{3.13}$$

and a similar formula for $T_{\rm II}$.

† M. Mooney, Journal Appl. Phys. *11* (1940) 582.

According to (IX, 3.9) and (IX, 3.1), the simple shear

$$x_1 = a_1 + 2\gamma a_2, \quad x_2 = a_2, \quad x_3 = a_3 \tag{3.14}$$

gives the strain tensors

$$B_{ij} = \begin{bmatrix} 1 + 4\gamma^2 & 2\gamma & 0 \\ 2\gamma & 1 & 0 \\ 0 & 0 & 1 \end{bmatrix}, \quad C_{ij} = \begin{bmatrix} 1 & -2\gamma & 0 \\ -2\gamma & 1 + 4\gamma^2 & 0 \\ 0 & 0 & 1 \end{bmatrix}. \tag{3.15}$$

If p in (3.7) is chosen so that $T_{33} = 0$, this constitutive law furnishes

$$\left.\begin{aligned} T_{11} &= 4\alpha\gamma^2, \quad T_{22} = 4\beta\gamma^2, \quad T_{33} = 0, \\ T_{12} &= 2(\alpha - \beta)\gamma, \quad T_{13} = T_{23} = 0. \end{aligned}\right\} \tag{3.16}$$

To compare these formulas with (VIII, 2.11), we must set $\gamma = ct$. For (3.16) to agree with (VIII, 2.11), we must have $\alpha = \mu$, $\beta = 0$. The special case $\beta = 0$ of Mooney's theory was discussed by Rivlin.†

As a less trivial last example, we discuss the flexure of a rectangular parallelepiped.‡ In addition to the rectangular coordinates a_1, a_2, a_3, the axes of which are parallel to the edges of the undeformed parallelogram, cylindrical coordinates ρ, θ, ζ will be used. It will be assumed that the flexure to be considered transforms the material planes $a_1 =$ constant, $a_2 =$ constant, and $a_3 =$ constant, of the initial state into the cylinders $\rho =$ constant and the planes $\theta =$ constant and $\zeta =$ constant of the instantaneous state. To the orthogonal directions of increasing values of a_1, a_2, a_3 in the initial state, there correspond the likewise orthogonal directions of increasing values of ρ, θ, ζ, which are the principal directions of **B** and **C**. Since the considered deformation is described by equations of the form

$$\rho = \rho(a_1), \quad \theta = \theta(a_2), \quad \zeta = \zeta(a_3), \tag{3.17}$$

the principal length ratios are given by the relations

$$\lambda_\rho = D_1\rho, \quad \lambda_\theta = \rho D_2\theta, \quad \lambda_\zeta = D_3\zeta, \tag{3.18}$$

in which D_i indicates differentiation with respect to a_i. The incompressibility of the material requires that

$$\lambda_\rho\lambda_\theta\lambda_\zeta = (\rho D_1\rho)(D_2\theta)(D_3\zeta) = 1. \tag{3.19}$$

Since the content of each of the three parentheses in (3.19) depends on another variable, this equation can only be satisfied if each of these parentheses has a constant value. Accordingly,

$$\rho = (2Aa_1 + B)^{1/2}, \quad \theta = Ca_2, \quad \zeta = a_3/(AC), \tag{3.20}$$

where A, B, C are constants of integration.

† R. S. Rivlin, Philos. Trans. Roy. Soc. (A) *240* (1948) 459.
‡ See R. S. Rivlin, Proc. Roy. Soc. London (A) *195* (1949) 463.

According to (IX, 3.10), the tensor **B** has the principal values

$$B_{\rho\rho} = \frac{A^2}{\rho^2}, \quad B_{\theta\theta} = C^2\rho^2, \quad B_{\zeta\zeta} = \frac{1}{A^2C^2}, \tag{3.21}$$

and the principal values of **C** are the reciprocals of those of **B**. By (3.21), the basic invariants $\mathscr{B}_{(1)}$ and $\mathscr{B}_{(2)}$ are independent of θ and ζ, and the same remark applies to the elastic potential E.

Let the undeformed parallelepiped be bounded by the planes $a_1 = a$, $a_1 = -a$, $a_2 = \pm b$, $a_3 = \pm c$ and the deformed body by the planes $\rho = \rho'$, $\rho = \rho''$, $\theta = \pm\theta'$, $\zeta = \pm\zeta'$. It follows then from (3.20) that

$$\left.\begin{aligned} 4aA &= \rho'^2 - \rho''^2, \quad 2B = \rho'^2 + \rho''^2, \\ bC &= \theta', \quad 4abc = (\rho'^2 - \rho''^2)\theta'\zeta'. \end{aligned}\right\} \tag{3.22}$$

When a, b, c are given, the deformation (3.20) is therefore uniquely determined by the values of ρ', θ' ζ'. Indeed, the last equation (3.22) then furnishes ρ''^2, and the constants A, B, C can be determined from the remaining equation (3.22).

From the constitutive equation (3.7), we now obtain the principal stresses

$$\left.\begin{aligned} T_{\rho\rho} &= -p + \alpha\frac{A^2}{\rho^2} + \beta\frac{\rho^2}{A^2}, \\ T_{\theta\theta} &= -p + \alpha C^2\rho^2 + \frac{\beta}{C^2\rho^2}, \\ T_{\zeta\zeta} &= -p + \frac{\alpha}{A^2C^2} + \beta A^2C^2. \end{aligned}\right\} \tag{3.23}$$

It then follows from the second and third equilibrium equation (I, 10.14) that p is independent of θ and ζ. The first equilibrium equation contains the expression $(T_{\rho\rho} - T_{\theta\theta})/\rho$, which by (3.23) can be written in the form

$$\frac{1}{\rho}(T_{\rho\rho} - T_{\theta\theta}) = \alpha\left(\frac{A^2}{\rho^3} - C^2\rho\right) + \beta\left(\frac{\rho}{A^2} - \frac{1}{C^2\rho^3}\right). \tag{3.24}$$

Since $\mathscr{C}_{(3)} = 1$, equations (3.21) and (2.24) yield

$$\left.\begin{aligned} \mathscr{B}_{(1)} &= \frac{A^2}{\rho^2} + C^2\rho^2 + \frac{1}{A^2C^2}, \\ \mathscr{B}_{(2)} &= -\mathscr{C}_{(1)} = -\left(\frac{\rho^2}{A^2} + \frac{1}{C^2\rho^2} + A^2C^2\right). \end{aligned}\right\} \tag{3.25}$$

By (3.6), (3.24), and (3.25), we have therefore

$$\frac{1}{\rho}(T_{\rho\rho} - T_{\theta\theta}) = -\frac{\partial E}{\partial \mathscr{B}_{(1)}}\frac{d\mathscr{B}_{(1)}}{d\rho} - 2\frac{\partial E}{\partial \mathscr{B}_{(2)}}\frac{d\mathscr{B}_{(2)}}{d\rho} = -\frac{dE}{d\rho}, \tag{3.26}$$

so that the first equation (I, 10.14) can be written as

$$\frac{d}{d\rho}(T_{\rho\rho} - E) = 0. \tag{3.27}$$

Accordingly, we have

$$T_{\rho\rho} = E + p_0, \tag{3.28}$$

where p_0 is a constant. Equations (3.26) and (3.28) furnish

$$T_{\theta\theta} = \frac{d}{d\rho}[\rho(E + p_0)]. \tag{3.29}$$

For the cylinders $\rho = \rho'$ and $\rho = \rho''$ to be stress-free, we must have

$$E(\rho') = E(\rho'') = -p_0 \tag{3.30}$$

by (3.28). As is shown by (3.29), the axial force transmitted in a typical section θ = constant, that is

$$\int_{\rho''}^{\rho'} T_{\theta\theta}\, d\rho = [\rho(E + p_0)]_{\rho''}^{\rho'} \tag{3.31}$$

then vanishes also. Since the relations (3.30) must be satisfied independent of the form of $E(\mathscr{B}_{(1)}, \mathscr{B}_{(2)})$, we must have

$$\mathscr{B}_{(1)}(\rho') = \mathscr{B}_{(1)}(\rho''), \quad \mathscr{B}_{(2)}(\rho') = \mathscr{B}_{(2)}(\rho''). \tag{3.32}$$

It then follows from (3.25) that

$$A = C\rho'\rho''. \tag{3.33}$$

Combination of (3.33) with the first and third equations (3.22) furnishes the relation

$$\theta' = \frac{b}{4a}\left(\frac{\rho'}{\rho''} - \frac{\rho''}{\rho'}\right), \tag{3.34}$$

which shows that the deformation (3.20) is already determined by the values of ρ' and ρ'', from which θ' and ζ' can be calculated by means of (3.34) and the last equation (3.22).

According to (3.29) and (3.30), the *bending moment* in the typical section θ = constant has the value

$$M_\theta = 2\zeta'\int_{\rho''}^{\rho'} \rho T_{\theta\theta}\, d\rho = -2\zeta'\int_{\rho''}^{\rho'} \rho(E + p_0)\, d\rho. \tag{3.35}$$

Finally, we obtain the stress $T_{\zeta\zeta}$ by forming the difference of the third and the first equation (3.23) and using (3.28). On account of (3.6), we thus find the relation

$$T_{\zeta\zeta} = E + p_0 + 2\left(\frac{1}{A^2C^2} - \frac{A^2}{\rho^2}\right)\left(\frac{\partial E}{\partial \mathscr{B}_{(1)}} - C^2\rho^2 \frac{\partial E}{\partial \mathscr{B}_{(2)}}\right), \tag{3.36}$$

in which the constants A and C are to be determined from the first and third equations (3.22) and (3.34). In the lateral surface $\zeta = \zeta'$, an infinitesimal normal force dN_ζ and an infinitesimal bending moment dM_ζ are transmitted between neighboring normal sections that form the angle $d\theta$:

$$dN_\zeta/d\theta = \int_{\rho''}^{\rho'} \rho T_{\zeta\zeta}\, d\rho, \quad dM_\zeta/d\theta = \int_{\rho'}^{\rho''} \rho^2 T_{\zeta\zeta}\, d\rho. \tag{3.37}$$

We leave it to the reader to evaluate the stresses (3.28), (3.29), (3.36) and the resultants (3.35), (3.37) for a specific form of the elastic potential $E(\mathscr{B}_{(1)}, \mathscr{B}_{(2)})$, for instance for Mooney's form (3.8).

4. Uniqueness and stability.† Consider a hyperelastic body that occupies the regular domain $\overline{V}$ with the surface $\overline{S}$ in its homogeneous stress-free initial state. What body forces and surface tractions must act on this body if it is to be in equilibrium in the deformed state specified by $x_i(a)$?

If the elastic potential $\overline{E}$ is regarded as a function of the derivatives $D_i x_j$, the Lagrangian stress field is

$$\overline{T}_{ij} = \frac{\partial \overline{E}}{\partial(D_i x_j)} \tag{4.1}$$

(see 2.10). To the surface element that initially had the area $d\overline{S}$ and the unit normal vector $\bar{\nu}_i$, the force

$$\overline{T}_j^{(\bar{\nu})}\, d\overline{S} = \bar{\nu}_i \overline{T}_{ij}\, d\overline{S} = \bar{\nu}_i \frac{\partial \overline{E}}{\partial(D_i x_j)}\, d\overline{S} \tag{4.2}$$

must therefore be applied in the deformed state (see IX, 4.2). Similarly, to the volume element with the initial volume $d\overline{V}$, the force

$$\bar{\rho}\overline{K}_j\, d\overline{V} = -D_i \overline{T}_{ij}\, d\overline{V} = -D_i\left(\frac{\partial \overline{E}}{\partial(D_i x_j)}\right) d\overline{V} \tag{4.3}$$

must be applied (see IX, 4.17).

The inverse of this problem, namely to find the equilibrium configuration $x_i(a)$ for given surface tractions $\overline{T}_j^{(\bar{\nu})}$ and specific body forces $\overline{K}_j$, may be generalized as in Section 4 of Chapter VIII by not giving all components of the surface traction $\overline{T}_j^{(\bar{\nu})}$ at the typical point of the surface $\overline{S}$ and pre-

† The exposition of this section essentially follows R. Hill's presentation (Journal Mech. Phys. Solids *5* (1957) 229) of the investigation of C. E. Pearson (Quarterly Appl. Math. *14* (1956) 133).

scribing instead the corresponding coordinates x_j of this point in the deformed state. A boundary condition will be called *statical* or *kinematical* according to whether it prescribes a component of the surface traction or a coordinate of a surface point.

For the analogous boundary value problem of classical elasticity a uniqueness proof was given in Section 4 of Chapter VIII, but for the finite deformations considered here this type of *uniqueness in the large* can hardly be expected. We shall therefore discuss *uniqueness in the small* in connection with the following boundary value problem: Given an equilibrium configuration $x_i(a)$ with the associated surface tractions $\overline{T}_j^{(\bar{\nu})}$ and specific body forces $\overline{K}_j$, to determine the infinitesimal displacements $\delta x_i(a)$ caused by given infinitesimal changes $\delta\overline{K}_j$ of the specific body force and given infinitesimal changes $\delta\overline{T}_j^{(\bar{\nu})}$ and δx_j of certain components of the surface traction and the complementary surface coordinates.

Let δx_i^* and δx_i^{**} denote the displacement fields and δT_{ij}^* and δT_{ij}^{**} the stress fields of two solutions of this boundary value problem. According to (4.1), we have

$$\delta\overline{T}_{ij}^* = \frac{\partial^2\overline{E}}{\partial(D_i x_j)\partial(D_k x_l)} D_k(\delta x_l^*), \tag{4.4}$$

and a similar formula holds for $\delta\overline{T}_{ij}^{**}$. In both formulas, the derivatives of the elastic potential have the same values, because they must be evaluated in the given equilibrium configuration $x_i(a)$. Since the stress changes $\delta\overline{T}_{ij}^*$ and $\delta\overline{T}_{ij}^{**}$ correspond to the same change $\delta\overline{K}_j$ of the specific body force, we have by (4.3)

$$D_i(\delta\overline{T}_{ij}^* - \delta\overline{T}_{ij}^{**}) = 0. \tag{4.5}$$

At a surface particle at which for example the first component $\delta\overline{T}_1^{(\bar{\nu})}$ of the change of the surface traction is given and also the components δx_2 and δx_3 of the surface displacement, we have

$$\bar{\nu}_i(\delta\overline{T}_{i1}^* - \delta\overline{T}_{i1}^{**}) = 0, \quad \delta x_2^* - \delta x_2^{**} = 0, \quad \delta x_3^* - \delta x_3^{**} = 0, \tag{4.6}$$

so that

$$\bar{\nu}_i(\delta\overline{T}_{ij} - \delta\overline{T}_{ij}^{**})(\delta x_j^* - \delta x_j^{**}) = 0. \tag{4.7}$$

For the considered boundary value problem, (4.7) holds in fact at any point of the surface $\overline{S}$, so that

$$\int \bar{\nu}_i(\delta\overline{T}_{ij}^* - \delta\overline{T}_{ij}^{**})(\delta x_j^* - \delta x_j^{**})\, d\overline{S} = 0. \tag{4.8}$$

Transformation of (4.8) by means of Gauss' theorem (I, 9.3) and use of (4.5) furnishes

$$\int (\delta\overline{T}_{ij}^* - \delta\overline{T}_{ij}^{**}) D_i(\delta x_j^* - \delta x_j^{**})\, d\overline{V} = 0. \tag{4.9}$$

Equation (4.9) corresponds to equation (VIII, 4.7) in the uniqueness proof of the classical theory of elasticity. There it follows from Hooke's law that the integral in (VIII, 4.7) can only vanish if the considered equilibrium configurations and the associated stress fields are identical. Since, with the use of (4.4), equation (4.9) can be written as

$$\int \frac{\partial^2 \bar{E}}{\partial(D_i x_j)\partial(D_k x_l)} D_i(\delta x_j^* - \delta x_j^{**}) D_k(\delta x_l^* - \delta x_l^{**})\, d\bar{V} = 0, \tag{4.10}$$

a similar conclusion could be drawn in the present case if the structure of the function $\bar{E}$ should be such that the quadratic form

$$\frac{\partial^2 \bar{E}}{\partial(D_i x_j)\partial(D_k x_l)} \eta_{ij}\eta_{kl} \tag{4.11}$$

in the nine variables η_{ij} would be positive definite for arbitrary values of the derivatives $D_i x_j$. This uniqueness in the small would however entail uniqueness in the large, since each infinitesimal step of the loading process would produce a unique change of configuration. Since uniqueness in the large is not to be expected, the condition that the quadratic form (4.11) should be positive, is in all probability too sweeping.

On the other hand, uniqueness in the small is already guaranteed if, for instance,

$$\frac{\partial^2 \bar{E}}{\partial(D_i x_j)\partial(D_k x_l)} D_i(\delta x_j) D_k(\delta x_l)\, d\bar{V} > 0 \tag{4.12}$$

for *all* displacement fields δx_j that do not represent a translation and have zero values of all components of the surface displacement that appear in the kinematical boundary conditions. Since these components vanish for the difference $\delta x_j^* - \delta x_j^{**}$, the relations (4.10) and (4.11) would contradict each other unless $D_i(\delta x_j^* - \delta x_j^{**}) = 0$. In this case, the difference between the two displacement fields would at most represent a translation, and this is not, as a rule, compatible with the kinematical boundary conditions.

An important special case of our boundary value problem arises when the prescribed changes of the body forces, surface tractions and surface coordinates are zero. If this problem has a solution, this is only determined to within a constant factor, on account of the homogeneity of the relevant differential equations and boundary conditions. In the neighborhood of the considered equilibrium configuration there exist then other equilibrium configurations for the same prescribed body forces, surface tractions and surface displacements. A state of equilibrium of this kind is called *indifferent*.

A state of equilibrium in which the criterium (4.12) is satisfied cannot be indifferent. We shall prove that such a state of equilibrium is *stable* in the following sense: In the course of any motion that starts with infinitesimal velocities from the considered state of equilibrium and during which the specific body forces are constant and the statical and kinematical boundary conditions are maintained, each particle remains within an infinitesimal neighborhood of its initial position.

Consider a field of infinitesimal displacements from the given equilibrium configuration $x_i(a)$ that satisfies the kinematical boundary conditions. Since this field can only be determined to within a constant factor λ, it will be denoted by $\lambda \delta x_i(a)$. The infinitesimal work of the prescribed surface tractions on these displacements can be written as $\int \lambda \bar{\nu}_i \bar{T}_{ij} \delta x_j \, d\bar{S}$, because $\bar{T}_j^{(\bar{\nu})} = \bar{\nu}_i \bar{T}_{ij}$ for any prescribed component of the surface traction, while the complementary displacement component δx_j vanishes for any component of the surface traction that is not prescribed. The work of all body forces and prescribed surface tractions thus equals

$$\begin{aligned} d\mathscr{A} &= \lambda \int \bar{\rho} \bar{K}_j \delta x_j \, d\bar{V} + \lambda \int \bar{\nu}_i \bar{T}_{ij} \delta x_j \, d\bar{S} \\ &= \lambda \int (\bar{\rho} \bar{K}_j + D_i \bar{T}_{ij}) \delta x_j \, d\bar{V} + \lambda \int \bar{T}_{ij} D_i(\delta x_j) \, d\bar{V}. \end{aligned} \tag{4.13}$$

In (4.13), Gauss' theorem has been used in the transition to the second line. Since the initial state $x_i(a)$ is an equilibrium state, the first integrand in the second line of (4.13) vanishes. To within higher order terms, the displacements δx_j change the energy of the body by

$$d\mathscr{E} = \lambda \int \frac{\partial \bar{E}}{\partial (D_i x_j)} D_i(\delta x_j) \, d\bar{V} + \frac{\lambda^2}{2} \int \frac{\partial^2 \bar{E}}{\partial (D_i x_j) \partial (D_k x_l)} D_i(\delta x_j) D_k(\delta x_l) \, d\bar{V}. \tag{4.14}$$

It follows from (4.11), (4.13) and (4.14), that to within terms of higher order

$$d\mathscr{E} - d\mathscr{A} = \frac{\lambda^2}{2} \int \frac{\partial^2 \bar{E}}{\partial (D_i x_j) \partial (D_k x_l)} D_i(\delta x_k) D_j(\delta x_l) \, d\bar{V}. \tag{4.15}$$

Let $d\mathscr{K}_0$ be the infinitesimal initial kinetic energy. If the body ever assumes the configuration $x_i + \lambda \delta x_i$ during the considered motion, its energy in this configuration is $d\mathscr{K} = d\mathscr{K}_0 - (d\mathscr{E} - d\mathscr{A})$ by the principle of conservation of energy. Using (4.15) and the condition that $d\mathscr{K}$ cannot be negative, we readily obtain an upper bound for λ if $d\mathscr{E} - d\mathscr{A}$ is positive. Moreover, as $d\mathscr{K}_0 \to 0$, this bound tends towards zero as the square root of $d\mathscr{K}_0$. If the criterion (4.12) is satisfied for *any* displacement field δx_j that is compatible with the kinematical boundary conditions, bounds can be set for the initial kinetic energy $d\mathscr{K}_0$ so that during the ensuing motion the distance of any particle from its initial position never exceeds a given infinitesimal length, no matter how the initial velocities are chosen within the restrictions imposed by the value of $d\mathcal{K}_0$. *For the considered equilibrium configuration, the criterion* (4.12) *thus guarantees not only uniqueness in the small but also stability.* Whereas this criterion is sufficient for uniqueness in the small, it can be shown to be not only sufficient but also necessary for stability. The proof of this would however exceed the scope of this book.

For easy application of the stability criterion, it is desirable to use as independent variables the coordinates x_i of the state, the stability of which is to be examined. According to (2.9), we have

$$\frac{\partial^2 \overline{E}}{\partial(D_p x_j)\partial(D_r x_l)} = \frac{\partial^2 \overline{E}}{\partial \overline{U}_{pq} \partial \overline{U}_{rs}} D_q x_j D_s x_l + \frac{\partial \overline{E}}{\partial \overline{U}_{pr}} \delta_{jl}. \tag{4.16}$$

With $D_p(\delta x_j) = D_p x_i \partial_i(\delta x_j)$, equation (4.16) can now be used to rewrite the integrand of (4.12) as follows:

$$\frac{\partial^2 \overline{E}}{\partial(D_p x_j)\partial(D_r x_l)} D_p(\delta x_j) D_r(\delta x_l) = \frac{\partial^2 \overline{E}}{\partial \overline{U}_{pq} \partial \overline{U}_{rs}} D_p x_i D_q x_j D_r x_k D_s x_l \partial_i(\delta x_j) \partial_k(\delta x_l) + \frac{\partial \overline{E}}{\partial \overline{U}_{pr}} D_p x_i D_r x_k \partial_i(\delta x_j) \partial_k(\delta x_j). \tag{4.17}$$

In view of the choice of the independent variables, the integration must now be extended over V, so that $d\overline{V}$ in (4.12) must be replaced by $(\rho/\bar{\rho})\, dV$. Use of (IX, 4.8) and (2.8) then enables us to write the stability criterium in the following form, which is due to Pearson: †

$$\int [T_{ik} \partial_i(\delta x_j) \partial_k(\delta x_j) + \overline{C}_{ijkl} \partial_i(\delta x_j) \partial_k(\delta x_l)]\, dV > 0; \tag{4.18}$$

here

$$\overline{C}_{ijkl} = \frac{\rho}{\bar{\rho}} \frac{\partial^2 \overline{E}}{\partial \overline{U}_{pq} \partial \overline{U}_{rs}} D_p x_i D_q x_j D_r x_k D_s x_l. \tag{4.19}$$

According to (2.6), the second derivative in (4.19) can also be written as the derivative of $\overline{S}_{pq}$ with respect to $\overline{U}_{rs}$. If the *elastic* behavior of the considered material is restricted to small strains, we may further simplify the criterion (4.18) for the stability of states of *elastic* equilibrium by not taking this derivative in the investigated state of equilibrium but evaluating it instead in the neighboring natural state. Since the difference between Lagrangian and Eulerian coordinates is irrelevant for infinitesimal deformations, it follows from (VIII, 3.6) that

$$\frac{\partial \overline{S}_{pq}}{\partial \overline{U}_{rs}} = \frac{\partial T_{pq}}{\partial U_{rs}} = \lambda \delta_{pq} \delta_{rs} + \mu(\delta_{pr}\delta_{qs} + \delta_{ps}\delta_{qr}). \tag{4.20}$$

† C. E. Pearson, Quarterly Appl. Math. *14* (1956) 133.

With the use of (IX, 3.9), equation (4.19) may then be written in the form

$$\bar{C}_{ijkl} = \frac{\rho}{\bar{\rho}} [\lambda B_{ij} B_{kl} + \mu(B_{ik} B_{jl} + B_{il} B_{jk})], \tag{4.21}$$

in which we may set $\rho/\bar{\rho} = 1$ and $B_{ij} = \delta_{ij}$ for the natural state. The stability criterion therefore reduces to

$$\int \{T_{ik} \partial_i(\delta x_j) \partial_k(\delta x_j) + \lambda \partial_i(\delta x_i) \partial_k(\delta x_k) + \mu[\partial_i(\delta x_k) \partial_i(\delta x_k) + \partial_i(\delta x_k) \partial_k(\delta x_i)]\} \, dV > 0. \tag{4.22}$$

Since the integrand in (4.22) is homogeneous in the derivatives of the infinitesimal displacements δx_i, these can be replaced by the corresponding derivatives of the components v_i of a velocity field that is compatible with the kinematical boundary conditions. Writing the typical derivative $\partial_i v_j$ as the sum of its symmetric part $\partial_{(i} v_{j)} = V_{ij}$ and its antisymmetric part $\partial_{[i} v_{j]}$, we finally obtain the stability criterium

$$\int [T_{ij} \partial_i v_k \partial_j v_k + \lambda V_{ii} V_{jj} + 2\mu V_{ij} V_{ij}] \, dV > 0. \tag{4.23}$$

As an example, we treat the buckling of a slender prismatic rod that is subjected to a uniform axial stress S. Let the axis of the unbuckled rod coincide with the x_3-axis, and let the end sections in the planes $x_3 = 0$ and $x_3 = l$ be so supported that the rod can only buckle in the x_1, x_3-plane. Denote the cross-sectional area of the rod by A and the moment of inertia of the cross section with respect to the x_2-axis by I. The *slenderness ratio* $l\sqrt{A/I}$ will be treated as large in comparison to 1.

Apply the stability criterion (4.23) to the velocity field given by the relations

$$v_1 = \varphi(x_3), \quad v_2 = 0, \quad v_3 = -x_1 \varphi'(x_3), \tag{4.24}$$

in which the prime indicates differentiation with respect to x_3. The velocity field (4.24) corresponds to the usual assumption that the material cross sections $x_3 =$ constant remain plane and normal to the material axis of the bar. Equations (4.24) neglect the effects of the lateral contraction or extension, which accompanies the axial extension or contraction of the fibers of the rod when this is bent. According to (VIII, 3.9) this neglect implies that in (4.24) Lamé's constant λ has been assumed to vanish. Accordingly, we shall set $\lambda = 0$ in evaluating the integral in (4.23).

The function $\varphi(x_3)$ in (4.24) has to satisfy boundary conditions for $x_3 = 0$ and $x_3 = l$ that specify the manner in which the ends of the rod are supported. If, for instance, the end sections are free to rotate about centroidal axes that are parallel to the x_2-axis, but cannot undergo any lateral translation, we have the boundary conditions

$$\varphi(0) = \varphi(l) = 0. \tag{4.25}$$

It follows from (4.24) that

$$\partial_i v_k = \begin{bmatrix} 0 & 0 & -\varphi' \\ 0 & 0 & 0 \\ \varphi' & 0 & -x_1\varphi'' \end{bmatrix}, \tag{4.26}$$

so that $V_{33} = -x_1\varphi''$ is the only nonvanishing component of V_{ij}. Since, furthermore, all stress components other than $T_{33} = -S$ vanish, the relation (4.23) with $\lambda = 0$ furnishes the following stability criterion:

$$-S\left(A\int_0^l \varphi'^2\,dx_3 + I\int_0^l \varphi''^2\,dx_3\right) + 2\mu I\int_0^l \varphi''^2\,dx_3 > 0. \tag{4.27}$$

In view of our assumption concerning the order of magnitude of the slenderness ratio, the second term in the parenthesis in (4.27) may be neglected. The compressed rod thus is stable if

$$S < 2\mu\,\frac{I}{A}\,\frac{\displaystyle\int_0^l \varphi''^2\,dx_3}{\displaystyle\int_0^l \varphi'^2\,dx_3}. \tag{4.28}$$

Since we have set $\lambda = 0$ in deriving this criterion, we may replace the factor 2μ by Young's modulus E (see VIII, 3.9). The *buckling load* $P = SA$ of the rod thus is given by

$$P = EI\,\mathrm{Min}\,\frac{\displaystyle\int_0^l \varphi''^2\,dx_3}{\displaystyle\int_0^l \varphi'^2\,dx_3}, \tag{4.29}$$

where the minimum is to be taken for the set of all twice continuously differentiable functions $\varphi(x_3)$ that satisfy the boundary conditions (4.25). The reader who is familiar with the calculus of variations will readily verify that the minimum, which is assumed for

$$\varphi \propto \sin\frac{\pi x_3}{l}, \tag{4.30}$$

has the value π^2/l^2, yielding the familiar Euler formula

$$P = \pi^2 EI/l^2. \tag{4.31}$$

If one does not care to use the methods of variational calculus, one may obtain an approximate value of the buckling load by using an expression for a twice continuously differentiable function φ that satisfies the boundary conditions (4.25) for any choice of the parameters contained in this expression. One then determines these parameters to minimize the quotient in (4.29). Since this method arbitrarily restricts the considered functions φ, it will furnish an upper bound for the buckling value, which may however be very close to the true value (4.31) if the expression for φ has not been chosen badly.

Index †

† Italicized page numbers refer to definitions or fundamental relations.